Child of the sun

Kyle Onstott and Lance Horner

Child of the sun

Pan Books London and Sydney

First published in Great Britain 1966 by W. H. Allen & Co Ltd
This edition published 1968 by Pan Books Ltd,
Cavaye Place, London sw10 9pg
9th printing 1977
© Kyle Onstott and Lance Horner 1966
isbn 0 330 02048 x
Printed and bound in Great Britain by
Hazell Watson & Viney Ltd, Aylesbury, Bucks

1

THE FULL SPLENDOUR of the late afternoon Syrian sun streamed into the courtyard of the palace at Emesa, gilding the patterned mosaic floor, highlighting the pillars of coloured marble and changing the jet of the fountain in the centre from crystal to liquid gold. Varius Avitus Bassianus, nephew of the Emperor Caracalla of Rome, stretched his naked limbs on the ivory couch under the canopy of wine-red gauze and sought a spot on the mattress which was not already dampened by his sweat. He adjusted the fold of black cloth that kept the full force of the sun from his eyes, turned over slowly so that the filtered rays could reach his back, punched the pillow into a more comfortable position and tried to recapture the voluptuously-peopled dream from which he had so recently awakened.

Ah, but it was useless. The clatter of horses' hooves outside and the shouts of his cousin Alexianus and his boorish companions had set a flock of pigeons to wheeling back and forth inside the courtyard which made further sleep impossible. He sat up, unwrapped the blindfold from his eyes and blinked into the sunlight. Slowly he inched over on the bed, keeping a precarious balance, until his hand encountered the ivory handle of a small mallet with which he struck a brass gong. Its echoing clamour started the pigeons wheeling again.

In the interval before the slave would appear in answer to his summons, Varius stretched himself languidly into wakefulness. His adolescent body and tawny golden skin had all the feline grace of the cheetah which dozed on the floor beside his couch. A tangle of black curls, now damp with sweat, covered his head, and dark brows, precisely plucked to an exact symmetry, framed his large liquid brown eyes. The nose was straight, chiselled in classic perfection which was marred only by the nostrils which were over-wide. A precisely dented upper lip, red, wet and bee-stung, seemed both petulent and sensual and the cleft chin, although well formed, was weak. Without the all too apparent evidence of the body, it would have been difficult to distinguish the sex of the face for it was girlish in its beauty and yet as masculine as that of any boy in his early teens. The slender body that stretched on the couch was well formed but delicate with immature muscles which promised future strength without magnitude.

Varius glanced up as the long, embroidered Babylonian curtains parted and a slave entered and glided across the floor. His movements, like those of the boy he was about to serve, were smooth and catlike; mincing and delicate as he lifted his feet gingerly from the sun-warmed mosaic. He was older than Varius by some five years and his hair, of a violent shade of orange, came to his shoulders in carefully arranged ringlets. It could not have been a natural colour – no man was ever born with hair of that shade – and the darker blackness at the scalp showed that it had been hennaed. Even at twenty, his face showed the ravages of dissipation which he had carefully tried to hide by painting his face with white lead, rouging his cheeks and darkening his eyes with antimony. He approached the couch, fluttered his hands in the air and laid a delicate finger on Varius's shoulder.

He shook his head and clucked with disapproval. 'My dear, dear boy! Either the sun was too strong today or the gauze awning not thick enough. You are far too brown. Only a golden colour, the priest said, just the kiss of the sun, and now,' he ran the finger along Varius's skin as if to erase the colour, 'you are actually tanned. Oh, dear! What will your lady mother say and what will Zenotabalus the High Priest say? Oh, but we must do something about it.'

Varius looked at his shoulder where the finger had been. He too ran his finger across his skin and frowned. He reached for the whip which lay on the floor beside the cheetah and before the slave could move back, Varius let the lash fall across the man's chest. Strangely enough the slave

6

did not seem to mind although a red welt appeared on his soft skin.

'It's your fault, Gannys,' Varius let the lash descend again and still the slave smiled, 'all your fault! You should take better care of me. Why didn't you order another layer of gauze? Why didn't you wake me sooner or at least turn me over? Why didn't you attend me? Where were you? In the kitchen, fondling the new slave? Keep your hands off him. I want him first. I've a mind to have you whipped, Gannys. You're lazy and now what shall we do? Oh, it's your fault.'

Gannys paid no more attention to the threat of whipping than he had to the lash. ''Tis nothing, my dear lad. We'll bleach it out in moments with the new cream I have received from Egypt. Oh, 'tis wonderful, with the loveliest perfume. Lotus, I think, although I've never smelled anything quite like it before. 'Twill send you into ecstasies. You'll adore it.'

Varius rose from the couch and walked across the courtyard. His walk lacked the mincing affectation of Gannys and yet he carried himself, naked as he was, as though he were trailing a court robe behind him. As he neared the curtains, he stopped, and listened with disapproval to the loud voices that were coming nearer.

'My cousin Alexianus arrives.' Wrinkles appeared in his forehead which he smoothed quickly away with his fingers. 'He's been hunting, I suppose.'

'Yes.' Gannys's painted face showed the same distaste as Varius's. 'Him and the palace boys that hang on his every word! Kill, kill, kill, that's all they want to do. Today it's falcons, tomorrow it's arrows and the next day it will be swords or spears. It matters not to them except that they bring back some poor dead bird or animal.'

'And how they stink when they return.' Varius's nose indicated the offence that such smells caused him. 'Once I offered Alexianus some attar of roses for his smelly armpits. He stank so much I could not sit next to him at table, and what do you think he said?'

'Something nasty as usual,' Gannys was quick to agree.

'He said that the stink of a little honest sweat would do

me good. Me, Gannys, who in three weeks when I pass my fourteenth birthday will be High Priest of Elagabalus, Son of the Sun.'

'Pay no attention to him. He's jealous. He has always been. You are older than he, handsomer, more intelligent and . . .' Gannys nodded his head in affirmation, 'you are to be the High Priest, not he, and besides,' he glanced coyly at Varius, 'the soldiers are all your friends.'

Varius basked in the compliments. 'Naturally he's jealous. Just a jealous boor. But . . . he's not bad looking, Gannys. In fact, he's very handsome.'

'Not as handsome as the new slave boy in the kitchen. And of course, he cannot be compared with you, dear Varius.' He stopped and raised his hands, 'Or should I begin to address you as Elagabalus. I shall soon have to.'

Varius disregarded the question.

'About the new slave boy! Then you were in the kitchen with him and I forbade you. I forbade you to touch him, Gannys. Oh, this time I will surely have you sent to the whips, I vow. You'll have a pretty criss-cross of welts on your back. Now you've spoiled him for me. I've been anticipating him all day but I do not want him after you have slobbered over him.'

Gannys was quick to defend himself. 'Of course I touched him, how else could I have bathed him. Think you that you would have enjoyed him smelling of leeks and garlics? But apart from bathing him, that is all. So, send me to the whips if you must but at least, he is clean and sweet smelling for you and awaits you in the bath. I am always thinking of you, my Varius,' he looked sideways at Varius, 'Elagabalus, I mean.'

Gannys always knew how to flatter to gain his own ends and he knew the hold he had over the boy – a hold strengthened by his willingness to pander to the burgeoning desires of the adolescent body. In this he had not only the approval of the boy's mother but of the priest of the Temple of the Sun as well, albeit for different reasons. Soaemias, the boy's mother was determined that no other female would

8

ever have any place in her son's affections, therefore Varius would never be permitted to love a woman. To the sun worshippers, the sun was a man, glorious and strong, who ruled by day. The moon was a woman who ruled by night, whose power diminished as she entered her periods of uncleanliness. Therefore a priest of the sun could have no dealings with a woman. To do so would rob him of his power and his cleanliness. So Zenotabalus, as well as Soaemias, had forbidden Varius to have any contact with women. Varius was apparently quite satisfied.

Instructions had been given to Gannys to indoctrinate Varius into the then fashionable vices of the East and no better teacher could have been found than he who, indeed, knew them all. He was most willing to lead Varius down such erotic paths for it gave him a hold over Varius, making the boy more amenable to discipline, easier to reward and more completely under Gannys's influence. Even at his present age of fourteen, Varius was well seasoned in the role he was to play during his life – that of a pawn in others' hands. Throughout his brief span of existence, Varius was to have no mind of his own – only his body, but this beautiful body was his and from it he would derive all the pleasure he could.

Gannys held up the curtain for Varius to pass through and as it fell behind them, they heard the voices, rough, loud and vulgar approaching down the long corridor.

'Sixteen birds today, Alexianus', one of the young ruffians was shouting. 'Sixteen to my five. Ah, boy, the sun favoured you today. Perhaps it is because your cousin is soon to be Son of the Sun.'

Alexianus's mouth pursed itself to accommodate the obscene noise he made. 'My cousin Varius. Bah! The little sissy! But quiet, here he comes, tripping alongside his painted Gannys. Of the two, I think I hate the slave the more.' He took up a position in the centre of the passageway.

All the good looks that Varius possessed were equalled in his younger cousin Alexianus. The brow was higher, the eyebrows natural instead of plucked, the nose better formed, the mouth less sensual and the chin stronger. But it was the boy's eyes which were his most prominent feature. Varius regarded the world through the thick veil of his lashes with an indifferent somnolence but Alexianus had eyes of such startling clarity and beauty that many found it impossible to look at him directly. Alexianus was all boy with none of the languid effeminacy of Varius. His face was frankly open and lacked the craftiness which distinguished that of Varius. His words were direct and honest, inspiring confidence. And yet, with all his beauty he lacked the intelligence of Varius.

He stood astride the passage, blocking the way, his friends, sons of the palace freedmen and slaves, behind him. His rough tunic of white cotton was stained with sweat and horse spittle. In his hands he carried a bulging cloth bag through which blood was seeping. As Varius drew near, he delved into the bag and drew out the mutilated body of a partridge.

'A gift to you, Cousin Varius.' He tossed the dead bird to Varius. It hit him on the chest and slithered down his belly to land on the floor – a misshapen lump of flesh and feathers.

Varius shrank from the contact. The smudge of blood stood out against the honey-coloured flesh.

'You and your dead birds!' Varius recoiled from the object on the floor. 'Think you of nothing but killing? I want not your gift, Alexianus. Neither your gift nor you.' As a final insult, Varius wrinkled his nose again, 'And you stink – a rank smell of horses.'

'Then crawl not to my bed tonight, for if you do, you'll get the same reception you got last night and the night before and the night before that. I'm no slave that you can whip into submission so save your caresses for those luckless bastards and for the soldiers of the Tenth Legion.'

Varius's face turned red under his tan. He reached out a hand and pushed Alexianus aside. However, Alexianus was not budged by the feeble push, instead he lowered his shoulder, caught Varius on the chest and heaved. Varius went backwards, flailed his arms vainly for a second and then fell, sprawling on the floor. Immediately he started yelling, as though he had been murdered.

Alexianus jumped on him, sitting on his chest. With one hand he grabbed his cousin's long hair, clutching a handful and banged Varius's head on the floor. Varius only howled the louder. Gannys, in the background until now, came forward, vainly trying to lift Alexianus from his master but a well directed backhand slap from the youngster sent Gannys into retreat, clutching his belly. Varius's screams rose above his sobs and with each scream, Alexianus raised his head and let it fall on the floor again.

'Mama, Mama, Mama!' The corridor echoed and re-echoed with Varius's howls as the companions of Alexianus sped away to absent themselves from the conflict. 'Mama, help me! Guards, attend me! Gannys, stop him! He's killing me. Mama!'

The last frantic wail produced results. A woman came running down the corridor, her silken draperies floating behind her; her hands outstretched; her face contorted with anger. She reached down, grabbed Alexianus by the hair and pulled him off Varius. Gannys, quite recovered from his blow, hastened to help her and between the two of them, they got the screaming Varius to his feet.

'Punish him, Mother, punish him.'

'He will be punished, Varius.' Her anxious fingers moved over his head. 'Are you hurt, my son?'

Varius's sobs subsided but he was trembling with anger.

'He dared to touch me. I, who in a few weeks time will be the most sacred person in the world.'

Alexianus did not retreat, although all his friends had run away. He was left alone to witness the torrent of maternal love that flowed over Varius. Soaemias was a most possessive mother. In her son Varius, she held the solitary key to all her hopes and ambitions. That she was a cousin to the Roman Emperor Caracalla; that her mother was sister to the Emperor's mother had gained her little but the exile of herself, her mother, her sister and her sister's child, Alexianus, to this provincial city. Caracalla, who lived in fear of the world, trusted his own family less than strangers.

Through her son Varius, Soaemias saw a possible stairway to greatness, the first step towards which would be the boy's elevation as High Priest of Elagabalus. All competition must be ruled out. No other woman must be allowed to replace her influence. No other contender against Varius must be allowed to rival him or exceed him. In her young nephew, her sister Mamaea's child, she had long sensed a possible rival.

Alexianus defied her. He pointed to the bloodstained bag on the floor.

'I but made a present to your puling Varius. A bird I killed this afternoon. I was about to suggest that Gannys take it to the kitchen and have it cooked for his supper but he did not want the gift.'

'And you knew that when you gave it to him. Do not cozen me, young whelp. Your gift was not made through love. You know that Varius hates anything that is dead, bloody, dirty or odorous. You had only in mind to plague him. Now run and tattle to your mother about all that has happened and let her relate it to our mother so that it will be the topic of conversation at dinner tonight. "Varius did this and Varius did that." Know you not that he is to be Priest of the Sun? Keep your hands off him.' She struck out at him but Alexianus side-stepped.

He stretched out his hands, palms up. Indeed they were dirty. He shrugged his shoulders, bowed with mock obeisance to Soaemias and then made an even deeper genuflection towards Varius.

'Lest I profane the air which the divine Varius breathes, I shall leave you. My mother awaits me but I shall not bother her with a thing so trivial as my banging my cousin's head on the floor. She would only applaud me and worry about some possible damage to the floor.' He turned on his heel and left.

Soaemias released Varius from the smothering restraint of her embrace and turned him over to Gannys.

'Bathe him and put cold compresses on his poor head. Perhaps you can find some way to amuse him and make him forget this ugly scene.' She pushed them protectively before her and watched them walk down the hall.

When they were out of hearing, Varius pinched Gannys's arm viciously. 'Hear! You are to amuse me. Mama said so, Gannys. And how will you amuse me? Tell me.'

Gannys rubbed the red spot on his arm.

'The new boy from the kitchen is waiting in the baths. That should amuse you. I picked him out especially for you.'

'And that means he's big and strong and handsome.' Varius bent over and kissed the red spot on Gannys's arm.

'That he is,' Gannys agreed.

'And being big and strong, perhaps I shall have to whip him to make him mind.' Varius brandished the slender lash which he had brought with him.

'Oh, undoubtedly,' Gannys agreed.

'Then I *will* be amused. I certainly will.' He reached out and drew Gannys's arm around his waist. 'Could anyone have a better slave than you, dear, dear Gannys?'

2

THE SWIMMING BATH was illuminated by an indigo light which filtered through the coloured glass inset in the ceiling. It bathed the room in a weird, unearthly light and as Varius swam through the sapphire water, it broke into a blue effervescence that drained the colour from his hands, making them ghostly white, despite the coloration of the sun. He dived underwater, leaving a trail of pale blue bubbles behind him and swam under the surface until he came to the white marble coping at the deep end of the pool. With fingers locked over the rim, he looked up at the boy standing on the edge of the pool – the new slave boy which Gannys had only that morning chosen from a new shipment of slaves and purchased in the slave market at Emesa.

Varius inventoried him carefully. He was pleased to see that the boy was of a peasant type, and he could see that Gannys had chosen carefully with his young master's particular preference in mind. Varius had no liking for willowy, pale Greek boys or the small-boned Arab youths with their airy affectations. This one, he noted, was perhaps eighteen and his eyes followed from the feet, which were broad and flat with thick, curved toes, to the stalwart legs with their bulging calves, then to the flat stomach and the wide chest with arms which showed the rounded muscles of hard labour. The face was pleasing and the hair crisply blond.

The blue eyes of the slave looked down at Varius, conscious of the careful scrutiny that was being made of him. Until a week ago, he had been a farmer. Now he did not know exactly what he was or what he was to be. He forced a smile to his face and his lips parted tentatively to show a row of strong white teeth. Varius did not return the smile.

'What is your name, slave,' he demanded.

'They call me Threnox.'

'Know you that you are my slave?'

The boy's smile disappeared. He nodded assent.

'And that you must do everything I ask of you? Everything? Because if you do not, I shall whip you and if I cannot whip you hard enough, I shall send you to the public whip-handler. He'll raise some fancy welts on your back, won't he, Gannys?'

'Indeed he will, Threnox.' Gannys shook a warning finger at the youth. 'Better do exactly as your new master commands,' Gannys winked at Varius.

'Then come swim with me now,' Varius commanded.

'But I cannot swim, my lord and master. On the farm where I lived there was no water – only a well. So I have never learned.'

'Well, then, I shall teach you. Come, jump in.'

Threnox hesitated. 'But it is over my head and I shall drown.'

Varius laughed. 'So, you drown! And tomorrow Gannys will buy me another slave and I shall not mourn you. Besides, it will be interesting to see a person drown. I have never seen that happen. Now I desire it. Jump, I tell you, jump in.'

Threnox reached one foot slowly down into the water and withdrew it. He was frightened. Here he was in this strange palace, where he had been bathed and rubbed with sweet-smelling oils. His clothes had been taken away from him and he had nothing wherewith to hide himself. Now he was in this dark room, in this weird light, looking down into the depths of this blue water into which he was supposed to jump. The boy who looked up at him frightened him. He shrank back but Varius reached up, grabbed one of his ankles and pulled. Threnox, with his feet firmly braced, re-sisted and although Varius exerted all his strength, he could not budge Threnox. Varius became angry. He abandoned his hold on Threnox and swam to the opposite end of the pool which was shallow and climbed out on the marble steps. The whip with which he had lashed Gannys was lying on the floor and as he ran around the pool, he picked it up. Threnox was still standing on the edge and as Varius approached him, he shrank back from the whip in Varius's hand.

It did not appear to be a formidable weapon – its deli-cately carved ivory handle held only a single strand of braided silk and leather but its lightness was deceiving. In Varius's hand it could inflict pain and he had had sufficient practice to assure himself of the results he desired. With the whip in his hand and the ability to make others cower be-fore him, he was able to forget the frustrations of his life, the domination of his mother and the existence which was so carefully charted for him by Gannys. The whip forced those that were stronger than himself to bow to his will and it was always foreordained that they must bow, because they knew if they did not there was a stronger whip, wielded by a more formidable hand which would be mercilessly laid upon them.

Threnox, like a trapped animal, sought a place to run but there was no escape – the pool was bordered by only a narrow gallery on all four sides. Gannys stood threatening on one side – Varius was advancing on the other. Threnox retreated to the wall but even before Varius reached him, he tasted the end of the lash.

Varius was jubilant. 'Into the pool, slave! Jump! It will amuse me to see you drown.' Now he was near enough so that the full force of the lash bit into Threnox's flesh. Again and again it descended and all his attempts to dodge and protect himself with his arms were of no avail. Slowly the sting of the lash forced him to the very edge of the pool. His foot hovered on the marble coping and then slipped and he fell backwards into the water.

Throwing the whip to Gannys, Varius dived in after him, swam underwater until he reached the flailing arms and the thrashing legs, then, just as Threnox managed to reach the surface, Varius pulled him under. Threnox's strength came to his rescue for he managed to fight Varius off and reach the surface again. He gulped air into his lungs only to have his head pushed under again by Varius. The struggle continued – Threnox fighting to rise and fill his bursting lungs and Varius forcing him down under, until Threnox, weakened by lack of air could struggle no more. He went limp in the water, his vain efforts to keep afloat ended.

Suddenly Varius's mood changed. That which he had lashed, tormented and nearly drowned now became the object of his tenderest solicitations. He lifted Threnox's body and swam with it to the shallow end of the pool, cradled Threnox's head in his arms and tenderly brushed the wet hair from the slave's face. Threnox gasped for air and opened his eyes. His glance of fear was returned with one of affectionate solicitude by Varius.

'Poor boy! Poor, dear boy!' They were now in shallow water and Varius helped Threnox to stand up, then supported him. With his arm around Threnox's waist, he guided him up the marble steps and through a curtained doorway that led to a small room almost completely filled by a large slab of white marble, supported on bronze legs with a low couch beside it. Still solicitous and gentle, Varius guided the dripping slave to the couch, forced him down and lifted his legs up on the couch. He plumped up the pillow under Threnox's head, clucking and cooing with sympathetic noises. Gannys followed and looked on indulgently.

'I saved your life, dear boy.' Varius had found a towel and was drying Threnox's body. 'Yes, had it not been for me, you would have drowned in the pool. Oh, at first I wanted you to drown but then I realized you would bring me more pleasure alive than dead, and besides,' his mouth drew down in disgust, 'had you drowned in the pool, I would never have wanted to swim there again. I hate dead things. But you are not dead, dear Threnox, and now you must show me how very grateful you are to me for saving your life.'

Threnox managed to speak, 'I thank you.'

'*My lord and master,*' Varius prompted him. 'You mustn't forget that, Threnox, for I am your lord and master.'

'My lord and master.'

Varius motioned Gannys to leave.

'So now, with your heart filled with gratitude for me, Threnox, move over on the couch and let me lie beside you. You are trembling. Ah, you shiver from the cold water but my body will warm you. Oh, how you must love me, Threnox, because now you live and breathe at this moment. Had I forced you to the bottom of the pool and stood on you, you would now be dead. So you are alive and you must become even more alive that you may show me the depths of this great love you have for me.'

Threnox grudgingly moved over on the couch and Varius accommodated himself to the narrow space that remained. Their damp bodies touched each other, and Varius's arms drew Threnox's face close to his own. His lips sought those of the slave, pressing hard to overcome their reluctance. Suddenly Varius sat up. Gannys was still standing in the doorway, the curtain upheld in one hand.

'Out! Oh you vile Gannys! I'll not have you spying on me. Here is somebody who loves me because I have just saved his life and I'll not have you gawking at us while he proves it.

Out and quickly, for my fingers already tell me that Threnox is ready to demonstrate his love.'

Gannys dropped the curtain but he remained standing on the other side. Slowly and carefully so as not to disturb the hanging folds, his fingers made a small opening between the edge of the curtain and the door jamb. He peeked through it, keeping his eye glued to the aperture for the next hour. At first he measured his breath carefully but after a while, he realized that the two on the couch were entirely oblivious to any outside sounds. Finally he dropped the curtain and smiled to himself. The red welt across his chest had not disappeared and he rubbed it with one hand as though he cherished it.

Varius was so easy to handle, especially if one let him think he was handling himself. His fingers lingered on the welt across his chest. He had enjoyed that. He had taught Varius how to use the whip for his own enjoyment, for Gannys had been brought up by the whip in the hands of his Egyptian master and he still had a fondness for it. He walked along the edge of the pool to another room and sat down before a table of citron wood which was cluttered with bottles, phials and jars. The mirror of polished silver over the table gave a clear reflection of his face. Gannys smiled at his silvered image then frowned as he noted a tell-tale line around his eyes. He opened a jar of ointment and with expert fingers, he re-touched his face, glancing from time to time towards the door, awaiting his summons from the other room. Finally it came – he heard Varius call his name.

He gathered up an armful of towels and a long robe of soft white wool and departed. As he approached the curtain to the rubbing room, he heard Varius's voice. The words throbbed – hoarse and husky, satisfied and satiated.

'It wasn't as bad as you thought it would be, was it Threnox?'

The answer was relaxed and sleepy. 'No, my lord and master, but I hope the next time you do not half-drown me to make me prove that I can love you.'

'Oh now, I shall not drown you again, Threnox. I shall

have to think of something different. But, dear Threnox, it will be some time before I see you again but I shall tell Gannys not to sell you for I must save your life again. It makes you so grateful.'

Gannys lifted the curtain and walked in. The two figures were still on the couch and from their position, Gannys could see that their roles had changed. Varius was no longer the master. He had become the victim, but the smile of satisfaction on his face assured Gannys that his master was satisfied.

Varius slowly extricated himself from the burden of Threnox.

'You chose wisely, my good Gannys. He performed beautifully. Send him back to the kitchen and bid him await my next call. See to it that he is not sold as I shall desire him again. He is so grateful when I save his life that I must do so often. Dear Threnox!' Varius kissed the slave and climbed to his feet.

'Now, off to the kitchen with you, Threnox.'

Gannys threw the boy a towel to wrap around his waist. Threnox remembered to bow low to Varius before he departed.

'And now, dear, kind, thoughtful Gannys,' Varius scrubbed himself with the towel, 'what shall I wear tonight; with what delightful scent will I perfume myself and,' he indicated the still moving folds of the curtain, 'whom have you arranged for me to sleep with tonight?'

Gannys lifted the curtain to see if Threnox had gone.

'One question at a time, Varius. As to what you shall wear tonight, there is a new tunic of saffron coloured silk, embroidered with gold phoenixes which just arrived this afternoon from the seamstress.'

'Wonderful! It will become my dark hair.'

'And with it, attar of roses.'

Varius shook his head. 'Never! I only wear that perfume with rose colour. With yellow I prefer mimosa.'

Gannys smiled knowingly.

'Ah, but this is attar of *yellow* roses.'

Varius embraced him. 'Dear Gannys, how thoughtful you are. Yellow roses! But of course.'

'And as for your bed companion for the night . . .'

'Yes, yes, go on, Gannys.'

'Remember the soldier that the Tribune Gaius Vitronius sent here for guard duty about a month ago. The Tribune was sure that he would please you and he did – so much so that you gave the man a hundred gold pieces.'

Varius clasped his hands together. 'Oh, Gannys, the one I have been asking for every night.' Varius closed his eyes the better to envision the bulky young German, bursting with blond vitality.

'The same! And at my orders, Gaius has kept him in close confinement for a month, during the which he has seen neither man nor woman, preparing himself for this night.'

Varius was in raptures. 'You are good to me. First Threnox, then the saffron robe and the attar of *yellow* roses and now the German whom I have been dying to see for so long. I must reward you, Gannys. What would you like?'

Gannys picked up the slender whip and handed it to Varius.

'A good beating, my lord and master, so that I shall never forget that I am slave to the world's best master.'

Varius took a firm grip on the whip as Gannys stripped off his tunic and turned his back.

'But not too hard, dear Varius.'

'Yet hard enough for you to enjoy it, what?'

3

THE FORMAL *triclinium* of the Emesa Palace was used as seldom as possible and only on state occasions because its frescoed walls kept it hot and airless. At all other times the evening meal was served on the roof, where an occasional breeze from the river wafted up a flat smell of muddy bottoms and brackish water. With the canopy of the stars overhead there was an illusion of coolness, if not the actuality.

Tonight, with only Eutychianus Comazon, the local Tribune of the Roman Army for a guest, the occasion was not considered sufficiently formal to warrant the family abandoning the coolness of the roof for the stifling heat of the indoor *triclinium*. Comazon was an old friend of the family – more than an old friend many said when speaking of his relationship with Soaemias. Comazon had been quick to use his charm and take advantage of Soaemias's near relationship to the Emperor Caracalla and, if she preferred to share her couch with him, he was not loath to use such means of obtaining advancement. Soaemias was interested in men and she had been flattered by the attentions of the handsome young soldier. The affair had begun shortly after her widowhood in Rome, even before Caracalla had banished his immediate family, with the exception of his mother Julia Domna, to Emesa. Emesa was a small, quite unimportant city in Syria, whose only claim to fame was that it contained the main temple of the Sun God Elagabalus.

Of late, Comazon's ardour for Soaemias had cooled considerably. At thirty-five, she had become stout and was already losing the beauty which had made her famous. More important still, Comazon's long association with her had gained him nothing better than the tribuneship of the legion at Emesa. With the Emperor's cousin for his mistress, he felt he should have advanced higher, but consoled himself that the easy post at Emesa was better than being an obscure soldier on the fighting front, freezing with the cold in Gaul or perishing with the heat in Libya. Comazon was still a young man, some five years younger than Soaemias, and he did not confine all his nights to her. Naturally, as he carefully explained to her, he had to put in many evenings at the barracks. Soaemias understood and minded very little. Among the retinue of palace slaves there was always one whose embraces pleased her more than those of Comazon, of which she had long grown weary, but Comazon represented the army and the army was necessary to her plans.

So, the outward appearance of their long dead affection was maintained for mutual advantage.

Six couches were laid at three sides of the long table on the roof and beside each of the couches, six slaves, or rather five slaves and a Roman soldier were standing, awaiting the entry of the diners. By one of the couches in the centre, an elderly man with carefully combed white hair and beard awaited the arrival of the matriarch, Julia Maesa, whose sister, Julia Domna was the mother of the Emperor Caracalla. Maesa's daughters, Soaemias and Mamaea were both widows, each with one son, Varius and Alexianus.

The Roman soldier, orderly to the Tribune Eutychianus Comazon, stood beside the next couch, a wreath of roses and laurel in his hand for his commander. Around the corner from him, a tall, well-built young Nubian moved his doe eyes in the direction of the stairway, awaiting the arrival of his mistress, Soaemias. At the next couch stood the elegant Gannys, whose apparel put that of the other slaves to shame. Across the table, at the other end, Mamaea's favourite Thracian slave was adjusting his already too short tunic and beside him a sun-bronzed lad with clumsy hands and plain white cotton tunic awaited the entrance of his master, Alexianus.

The old man frowned at the buzz of whispers that were being hissed back and forth among the slaves. Gossip about their masters and mistresses was strictly forbidden, but when their slaves knew more about them than they knew themselves, it was most natural that they should talk whenever they got together and mealtime was one of the few occasions when the opposing factions of the household met on neutral ground.

Apol, the heavy-handed young slave of Alexianus and his constant hunting companion, leaned forward, his chin thrust out. He made an obscene gesture with his fingers across the table at Gannys.

'So, your young sissy got his pretty little head banged on the pavement today! Did mama's boy cry?' Apol shared his young master's dislike for both Varius and Gannys.

Gannys made an even dirtier gesture with his fingers. 'That to the young bully who is your master. He'll soon find out who's in power here. Varius will be High Priest and then your little bastard, Alexianus, had better keep his hands off or he will profane Varius's sacred body.'

Metrax, the Thracian slave of Mamaea snorted. 'Will his body be so sacred that he'll have to stop sleeping with soldiers?

Young Publius, the legionary, would take no derogatory remarks about the legion. 'Every Roman soldier in Emesa today loves and honours Prince Varius. He's a favourite with the whole legion.'

'Speak you for yourself, Publius?' Apol laughed. 'I suppose you do because you wear the gold medallion Varius gives to all whom he finds satisfactory at stud. How many gold pieces have you already collected from Varius?'

Publius's face reddened under his tan. 'As a soldier and a free man I will not discuss the matter with slaves.'

'Hush, hush,' Old Vatron tried to calm the others. 'It is forbidden to talk here. You must listen to me.'

'To you, old man?' Gigex the Nubian chuckled, showing his white teeth. 'Who's going to listen to you? You've not been able to get it up for poor old Julia Maesa for the last ten years. Now . . . if you only had something like this,' he hoisted up the front of his tunic and pointed down, 'then you'd have something to crow about.'

Mamaea's Thracian spat on the floor. 'If Soaemias wants that black monstrosity, she's welcome to it, but big as it is, I suppose it seems like hanging it out of the window to you. 'Tis said your mistress has only to spread her legs and a chariot and four can find shelter for the night. Now my mistress appreciates talent. She says my sergeant-at-arms may not be the biggest in the world but it is the most playful.'

'After you've had three doses of satyrion. That's the only way you could get it up.'

'Men, men, you must be quiet. They will be coming soon.' Vatron held up both hands to quiet them.

'Call you us men, Father Vatron?' Gannys simpered. 'Alas we are not men but slaves, except young Publius here.'

'Men! Ho ho!' Metrax and Apol slapped each other on the back. 'Men! Look who's talking about men! The slut Gannys with his painted face and dyed hair. Men? Ha!'

'I know more about men than you'll ever know,' Gannys glared at Apol, 'and who are you to talk so high and mighty? What were you and the young Alexianus doing down behind the stable the other day? I caught you.'

'Nothing more than other boys our age do.' Apol was quick to defend himself. 'And certainly nothing like your Varius does. Even tonight, the new slave, Threnox, was talking about him in the kitchens.'

'Which means the bragging little kern will be sent to the whips tomorrow.' Gannys stopped talking and placed a warning finger on his lips. 'Quiet everybody or we'll all be sent to the whips. They come, our high and mighty owners.'

There was a prattling of voices on the stairs which resolved into the strained falsetto notes of women who are trying hard to be polite in order to conceal their intense hatred of each other from a guest. The curtain at the head of the stairs parted and the company walked across the comparative obscurity of the roof to ascend the few steps to the brilliantly lighted domed enclosure where the table was set.

Julia Maesa, her hand resting lightly on the gold bracelets which covered Comazon's arm, led the little procession. She was a woman in her sixties who made little or no effort to conceal her age. She had never been a great beauty like her sister, Julia Domna, but she was still a fine looking woman, with iron grey hair, meticulously waved, parted in the middle and drawn back severely. Her long tunic of light grey silk was caught at the waist with a belt of wrought silver, otherwise she wore no jewellery.

Behind her came Soaemias, puffing slightly from the ascent of the stairs. Her arm was protectingly around the saffron tunicked Varius who exuded an overpowering smell of roses – yellow roses to be sure, Soaemias's younger sister Mamaea followed behind with Alexianus. In contrast to the

elaborate costume and the profusion of jewels which Soaemias wore, Mamaea's dress was of pleated white linen,
gathered at the waist with a plaited girdle of coloured cords
and her son was dressed in a similar rough tunic to that of
the slave Apol who was to wait on him. It was evident that
Mamaea and Alexianus were the poor relations, destined
always to be eclipsed by Soaemias and the favoured Varius.

Followed the usual flutter of place seeking, bowing the
ladies to their couches, adjusting the pillows and whispering
words of instructions to the several slaves. Finally the last
pillow was plumped up and bowls of rose water were passed
into which the diners dipped their fingers and then dried
them on the linen towels which hung over the arms of their
slaves.

At a signal from Vatron, a group of serving slaves appeared
from the shadows with bowls of snow, each of which held a
goblet of wine. When those on the couches had each been
served, Julia Maesa took the wreath and placed it on Comazon's head, thus crowning him both the guest of honour and
the *captain* of the dinner. It was he who would choose the
topics of conversation, regulate the watering of the wine,
taste first from the various meats and act as host.

He rose on his elbow, bowed to Julia Maesa and then to
Soaemias and Mamaea. This formality over, he addressed
Varius.

'Noble Varius, do you now propose a toast to the divine
Marcus Aurelius Antoninus, Emperor of Rome and your
kinsman.' (Caracalla's real name was as above – the name
Caracalla was a nickname from the long cloak which he
always wore, but this name was never used in his presence.)

Varius raised his goblet languidly.

'To my divine cousin, Caracalla, but first, dear Eutychianus, a libation to the god Elagabalus, whose divinity exceeds
even that of my cousin as he would be the first to admit.' He
poured a few drops of wine on the table and Comazon dis-
comfited by his omission and his correction, sprinkled an
even larger libation which was followed by all at the table.

'And now to Caracalla,' Varius raised his goblet but

whereas the others took only polite sips, he drained his and held out the empty goblet to Gannys to be refilled.

Soaemias caught Gannys's eye and nodded her head. Varius was being indoctrinated into the pleasurable and stultifying effects of alcohol. Comazon caught the look and smiled. Julia Maesa had also seen it but preferred to ignore it. Only Mamaea spoke.

'Soaemias, the wine is unwatered as yet.'

She scowled at the interruption. 'But Varius likes it better that way.'

'Yes, I do, Aunt Mamaea.' Varius took another swallow.

'And what you want you get.'

Julia Maesa rapped the table. 'Our noble guest, Eutychianus Comazon will lead the conversation. Let not family matters intrude.' She turned to Comazon, 'And what shall we discuss, Tribune?'

'I would not want to bore you with my profession, but I would speak of the army, particularly of a demonstration today at the camp in honour of your grandson, Varius. He is a great favourite of the soldiers and today they showed their love for him in a most remarkable way.'

Varius sat up on the couch, both arms gracefully outstretched towards Comazon.

'My dear Tribune, how wonderful! Do tell me what happened.'

'Well, out of their meagre pay each soldier in the Legion contributed something and from the sum total, they have had a suit of armour fashioned for you – the breastplate gilded with an embossed sun in token of your coming elevation to the priesthood of Elagabalus.'

'Wonderful, wonderful, wonderful!' Varius clapped his hands, 'And when shall I see this?'

'Today was the public viewing for the Legion. Now they think to prepare a fête in order to present it to you. 'Twill probably be several weeks before all the details are worked out as it will be a most elaborate affair, to take place after your elevation to the priesthood.'

'A toast to the Legion.' Varius tossed off the goblet of wine and the others acknowledged with sips. 'My soldiers all! Tell them, dear Eutychianus, that I love every one of them, and I love you too, you have been a father to me.'

Gannys filled his goblet again. The slaves appeared with the first course, and for the next few minutes nothing was said as the diners made their choice from the many delicacies.

Comazon leaned over and wiped the tips of his fingers on the towel which hung from Publius's arm.

'Yes, illustrious Varius, the man who has the love of the Legion is indeed a fortunate man.'

'Most fortunate,' Julia Maesa agreed. 'It was the army that put Caracalla in power and it is the army that keeps him there. Every Emperor of Rome since Nero has ascended to his purple through the strength of the soldiers behind him.' She turned to the Tribune. 'Naturally I am glad that the Legion here at Emesa is so attached to my grandson. But, Eutychianus, that is only one legion out of the many which make up the Roman army, scattered throughout the Empire.'

Comazon smiled with the secret knowledge of a man who has already accomplished something difficult. 'The Fifth and Sixteenth, stationed at Antioch have heard of the illustrious Varius. I have an agreement with the Tribunes in Antioch to transfer legionaries from time to time so that more and more soldiers may become acquainted with Varius and the rewards that acquaintance entails. Already the Fifth and the Sixteenth are favourable to Varius. Soon they will be even more favourable.'

Soaemias looked up quickly. 'How?'

'Apollo is worshipped at Antioch. His temple at Daphne is the largest in the world. Apollo is the Roman God of the Sun, merely another name for Elagabalus. When Varius becomes High Priest of Elagabalus, as he will be soon, he will be invited to appear at the Temple of Apollo in Antioch. Worship at the temple that day will be compulsory for all the soldiers stationed there. We shall make it a festival, with special awards for all who attend. There is nothing a Roman soldier likes more than a few extra *denarii*. He will have Varius to thank for them and he will cheer Varius to the rooftops.'

Julia Maesa shook her head, her disbelief written plainly on her face. 'But even with one legion at Emesa and two at Antioch, we can hardly hope to change the course of Empire.'

'Ah, allow me to contradict you, dear Julia Maesa,' Comazon reached out and laid a hand on her arm. 'Three legions are quite enough. Once they have accepted, others will follow. Look back in history! How many did it take to make Otho Emperor, or Vespasian or Domitian? What starts in one legion spreads like fire to others and remember, we shall have three, not one.'

Mamaea spoke for the first time. 'And what do *you* expect to gain from all this, Eutychianus, provided the time ever comes for you to act?'

Comazon recognized the hostility of her tone. 'Perhaps nothing, my dear Mamaea, perhaps much. That will be for Julia Maesa to say,' he bowed to the older woman.

Her glance disapproved of Mamaea's words. She pushed the food aside on her plate, sipped the rest of the wine in her goblet and signalled to old Vatron to help her from her couch. She noted Varius's face, flushed with wine, and his nodding head. A move of her fingers signalled Gannys to rouse him. Varius sat up quickly at Gannys's prodding, opening his eyes wide to disguise the fact that he had been dozing.

Comazon recognized the signal for dismissal and swung his foot over the edge of the couch. As he did so, he met Varius's eyes.

'You will be well guarded tonight, dear lad. I have ordered one of your favourite soldiers to be in attendance.'

Alexianus slipped from his couch and stood on the floor beside his slave. His tone was polite, his words carefully chosen, his eyes bright and straightforward. 'Dear Cousin,' he bowed with mock formality to Varius, 'I bid you good night. May you sleep well, and to that end I hope your soldier's armpits do not stink of sweat as mine do.'

Varius's hand was lifting a goblet full of wine to his lips. He flung the contents at Alexianus and the goblet followed to crash on the floor. A purple stain spread down the rough cloth of Alexianus's tunic.

'Have your brat keep a civil tongue in his head,' Soaemias glared at her sister.

Julia Maesa held up a hand for silence. 'Alexianus's words were ill chosen. So was Varius's action. He has broken one of my murrhine goblets. Mamaea, I charge you to see that your son does not provoke Varius after this.' She turned to Comazon. 'Come, old friend, you and I have much to discuss in private and you, Soaemias, accompany me. Bid your black man wait here, and you, Comazon, dismiss your soldier. What we have to discuss is not for the ears of slaves or common soldiers. My nephew Caracalla is in Antioch. I have received a courier just today. Macrinus is fomenting a revolt against Caracalla. Unwittingly the fool is playing into our hands. Come Eutychianus, come Soaemias, we have much to discuss.'

The three walked across the dark roof, talking in low tones. Gannys helped Varius to sit up and get his feet on the floor. He swayed slightly in the slave's arms. Alexianus had not moved. Mamaea was still on the couch.

'They are trying to make you Emperor of Rome, Varius, and I hope they do.' Mamaea's voice had lost its bitterness. There was even a trace of pity in it. 'As Emperor you will not last long.'

'Then I suppose it will be Alexianus's turn. But that will never happen, dear Aunt. You heard tonight how the soldiers love me. You know that I am soon to be High Priest. I shall reign a long time for my person will be sacred and I shall have the protection of my dear soldiers.'

'At least you will be protected tonight,' Alexianus mocked him.

'Thank you, dear cousin, and that you may sleep without further worry about me, let me tell you that Gannys will anoint the German's armpits so they will not stink like yours.'

Somewhat unsteadily Varius took Gannys's arm. Julia Maesa, Comazon and Soaemias were waiting for him at the head of the stairs. They were swallowed up in the darkness.

Mamaea laid a restraining hand on Alexianus. 'You have a hard lesson to learn, my son, but you must start learning it tonight. Play up to Varius. Flatter him, pretend to like him. Never antagonize him again. Your grandmother, together with Comazon and Soaemias are plotting to put him on the imperial throne. It is better that he be your friend than your enemy. Do not blame Varius too much for what he is.'

'But he is such a snivelling sissy, mama.'

'Blame him not. His grandmother, his own mother, Comazon, the priest Zenotabalus and that debauched Gannys are all conspiring to make him as evil as possible in order to gain their own ends. Varius could have been as fine a person as you are but he has been taught to think of nothing but the pleasures of his own young body.' She sighed. 'Perhaps it is as well. Your chances will be better in the end. But, swear one thing, Alexianus. Swear on the love you have for your mother. Never, never, never follow your cousin in any of his ways. Guide your own life by choosing exactly the opposite path. Whatever he does, shun it. Whatever he does not do, make it your own.'

She leaned over and kissed her son and led him away.

They had spoken too low for the slaves to hear but now that they were gone, the hum of conversation started. Gigex, the Numidian, raised his voice above the others.

'Looks to me as though we should all start packing for Rome.'

'Bah, what have you to pack?' Metrax, Mamaea's Thracian grinned.

Once again the black man raised his tunic and pointed down. 'I carry my most precious possession always with me,' he grinned too. " 'Tis a heavy weight, I vow, but it will make my fortune.'

'And one cut of the knife could deprive you of all your worldly goods.'

4

JULIA MAESA LED the way down the dark and rather narrow flight of steps which led from the roof to the second floor. Varius, leaning heavily on the arm of Gannys, followed behind her and Soaemias and Comazon came last. As Maesa paused to lift the drapery that covered the doorway at the foot of the stairs, she looked back up their dim length. Soaemias and Comazon were locked in a tight embrace and Maesa smiled to herself as she realized how perfunctory it probably was. Neither cared anything for the other but both needed the other. So, they kept up the pretence of love. Who was fooling whom? At least neither of them were fooling Maesa.

She was a competent general and she was managing a very difficult campaign whose purpose was to put the empty-headed Varius on the throne of the Caesars. Dress him in the imperial purple. Circle his head with the golden laurel leaves. Seat him in the ivory curule chair in Rome. Indoctrinate him so thoroughly into the pleasures to be derived from his healthy young body that he would have no desire to interfere with Maesa's plans for power. Keep him from ever caring for another woman so that there would never be any opposition to her own indomitable will. Install him as High Priest of Elagabalus so that he would be regarded as sacred. Curry favour for him with the army. Keep her daughter Soaemias under her thumb, and keep her other daughter, Mamaea, and her son, Alexianus, away from Varius but never alienate them entirely as Alexianus must be kept in reserve to take Varius's place if anything should happen to him. Tie Eutychianus and his prestige as Tribune of the

Army closer to her cause. These were the immediate problems that Maesa had to face. There were others. There was the Emperor Caracalla!

She waited at the foot of the stairs for Varius and Gannys and for Soaemias and Eutychianus. Her smile was that of an indulgent mother who had discovered her children doing something of which she disapproved but which she did not care to mention. She embraced Varius, inhaling the wine-sodden breath of the boy and returning the slobbering kiss he gave her. He turned and faced Soaemias, threw his arms around her and kissed her, calling her the dearest of all mothers. Comazon held out his arms to the boy and Varius kissed his mother's lover, but whereas the kiss he had given his mother was a dutiful one, his lips lingered on those of Comazon, until Comazon pushed him gently away, turned his head sideways and whispered in his ear.

'You will be well guarded tonight, dear Varius. The young German has had his drink laced with satyrion.'

'As was my wine too, Eutychianus. Gannys saw to that. I can scarcely wait to get to my room. Will he be waiting for me?'

'He will.' Eutychianus released him and turned him over to Gannys.

'Conduct your master to his room,' Maesa addressed Gannys without looking at him. 'Prepare him for bed. And you, Eutychianus and Soaemias, follow me.' She beckoned to them. 'A courier from Antioch arrived this afternoon. I have news – important news.'

She led them down the gallery that surrounded the *peristylium* below, to a door that opened into her own apartments, then took them across her bedroom into a smaller, windowless room which served as a wardrobe. When they were inside, she closed the carved cedar door. It was stifling hot and breathless in the little room. Without a word, she handed Soaemias a peacock feather fan and Eutychianus a linen towel to wipe the beads of perspiration from his forehead.

'I know it is hot in here, but it is safe,' she excused their discomfort. 'We have important matters to discuss.' She swept a pile of garments from two chairs for them and seated herself on the edge of a wooden bench which served as a rack for sandals. As Soaemias fanned and Eutychianus mopped his forehead, she continued.

'It was ill-advised to speak of the army at dinner tonight. I felt, however, if I changed the subject it might call even more attention to it. But I do not believe that anything we said could be considered dangerous. We must never discuss such things before slaves.'

'Oh, Mother, don't be so suspicious!' Soaemias waved the fan frantically. 'I know that my Gigex would never repeat a word. He is devoted to me. And as for Gannys . . .'

'I trust that one only because I've got enough on him to crucify him tomorrow. Never trust a filthy catamite. They're unstable. They'll turn on you in a moment. And as for your black stud, Gigex, remember, he's only a slave with one thing to recommend him. Don't think he's so devoted to you but what he can be bought.'

'My soldier, Publius, is a good boy,' Eutychianus nodded his head. 'Like your Gannys, Julia Maesa, I have enough on him to hang him tomorrow. He knows enough to keep silent.'

'Of course I can vouch for old Vatron,' Maesa said, 'but I am not sure of Mamaea's Thracian, or that brat that waits on Alexianus. As for that matter, I'm not sure of Mamaea herself. She wants to put Alexianus on the throne but,' she shook a warning finger at the other two, 'he's too young and, perhaps even more important, she has brought him up to have a mind of his own. Once on the throne, nobody but Mamaea could handle him and that would not agree with our plans.'

'Varius seems more and more amenable,' Eutychianus unhooked the clasp that held his toga over his shoulder and lowered it so that he could mop under his arms, 'you will never have any trouble with him.'

Maesa shook her head, her lips grimly together in a thin line.

'No, thanks to the efforts of Soaemias and the ministrations of Gannys, Varius is falling into line. He will never give us any trouble. Give him wine to drink and a man to bed with and he will be contented. Let him have all the pretty clothes he wants and a table full of perfumes and he'll not care how Rome is governed. Soon he'll be a priest of Elagabalus and he will delight in the trumpery of temple processions and the fact that he heads them in rare and elegant regalia.'

'Varius will even enjoy prostituting himself on the temple steps at night.' Eutychianus continued to mop.

'And as Emperor of Rome, he will not desire to rule more than the palace itself,' Soaemias looked up at her mother, 'while we rule the Empire.'

Maesa nodded briefly.

'The courier?' Eutychianus asked. 'Did he bring dispatches?'

Maesa put her fingers to her lips and tiptoed across the room and opened the door quickly. There was nobody on the other side. 'I half expected that Thracian of Mamaea's to come tumbling in.' She shut the door and resumed her seat. 'No, the courier brought no dispatches as he had committed his message to memory. As soon as he had finished speaking, a piece of catgut was slipped around his throat from behind and the message perished with him.'

Soaemias threw the fan with a gesture of impatience. It fell to the floor and the slender handle of tortoiseshell broke. 'Before we are fried in this miserable room, tell us what he said.'

'You must learn to cultivate patience,' Maesa admonished her gently.

'Patience! I'll cultivate it on some cool balcony or up on the roof, not here in this oven. Come, Mother, let us get this discussion over with.'

'Agreed.' Maesa lowered her voice and leaned forward. 'Caracalla has left Antioch with only a small bodyguard for Edessa.'

34

Soaemias forgot the discomfort of the heat. 'Did you say Emesa, Mother?'

'No, Edessa which is quite another matter.'

'Why does he go there?' Eutychianus asked.

'The astrologers have told him that he must visit the shrine of Luna, the Moon Goddess, at Carrhae.'

'Then he is deserting the worship of Elagabalus. Alas, he is doomed.' Soaemias sank back in her chair.

'You know Caracalla.' Maesa made a disparaging gesture with the palm of her hand. 'He's always been ruled by superstition, ever since he killed Geta. He thinks his brother's shade is haunting him. Yes, he goes to Carrhae.'

' 'Twill bring him bad luck to worship the Moon Goddess.'

'Let us hope so. But, here is the important thing. Opellius Macrinus in Antioch plots to murder Caracalla. Macrinus thinks because he is Prefect of the Praetorian Guard he will be next in line for Emperor. Caracalla is losing popularity with the army because he has not given a pay increase for two years. It is the army that has kept him in power. The only reason he wears that silly cape is to identify himself with his soldiers but, as much as they love him, even they have grown tired of his madness. Caracalla's days are numbered.'

'But if Macrinus succeeds to the purple, then we are lost.' Soaemias was trembling. Suddenly she saw all her carefully laid plans being swept away. She would not be the Divine Augusta, mother of the Emperor. She would never return to the Imperial Palace in Rome to be first lady of the Empire. Instead she would be forced to stay here in this backwater of a Syrian city with only her mother and this lout, Eutychianus, for company. Well, she had Gigex! That was one consolation but even Gigex could not recompense her for becoming the mother of Caesar.

'Macrinus!' Maesa was too much of a lady to spit on the floor but she saved herself from doing so only by swallowing the ready saliva which was in her mouth. 'He's a stupid fool. I hope he does have Caracalla murdered. It will save us from having to do it ourselves and there will be no divine blood on our hands. Macrinus has only his Praetorians to support him. He'll not last more than a few months then . . .' She stood up and looked over the heads of Eutychianus and Soaemias. Seemingly she saw beyond the stuccoed walls of the hot little room, beyond the fertile plains of seaboard Syria and over the broad expanse of the Mediterranean to where the white marble Palace of the Caesars stood on the Palatine Hill in Rome. 'Only a few months and then Varius will wear the golden laurel leaves.'

'If the army so wills,' Eutychianus added.

'The army will,' Maesa came back to the little room. 'That is your job, Eutychianus. I cannot do it all.'

'But Varius is not Caracalla's heir. Caesar has never been willing to sign the adoption papers.'

'Varius is not only Caracalla's heir but his son – his own son.'

'Mother, don't be foolish. Varius is the son of Varius Marcellus.'

'Call you me foolish, Soaemias? I would slap your face, were it not that I am too warm to make the effort. Of course he's Caracalla's son. Caracalla fathered him one night in Rome when you shared your busy bed with him.'

'And who will believe that?' Soaemias took a long breath and expelled it noisily. 'And even if they did, what would that make me?'

'A whore! But it is no more of a disgrace to have slept with Caracalla who, after all, is Emperor of Rome, than it is to have slept with Eutychianus who is only a Tribune, and all Rome knows about that. Certainly it is not half as bad as to abandon yourself to that black stud you gambol with every night. Yes, Soaemias, I say that you slept with Caracalla, not once but many times. I say that as a result of those nights of love for your dear cousin, you birthed Varius and if anyone doubts it they have only to look at the boy. He looks enough like Caracalla to be his own son.'

'Well, he's his own cousin,' Eutychianus corroborated.

'Once removed,' Maesa added.

'Then I'm to go down in history as the imperial slut?'
Soaemias seemed strangely perturbed over her reputation.

'You will and were. Fool!' Maesa reached down and
picked up the broken stick of the fan and flung the pieces in
Soaemias's lap. 'Utter fool that you are. What care you what
a few gabbling tongues say? You will be the Mother-Augusta of Rome, when Varius is Emperor. So, you slept with
Caracalla! It's a small price to pay.'

Soaemias got up and walked the few steps to the door.
With one hand on the bronze latch, she paused and turned
back to face her mother and Eutychianus.

'I shall not have to lie when I say that I slept with my
cousin, Caracalla.' She smiled. 'I did, many times – and that
is one thing, dear mother, you never found out about. Yes, I
slept with him and at that time I loved him but,' she laughed
aloud, 'for the life of me I cannot tell you whether it was before or after Varius was born.'

'And who cares, dear Soaemias.' Eutychianus got up and
stood beside her. 'Who cares? Both your mother and I can
vouch for one thing.'

'What, Eutychianus?'

'That it was *before* Varius was born, of course.'

Maesa chuckled as she nudged him in the ribs. 'Of course
it was before, wasn't it Eutychianus?'

'It was.'

'Ah but, dear Mother, I have a better witness than either
you or Eutychianus. Sempronia Cilia helped me with the
rendezvous and each time she arranged for Caracalla to
come to my rooms.'

'Sempronia! By all the Gods! Perfect!' Maesa's chuckle
had turned into a loud laugh. 'The biggest gossip in all
Rome. How does it happen she has kept her mouth closed
so long?'

'She never dared speak with Caracalla alive.'

'Then soon she will be spreading it all over Rome. She's an
old busybody but, strangely enough, everyone believes her.
Darling,' she wrapped one arm around Soaemias and the
other around Eutychianus. 'Open the door and let's get out

of this place before I melt. You're not as stupid as I thought you were. So you actually did sleep with Caracalla?'

Soaemias nodded as they stepped out into the cooler air.

'And how was he?' Eutychianus smiled as he asked the question.

'Oh, a thousand times better than you, dear Eutychianus, a thousand times better.'

'But not better than the ebon skinned Gigex?'

Soaemias stroked his cheek with the tip of her finger. 'Of course not. That would be impossible.'

5

THE ROAD THAT led from Edessa to Carrhae passed through peaceful country, therefore there was no need for an advance guard and Marcus Aurelius Antoninus, Emperor of Rome – known to millions as Caracalla from the voluminous soldier's cape which he always wore – rode ahead of the small detachment of soldiers. He tried hard to be one of them, a soldier among soldiers, and he asked for no special protection. To do so would set him apart and his only desire was to be a soldier and to be accepted as one by the men in the ranks. An Emperor of Rome could only survive through the grace of the army and from the moment he had become Caesar, Caracalla had thought first of himself and then of his army. He had paid them better, fed them better, clothed and quartered them better than any other emperor before him and now ... he hoped they loved him better but he was not sure.

He was not sure of anything. He never had been since the day his brother Geta ran to their mother's arms, screaming for safety. But Julia Domna had not been able to protect Geta. The swords had slashed and Geta had died in her arms. If she had resisted she would have died too. Now Caracalla was glad she had lived. He trusted his mother. Well, he trusted her a little more than anyone else, at least enough to leave her in Rome to guard his interests there. No by two-faced Janus, he didn't trust her. She had loved Geta more than she had ever loved him. She had never forgiven him for murdering his brother.

He had loved Geta too. He remembered the day his father, the Emperor Septimius Severus, had died. It was cold and rainy and bleak, that day in Britain, but he had donned the long cloak of a soldier and had taken Geta by the hand and appeared with him before the army. They had been proclaimed co-emperors of Rome. Geta was a handsome boy. Caracalla had loved him. Then why did he kill him? Why? Because there could be only one emperor in Rome. If he had not killed Geta, Geta would have killed him. But if Geta had killed him, he would not have come back every night to haunt Geta, like Geta's shade haunted him. Geta's shade was plotting his death. He knew it. He was never safe. He looked back over his shoulder to the soldiers behind him. Of course he was safe now, out here on the open road, and away from the confining walls of palaces and barracks. He was alone with his men, his soldiers, his friends. There was nothing for him to fear.

The sun had gone down and there was a chill in the air. Soon they would be stopping for the night and there would be the blaze of the camp fire with its welcome light and heat. The men would talk and Caracalla would pass the wine cups around and later he could roll himself in his long cloak and sleep alongside his soldiers – his friends. Then, Caracalla shivered at the thought of it, Geta would come, pointing the finger of death at him and he would awake screaming.

Yes, the sun had gone down and Elagabalus the Sun God was dead. The sun had perished; the godhead had been slain by the forces of darkness and only the long nightly sacrifice in the holy Temple of the Sun God at Emesa could bring the sun back to life so that he would appear tomorrow morning in all his splendour and all his glory. Night after night, the rites must take place in the temple at Emesa. Emesa! That was where he had banished his Aunt Julia Maesa and her two daughters. And there were two sons – what were their names? Alexianus and Varius, Alexianus was Soaemias's son. No, her son's name was Varius, so Alexianus must be Mamaea's son. He had never liked Mamaea – she was cold and calculating and she had never liked him. But he remembered Soaemias and her beauty and the warm bed he had shared with her in Rome. Perhaps after his visit to Carrhae was over, he would ride to Emesa and see his family. No, by Elagabalus, he wouldn't dare to. They would murder him in his bed.

Why did he swear by Elagabalus? The Sun God had deserted him. He, Caracalla, was as divine as the Sun God. He was Caesar, one of the divine Antonines. He was a god himself. So why should he worship Elagabalus when Elagabalus had done nothing for him, had forsaken him? Let the sun die! Forbid the nightly rituals at Emesa that would bring the sun back to life. Let Luna rule! That was where he was going; to the Temple of the Goddess of the Moon, the mighty Luna, at Carrhae. His astrologer had told him to go. Let the worship of Elagabalus be abandoned throughout the Empire and let Luna be the chief goddess of Rome. He could make Luna the most powerful of all the gods if she would only deliver him from Geta. She could! Geta came only at night and Luna ruled the night. How stupid, oh how abysmally stupid he had been all these years to worship the divinity of the sun just because his grandfather had been priest of Elagabalus. And, he was only an honorary priest because he had married and the priests of Elagabalus never married. How could the God of the Sun help him when his godhead struggled for life every night, aided only by the filthy rites at the temple in Emesa.

Filthy? Of course they were filthy! He, Caracalla, knew all about them for he had spent one night in the Temple of Elah-ga-baal at Emesa and he had seen what happened. He was disgusted. He had seen how the High Priest had fortified himself with the virility of other men so that he would gain strength to bring the male sun back in the morning. He had seen the obscene black stone, the gigantic phallus of the sun, glistening wet from the sacrifices of men – the more men and the stronger they were the more strength the sun gained in its passage from nightly death to life.

And now, his cousin, the young Varius was about to become the High Priest of Elah-ga-baal. Only fourteen years old! What a life for any boy. He would be denied all the pleasures of women. Well that was one thing that he, Caracalla, had never denied himself. Women liked him and, by Eros, he liked them.

He might go on to Emesa anyway. He'd like to see Aunt Maesa. She would remind him of his mother. Probably Aunt Maesa hated him for having exiled her to Emesa. She was better off there than in Rome for Aunt Maesa was a trouble-maker and she was rich. There was nothing more dangerous than a meddling rich woman, especially if she were as clever as Aunt Maesa. Soaemias would be there. How he would like to sleep with Soaemias again. Now there was a woman whom even he could not satisfy. Soaemias had loved him in Rome. No, of course she didn't love him. Nobody ever loved him. His own mother didn't love him. Nobody ever loved an emperor except his soldiers, his friends. He looked back over his shoulder to the dim forms riding behind him. It was getting dark. They must stop for the night. He pulled up on his reins and halted his horse.

What was the young soldier's name – the one Macrinus had sent from Antioch a few days ago? Macrinus had recommended him so highly. Ah, yes! Martialis.

Caracalla called out his name, 'Martialis, attend me.'

A young soldier rode up beside the Emperor and bowed low in the saddle.

Caracalla reached over and cupped the soldier's chin in his hand and lifted his head. 'You are but recently arrived and are unaccustomed to our procedure here. I am a soldier like yourself and one soldier does not make obeisance to another. Do not bow to me.'

'Yes, Caesar.'

It had grown too dark for Caracalla to see the other's face.

He thought he detected a trace of sarcasm in the fellow's words but he decided to ignore it.

'We must camp for the night. Ride ahead and find a suitable spot. Let it be sheltered by rocks so the fire will burn brightly and not be blown by the wind. Light a fire if you have time and it will serve as a beacon for us. Ride, Martialis.'

The soldier slapped his horse's rump and galloped off, soon lost in the quickening dusk. Caracalla dropped back so that he would be with the other men. The gathering darkness seemed unfriendly and he wanted human companionship, the brightness of the fire and the fraternity of his men. He hoped Martialis would find a place soon. He had to piss. By Priapus, he had to piss! Should he stop now? No, better ride on. It would only delay matters and he could stand the dull ache in his bladder a little longer. He signalled to two of the company to ride close to him and they brought their horses so close to his own that he could feel their bare knees through the folds of his cloak – the *caracallus*.

Caracalla! That was what they called him although never to his face. He was proud of the name. It signified the cloak that he wore and that stamped him as a soldier. Caracalla! What a name to call an emperor of Rome, a Divine Caesar. They had called Tiberius's son Caligula from the *Caligulae*, the soldier's boots he always wore. Caligula – soldier's boots! Caracalla – soldier's cape! Fine name for emperors of Rome. But Caligula had been murdered. They said he was a bloodthirsty monster. Well, nobody could say that about Caracalla. He had had people murdered but it had been necessary. He had had to murder his own brother, Geta.

'Look, Caesar,' one of the soldiers pointed ahead. There was a fire burning. 'Martialis has discovered a camp spot for the night and lighted a fire.'

'A hundred *drachmae* to the man who arrives second. I shall be the first for divine though I am, I need to piss like any man.'

The camp site was as Caracalla had ordered, at the base of a rocky cliff, well sheltered from the wind. A small fire of

42

grass and hastily gathered brush was burning and Martialis, the soldier was gathering other wood as they rode up. He dropped the armful of faggots on the fire, making it blaze up, gilding the soldiers' armour and causing their faces to shine redly. Caracalla hoisted one heavy leg over his saddle and jumped to the ground. A clump of low bushes, growing at the summit of a rise, shielded him as he turned his back to the soldiers. They heard the stream of urine frothing against the rocks and Caracalla's voice.

'Ho, Martialis, there is plenty of wood here. Come and I will help you gather it.'

The soldier started towards Caracalla as the other soldiers dismounted, removed their saddle bags and began to set up the meagre camp for the night.

Suddenly they heard a scream from the bushes.

'Geta! Geta! Not here! Not now!' The scream ended in a high note of horror.

The big body, enveloped in the long cloak plunged forward, fell into the bushes with a crash and rolled down the hill. The soldier, Martialis, wiped the blood from his sword on the edge of his tunic and thrust it back into his scabbard.

'Death to the tyrant, Caracalla. Long live Opellius Macrinus, the new caesar.'

The other soldiers ran to where he was standing and quickly surrounded him.

'You have killed Caracalla!' One of the soldiers grabbed Martialis from behind, his arms around his neck, choking off his wind.

'Free him, Dacius,' the others shouted, 'we would learn what he has to say.'

'Kill him! He has murdered Caesar.' The massive brute, Dacius, tightened his arm, lifting Martialis off his feet.

'Yes, kill him! But first make him sign a confession that he killed Caracalla, else we shall all be crucified.'

Dacius released his hold and Martialis fell to the ground, gasping for breath. He looked up at the ring of soldiers' boots around him. As he raised himself on one elbow, he managed to stutter.

'You will not be crucified. You will be rewarded. I acted on orders of Opellius Macrinus, Prefect of the Praetorian Guard. He sent me from Antioch to kill the beast. Now, Macrinus will be Emperor. Five hundred *drachmae* to each of you. That is what he bade me promise you.'

'Stingy bastard! Caracalla would have given me that for being second to the camp site tonight.' Dacius kicked Martialis to the ground. 'Dion, you are the scribe. Hand this man your tablet and stylus.'

Another soldier fumbled inside his robe and drew out a brass bound wax tablet with a steel stylus and handed them to Dacius.

Dacius knelt on the ground beside Martialis. 'Write here! "I murdered Caracalla this night by order of Macrinus" and sign your name.' He pushed the tablet and the stylus into Martialis's hands.

'It will mean a promotion for all of you. Macrinus will not forget his friends.' Martialis slowly printed the words on the soft wax, closed the tablet and handed it back to Dacius who in turn handed it to Dion. Martialis was smiling now and he started to get up but Dacius pushed him down. His sword flashed in the light of the blazing camp fire.

A ring of raised steel surrounded Martialis and in its quick descent, he had only time to half raise his arms in a futile gesture of self-defence. As they withdrew their swords, Dacius leaned over and decapitated the corpse. He grabbed the brush of the helmet and raised the severed head high, looking into the frightened eyes.

'You did not die, lad, because you killed an Emperor of Rome. Caracalla was a poor emperor, an empty-headed piss-pot of a man. But, my lad, he was a good soldier and he was my friend.' He flung the head to the ground and the steel helmet rang out as it hit the stones.

They left it lying there and went down into the clump of bushes and found Caracalla's body. He was a powerful man and they struggled up the hill under his weight. When they had lain him down by the fire and folded his arms across his armour and wrapped him in his long cloak, they knelt beside

44

him. In death his face had lost the harsh lines of dissipation and become young and handsome again. They took a long, sorrowful look at his face, the flashing eyes now closed, the handsome straight line of the nose, the flaring nostrils, the fleshy lips and the hair that curled from his head down the sides of his face to his chin. Slowly they covered his face with a corner of his cloak – the *caracallus* that had named him.

One by one the kneeling soldiers paid tribute to him.

'He shared his meal with me one night, dividing the bread and beans of a common soldier and he gave me the major part.'

'Only a meal! He shared a whore with me once in Antioch. We had a wager who could mount her the most times. He won but he paid me the wager.'

'When my wife sickened in Rome, he heard about it and sent his own physician. She was cured.'

'We once rode from Rome to Neapolis together. He talked with me like a common soldier. He was my friend.'

'And mine!'

'And mine!'

'And mine!'

They were hard men – men who had endured hunger, cold and every kind of hardship but they wept for Caracalla, not for Caesar but for Caracalla, their friend.

6

BARRACKS OF THE PRAETORIAN GUARD, ANTIOCH, SYRIA.
                                                    OPELLIUS MACRINUS

T H E S M O K I N G L A M P S cast a flickering and fitful illumination on the surging mob of men below. They were lifting Opellius Macrinus to their shoulders with hoarse shouts of '*Ave* Caesar!' Caracalla was dead! Now the proud Praetorians – the pampered bullies of the Roman Army – harangued by a well-bribed few, and confident of their own power,

45

were electing their own man, their Prefect, to the Roman purple. 'Ave Caesar!'

Macrinus smiled down from the precarious position he had finally achieved on the shoulders of two guards. He stroked the sparse beard which he had grown to cover the weakness of his chin. So, Caracalla was dead! So, 'Ave Caesar!' that meant himself. He would now be Emperor of Rome. Not would be but already was, because his Praetorians had elected him. The Senate would confirm him if the army said so. Tomorrow he would don the golden laurel leaves. Tomorrow? Why not tonight? He was master of the world. Caracalla was dead. There was no other claimant to the throne. 'Ave Caesar!'

No other claimant? Well, there was that cousin of sorts in Emesa. What was his name? Varius Avitus. But . . . he had no claim to the throne and by all reports he was a weakling – only fourteen years old and soon to be a priest of Elah-ga-baal. That was enough to disqualify him if what they said about the Sun God priests was true and undoubtedly it was. These Syrians were a degenerate lot and the priests of Elah-ga-baal were the worst.

Yes, Caracalla was dead and he, Macrinus, had been wise to send Martialis to kill him. Martialis had always hated Caracalla because Caracalla had killed his brother. Just because he was a friend of Geta's. There was no blood on Macrinus's hands anyway. Nobody knew that he had sent Martialis. Nobody except Martialis himself and he was dead. Just as well! Emperor of Rome. Divine Caesar! Well, perhaps not divine because he was not of the Antonine house, but he would have the Senate confer divinity on him.

He steadied himself on his Praetorians' shoulders and patted one of them on the cheek. 'Ave Caesar!' Perhaps it would be wise to strangle the young Varius. But that posed a problem. The worship of Elah-ga-baal was strong here in the East. He might make enemies. Alas, he could not afford that luxury. Well let the brat live. By no stretch of the imagination could he prove a serious rival.

He must have a purple robe to wear tomorrow. Anything

46

that Caracalla had would be too big for him. Caracalla was a big man. But . . . he would search Caracalla's chests and find one and even if his wife had to sit up all night, she could alter it to fit. The scrawny bitch! Before he married her she had been a seamstress, employed by a maker of robes near the Ostian Gate. She could still thread a needle – if she would only keep her infernal mouth still long enough. She could spend her first night as Augusta of Rome stitching one of Caracalla's togas. Now, he'd no longer be bound to the bony old drab. As Emperor of Rome he could have his choice of all those high born Romen women, even that snobbish cousin of Caracalla's, that high-breasted Soaemias who had never looked twice at him. What a woman to bed!

'*Ave* Caesar!'

THE IMPERIAL APARTMENTS IN THE PALACE, ANTIOCH, SYRIA
JULIA PIADOMNA

'I should weep. I know I should weep because my son is dead. But . . . I cannot weep. I wept when Caracalla killed Geta. Poor boy! He had fled to my arms for sanctuary and I could not help him. I would have wept then but Caracalla would not let me weep. "No trace of tears", that is what he said. No trace of tears if I valued my life. He would have killed me as quickly as he killed Geta, his own brother.

'What was wrong with my son? Caracalla was such a handsome boy, so headstrong, so sure of himself. Yet, he was cruel. He learned that from Plautinus. Vile Plautinus, who under guise of friendship for my husband, undermined my son. Oh, Caracalla! I call you that because everyone called you that and yet I should call you by your own name. Some called you Tarantas because you were so cruel. Tarantas or Caracalla, what does it matter. I only know that the Marcus Aurelius who was once my son died years ago and an Emperor of Rome took his place. No wonder I cannot weep for you, Marcus. Twenty thousand Romans perished at the word of Caracalla. And countless Alexandrines were slaughtered, all because they were friendly to Geta. And . . . Caracalla,

Geta never plotted your life. Never! Oh, if I could only squeeze one small tear for you, Marcus.

'I remember once when you were a little boy and you fell while running down the path in the garden. You scraped your pretty face and you came to my arms, crying in your little-boy pain. I held you and comforted you and I thought then that no mother had a more beautiful son than you for you were beautiful, little Marcus. You were always beautiful, even when your face was only a handsome mask for the evil thoughts that ate your brain like worms. Sometimes I think you were mad.

'But now you are with Geta. I hope your shades will be reconciled. I shall pray to Elah-ga-baal. I shall pray, Caracalla, but I cannot weep. Opellius Macrinus is now Caesar. His guards will order me out of the palace. Where shall I go? I wish I could be with Maesa. At a time like this I need my sister. She would comfort me – but no, Maesa is too cold. She has no warmth of sympathy in her heart. Her grandson Varius looks like you, Caracalla, only he is even more beautiful. Yet he is weak. Weaker than you ever were. At least you were a man. Maesa has made a simpering catamite out of Varius. Probably she is even now plotting how she can put him on the throne, but she cannot. He has no legitimate claim to it.

'I must pack my jewels. I will be forced out tomorrow. How little I mind. I shall go back to Rome and live at the villa in the Campania. No palace has ever brought me joy. I have been the wife of Caesar and the mother of Caesar – Julia Domna, Augusta of Rome, Mother of Rome. Now, for the rest of my life I shall be just Julia Pia. I am glad. Poor Marcus. As the months pass I shall try to weep for you. I will try, Marcus, I will.'

THE BASSIANUS PALACE,
EMESA, SYRIA   *VARIUS AVITUS*

'Why do I awaken so early? There is something I must think about – something that happened last night. Oh yes, a courier arrived with the news that my cousin Caracalla is dead, murdered. By all the gods, Caracalla was handsome, unless the bust in the atrium flatters him. Once I fell in love with that bust and every time I passed it, if nobody was looking, I kissed those cold marble lips, wishing that they could kiss me back. I wanted Caracalla. Now he is dead and grandmother says I shall be Caesar. That homely old man, Opellius Macrinus, is now Caesar but she says he won't be for long and then it will be my turn because Caracalla was my father. Imagine! Wanting to sleep with my own father. Well, it would have been an experience. At least I'd have known what made me.

'They say that Caracalla never slept with boys. How stupid of him. What a lot of fun he missed. This soldier's arm rests heavy on my chest and his body is hot against mine. He sleeps and no wonder. I gave him little chance to rest last night. Let me look at him. How his black hair curls over his forehead and it is wet with his sweat. He told me he is twenty-eight years old and before he entered the legion, he was a sailor from Gades in Hispania. How strong his hands are. They are big and calloused and the nails are bitten down to the quick. He is very handsome and very strong and very cruel and yet I wanted him to be cruel. Last night I did not want to wield the whip. Perhaps I am getting to be like Gannys. Perhaps I shall grow to like it as well as he does. Oh, but it is thrilling to have a strong man force me to his will.

'So, I am to be Caesar. At least grandmother says so and she is always right. We'll leave Emesa and go to Rome. I do not remember Rome very well. I wonder if I shall like it there. When I am Caesar I will be able to have anything I want and do anything I want. Anything! Anything in the world, for Rome is the world and I shall be Emperor of Rome. I shall send Gannys all over the Empire to pick a bodyguard for me. Gannys knows the ones I like. I shall have the strongest, the handsomest, the most virile men in the world and . . . the wickedest. I'll train them all to be chariot drivers. No, I'll make soldiers of them and place Eutychianus Comazon over them. And I will dress in a robe entirely of gold, covered with gems and review my troops by lifting up their tunics one by one, I shall be Caesar!

'Ah, the soldier is stirring. His arm tightens around me. He still sleeps. Shall I awaken him? After last night, he will be useless to me. But no, in his sleep his strength grows and I can feel it pressing against my thigh. His arms are tighter. His lips are near mine. His mouth opens and I can see his white teeth and the red tip of his tongue. And now I shall reach down my hand and discover again what a wondrous thing is a man. When I am Caesar, I shall have ten of my guardsmen every night, all in one big bed that covers the whole floor. He awakens. He opens his eyes. They are dark, almost black and his lashes are long and sooty. He smiles at me and whispers "Pretty boy, see what you've done now." Again, sailor from Gades? Can you? But of course. Some day you will say that you bedded Caesar.

'Again? But no, sailor from Gades. You do not get what you want just by whispering "pretty boy" to me. It is not so easy. I yield not my virtue without a struggle. Would you kill me? Then do! Do! Do! Remind me to give you a double ration of gold for the double measure of pleasure you are giving me. Why did you stop, sailor from Gades? Oh, why? Why do you men spend yourselves so soon?'

JULIA MAESA

'The night has gone and the sun is rising and still I have not slept. There is so much to do, I do not know where first to start. Well, at last Caracalla is dead and he died without my having to do anything about it. It is just as well – better that way. He was Pia's son and I would not want his blood on my hands – my own nephew. I wonder if Pia will weep for him as she wanted to weep for Geta. Of the two, Caracalla was my favourite, at least he was more of a man than Geta was. Or more of a man than Varius is. But Varius is as I want him. Soaemias and I have trained him well and he will cause us no trouble. Perhaps the world will judge me ruthless to have made a pervert of my grandson but what care I for the world. I care only for Rome. Varius will never have a mind of his own but Alexianus will. I must admit it, I love Alexianus best. What we have made out of Varius disgusts me. I have always hated effeminate men. Varius is not stupid, but Alexianus is cleverer. What a ruler he would make, but he would rule by himself with some help from Mamaea and none at all from me. How I have always wanted to rule Rome. I have sat and watched the stupid mistakes that others have made. Septimius was not stupid but he let himself be influenced by that fool, Plautinus, and that was a mistake. Caracalla was really stupid. All he wanted was to be a common legionary but perhaps he was wiser than I give him credit. The army loved him. Yet their love did not save him for he was killed by a soldier. And now, Macrinus is to be Emperor. For how long? I'll give him six months on the throne. Yes, I must write to King Artabanus. Trouble is already brewing in Parthia. Artabanus was a friend of Caracalla's who almost married his daughter. Artabanus will fight to free Parthia from Rome and then Macrinus will have to act. He'll lead whatever legions are faithful to himself against Artabanus, and the legions that Comazon has won to Varius will revolt and Macrinus will be caught between two fires. We have honeycombed the legions with bribes. It has taken most of my fortune but when I have Rome in my hands, I'll have a far greater wealth. The legions are rotten with bribes and when these here revolt, others will follow.

'We must build up the image of Varius as the son of Caracalla. Then the legions will remember their love for Caracalla and will be all the more anxious to desert to Varius. Oh, I am sleepy but there is no time to sleep now. I must write more letters. I must write to Julius Paulus. He is the most influential person in Rome today and he has a daughter who is but a few years older than Varius. According to Roman law, Varius must wed although a lot of good he will do the woman he marries. Paulus's daughter is an empty-headed chit and she will do for Varius.

'Comazon must attend me first thing in the morning and if I can pry that black stallion off Soaemias, she must be present too. Soaemias is clever. But she thinks too much of her

Gigex these days. Yet, if I get rid of him she will hate me and I need her because she handles Varius better than I can. Where is my stylus? Now let me see, the first letter to Artabanus. "Your Exalted Majesty. You have my word for it. Once my grandson becomes Emperor, suitable terms will be arranged whereby all Parthia becomes an independent monarchy with you on the throne. However, in order for my grandson to become Emperor, we must first put down the imposter Macrinus that now claims to be Caesar. My grandson, who is soon to become High Priest of Elah-ga-baal will invoke the blessing of the Sun God upon you and your armies."

'Oh, there is so much to do, so much, so much, so much and only I to do it. If I had been a man I would have been a general. Alas, I am only a woman but I shall still be Emperor of Rome.'

SOAEMIAS

'Gigex, don't leave me. It is still early and you already speak of going. Do I not please you any more? Last night you were so different. You were tired; you had a headache; you wanted to sleep. Why do you think you are here? Certainly it is not to have a headache, to sleep or to be tired. Tired? Why should you be tired? You do nothing all day. You have an easy life for a slave. Too easy, too easy! You seem to forget that you are a slave and that if I wish, I can send you to the whips. I can have you crucified. Have your arms stretched out on a cross. I command you. Come back here to bed or by any god you name, I shall send you to the cross. This very day I'll have you whipped.

'Oh, Gigex dear, I didn't mean it, I didn't. I would not harm you. I would not have a mark on that glorious satin-soft skin of yours. I love you too much. Oh, Gigex, that is better. Your lips entrance me, they are large and soft, like two enormous cushions for me to rest mine on. Your teeth are so white and clean and your tongue a potent instrument. How big your nipples are. Let me squeeze them in my fingers. Your belly is so flat, Gigex and oh the wondrous joy of you.

'I am sorry that you drank so much last night while you waited for me. You drank trying to forget me? Because you were impatient and couldn't wait? I was with my mother until so late, no wonder you were impatient. No wonder you drank. You were lonely without your Soaemias. How well I understand and I'm sorry about what I said, about sending you to the whips. Of course I didn't mean it. Your beautiful back, darling Gigex. No welts must ever mar it.

'Would you like to go to Rome. Would you like to be head man over all the slaves in the Imperial Palace. No? Why not? You want to be a freedman? Well, why not? Yes, Gigex, you shall be free when we arrive in Rome, Varius will be Emperor and I the Mother-Augusta. Oh, Gigex, wait until you see Rome – the Palace, the Circus Maximus, the Forum and the wonderful baths which Caracalla had almost finished. What a sensation you will cause when you walk through the baths naked. Half of Rome will be slavering and crawling after you.

'But you are not a freedman yet, Gigex. Don't forget you are still my slave and you will have to earn your freedom. If you want to be free, you will have to love me. No more headaches, no more drinking too much, no more feeling tired.

'Oh, that's better. Yes, Gigex, that is the way I love you. Faster, Gigex. No, wait. Let's not finish all at once. Lie beside me and let me play.

'Do be friendly with Varius, Gigex. No, not that friendly. Never! I refuse to share you with him. Yes, I know he has had his eyes on you but you must put him off. Make excuses. I'll talk to him. I can always persuade him to my way of thinking. I know – the colour of your skin. Darkness stands for night and night is cursed to the priests of Elah-ga-baal although I think they enjoy their nights more than their days. I'll tell Varius that it would be a bad omen for him to touch you. He's superstitious, and if I tell him that, he will leave you alone.

Oh, Gigex, you are impatient. Yes, now! Oh, now, Gegex, now! I can wait no longer and neither can you. Oh, Gigex, now!'

MAMAEA

'Caracalla is dead and there is nobody to mourn him. Not even Aunt Pia will weep for him for she shed all her tears in secret for Geta. I am the only one that will ever weep for Caracalla and I too must hide my tears for nobody must ever know I loved him. At least I never let him know. I did not throw myself at him the way Soaemias did, dragging him into her bed and tasting the delights I so longed for. Then I would not take him even if he had looked at me. I will not take Soaemias's left-overs – the slut! She has spoiled my whole life for me. Whenever I wanted anything, she always took it first. Even now, she is planning to put her ninny, Varius, on the throne of Rome.

'By right it should go to my son. Alexianus is strong where Varius is weak. He is a man, whereas Varius is nothing but a silly girl, disguised as a man. That ridiculous little queen with his silken robes, his affectations, his painted face and his soldier bed-mates. Yet, through some strange perversity of fate, he has charmed the army. Strange that men, soldiers, the embodiment of all that is male, should love this weird hermaphrodite and yet they do. Naturally. He has bought them with Mother's gold.

'I suppose he will be Caesar and we shall be off to Rome again. But, I must remember, even while I weep for Caracalla, that his death brings my son one step nearer to the purple. Macrinus cannot last long. He is weak and brainless, an insufferable poseur who will quickly lose what little popularity he has. Mother is already plotting his downfall in order to put Varius on the throne. Then Varius will fall and it will be Alexianus's turn. Oh Rome! How you will suffer until the time comes that Alexianus governs. You will be torn between Varius's feminine wiles, Soaemias's lusts and my mother's indomitable will. Then, with Alexianus will come peace. Alexianus will be a second Augustus.

'Yes, Caracalla, I weep for you and for myself. How often have I looked at your lips and wished that I could kiss them. How often have I wondered at the strength of your arms and longed for their embrace? Soaemias knew them – she felt your lips, she gloried in the strength of your arms and all the intimate passions that you gave her, but she never knew that I wanted you. Had she known she would have enjoyed it even more for she would have felt she was depriving me of something I wanted and that is her greatest joy. But my turn will come. Varius, poor weak womanly Varius will be hounded from the palace. Soaemias will go with him. Mother may perish with them and then there will be only Alexanius and I. If Soaemias can lay claim to sleeping with Caracalla, so can I. Who can prove that Alexianus is not an imperial bastard too. They say that Varius resembles Caracalla. Bah! Caracalla was a man, every inch of him, so how could the pretty painted Varius resemble him. Alexianus resembles him far more and Alexianus will be a man. I promise that. Oh, my son! Tonight you have changed fathers. Caracalla fathered you and if I swear it who can dispute me. Soaemias? No! For even though she had him, she cannot prove he did not leave her musky sheets, hot with their lust and damp with their sweat and seek the coolness of my own for a welcome relief.

'Macrinus! A year at the most with Mother, Soaemias and Comazon to undermine him. Then Varius! Six months, a year, Rome will soon weary of his abnormal licentiousness. Then, Alexianus and golden days for Rome.

'Wake up, Metrax, and leave. I cannot sleep with you snoring beside me. It is too hot to sleep with another. I only keep you because Soaemias has her Gigex but I have no desire for you. Tonight I would weep and I prefer to weep alone. Oh, Caracalla!'

TRIBUNE'S APARTMENT

EUTYCHIANUS COMAZON

'Rome lost a good soldier in Caracalla. If he had not been Emperor he would have made a good legionary – the kind that fights well in all sorts of weather and asks nothing more than a few *denarii* to spend on a whore. Would that we had more like him in the ranks.

'And now that stupid Opellius Macrinus! Setting himself up to be Emperor. Doesn't the fool know that the only reason he became Praetorian Prefect was because Caracalla was so lazy, he didn't realize how stupid Macrinus really was. Macrinus fawned and flattered himself all the way to the top and now there is nobody left for him to flatter so he will fall down as quickly as he climbed up.

'Maesa is clever! She has already made King Artabanus think that this would be a good time to overthrow the Roman yoke. Now it's up to me to set the legions against Macrinus so that he'll lose the war. Set them against Macrinus and bind them over close to Varius. Strange that I should like the boy but I really do. I've never bedded a boy in my life but he is too damned beautiful. At times I have been tempted and if what my soldiers say is true, it might be worth my while. Certainly they are devoted to Varius. He has charmed them and, by Eros, he has nearly charmed me. He's a good boy under all his airs and affectations, good hearted and generous. What he is is the fault of his grandmother and mother.

'Soaemias – what a bitch she is! But what a woman! Even now, after all these years, she can make me feel as no other woman ever could. I wonder if she gives that black stud, Gigex, the wonderful times she once gave me – and Caracalla too. No wonder he loved her. Any man would. But Gigex doesn't. It's something to bed a woman because you love her but something else again when you are commanded. Imagine trying to satisfy Soaemias *every* night. The poor fellow must have to fortify himself with a quart of satyrion and even then, Soaemias would not be satisfied. They say Varius is like her. The soldiers say they cannot satisfy him. He's insatiable. Well, from what I have seen of my poor boys, crawling back to camp almost on their hands and knees, I imagine Varius is like his mother. But Varius almost met his match in the young German. What a stallion that boy was but Varius wore him down and left him as limp as a rag. He needed a week to rest.

'I must find out about this Aurelius Zoticus, the young athlete that's stationed with the Thirteenth Legion in Alexandria. His fame had already spread through the army and even Gannys has heard about him. Gannys thinks he would be a good match for young Varius. Well, if this Zoticus is anything like the reputation he has been credited with, he ought to be able to satisfy Varius. I'll write to Publius Aemilianus in Alexandria and have the boy transferred to Emesa. Publius was no particular friend to Caracalla but he'll hate Macrinus because he was Caracalla's tool. And Publius is wise enough to know that the wind is blowing in the direction of Varius. He'll be willing to sacrifice the pride of the Thirteenth.

'There's a lot of things to do tomorrow. The most important is to bolster Varius's popularity. In a few weeks, he'll be High Priest of Elah-ga-baal. Time to get this Zoticus here. Zoticus will be a fit initiation for the first night Varius spends in the temple. And when Varius knows that I supplied Zoticus, he'll be more grateful to me than ever. And then I'll tell him that Publius Aemilianus sent him and he'll send off a gift to Publius. I must remember to send the courier to Alexandria tomorrow, telling him to return with Zoticus even if he has to kidnap him.

'Perhaps I'd better go to Parthia myself and see King Artabanus. But I'll wait until after Varius has been made High Priest. There are a lot of things I must do before that event. There's a donative to the soldiers on the occasion of Varius entering the priesthood. I'll suggest 300 *drachmae* and Maesa will howl like a hyena but she'll settle for 150 *drachmae* and that will be as much as Caracalla ever gave them. I'll not be able to get it to the men in Antioch now because Macrinus is there, but I'll send word to them that it is theirs, only being held in abeyance for them. That will make them love Varius all the more and weaken Macrinus's hold over them.

'I've got a nice lad to send to Varius tomorrow night. He's

a Nubian, as black as Soaemias's Gigex. Varius has had his eyes on Gigex for some time but Soaemias will not part with him. So, Varius will be grateful for the Nubian and the Nubian will be grateful to me for the gold Varius gives him. He'll treat all his friends to wine and they'll all toast Varius. So far the boy has had every soldier in the Legion under thirty, and the older men have had gifts. How they'll cheer when he appears on the steps of the temple.

'I wonder if it's too late to go to the palace tonight. Perhaps Soaemias would dispense with her Gigex for one night. Tonight I would appreciate her. 'Twould be like reading an interesting book all over again. I would know the ending but the story would be sweet. I wonder about Mamaea. She is so cold, perhaps there's a fire in her like Soaemias but she has never shown it. She doesn't like me. Oh well, what does it matter.

'It's too late to go tonight. I'll sound out Soaemias about tomorrow night. Maybe she'll enjoy a change of colour and the black would enjoy a night of rest. A courier to Alexandria in the morning! A letter to King Artabanus telling him my visit must be kept secret. A short briefing of the Nubian lad. See Soaemias and find out about tomorrow night. Get Maesa to agree to the donative. And now, to sleep. The first step is accomplished – Caracalla is dead. Soon we shall all be back in Rome, hiding under the silken skirt of young Varius. Perhaps I'll finally succumb to his charm. Might help me in the future. Well, soon I'll be Prefect of the Praetorians – more than that, I'll be Emperor of Rome – the real Emperor while I keep Varius amused.'

THE BASSIANUS PALACE,
EMESA   *ALEXIANUS*

'Mother says I must make up with Varius and be friendly with him. How I hate him, but I'll make up with him. I'll flatter him and pretend that I like him but one thing I will not do. I'll not let him come to my bed at night. No! I hope he doesn't try it tonight, but he won't. He has a soldier to slobber over and he'll stay away from me. I'll keep him away even if I have to rub cow dung on myself. He'd hate that. He hates stinks. If he comes sniffing around me and smells that, he'll jump away like a burned cat.

'I wonder if Apol fed my hawks tonight. I told him not to because we are going to use them tomorrow. I want to go to the bend in the river where the reeds grow tall. There should be some wild ducks there and if the hawks cannot get them, we'll use arrows. Mama said I could have a new horse when Varius becomes High Priest. I want a white horse, an Arabian. If Varius can have a crown of gold because he's High Priest, I imagine I can have a new horse. And I want a real bow like the Scythian archers have. I'd ask Comazon to get me one, but he's Varius's man and he wouldn't do anything for me. It make me so angry! Aunt Soaemias has all the new robes and the beautiful jewels and mama has nothing. Varius has everything he wants and I'm treated little better than a slave. But mama says the time will come when I shall have all Rome at my feet. But first, I must be friends with Varius.

'I wish I could have known my cousin Caracalla. They say he was a real soldier. Apol said that he was one of the strongest men in the army. He could lift a chariot. Varius wants to learn to drive a chariot. It's only because he wants to hang around with the charioteers. I'd like to learn to drive a chariot too. Varius and I could have a race and I'd beat him. I don't suppose I'll ever have a chance to learn to drive. Varius always gets everything he wants. But, mama has promised me the new horse. I'll get a new horse and Varius will get a chariot with four and all of them better than the one I get.

'Sometimes I wish I could be a slave like Apol. He has all the luck. Wonder if what he told me about the slave girl is true. He says she is the one who has charge of the linen press in grandmother's apartments. She's only fifteen but Apol says she knows how to do it and loves it. He says he meets her every night on her way back from supper in the kitchen. They go to the tool house at the far end of the garden and Apol gives it to her there. He says he'll arrange it for me some night but I've asked him and asked him and asked him and he always has some excuse! She's busy or she can't get away or she is at a particular time of month. I think he's just boasting. I'll seek her out myself, push her up against the wall and put it in her hand and we'll see if Apol is lying as I'm sure he is.

'Oh, I'm so sleepy. What was I thinking about? Apol! He's always bragging just because he's older than me and because he's had a woman and I haven't. Wonder what it is like. Apol says it's more fun than what we do down behind the stables. But, if he has a woman so often, why does he always want me to come with him behind the stables? I think he's lying but I'm going to find out. I'll put it in her hand. Oh, what difference does it make. Now I don't care whether I ever see her or not. I'll go to sleep. Apol is lying. I know he is . . . I know . . . I k-n-o-w . . .'

EARLY MORNING ON A STREET LEADING TO THE BARRACKS, ALEXANDRIA, EGYPT   *AURELIUS ZOTICUS*

'A hundred *drachmae* – a hundred lousy *drachmae*! That's all I get for spending the night with that fat, greasy Syrian. After all his sweet words and big promises. Him and his slimy dark skin! I earned that money and now back to the barracks and practice all day. What a life! Because I'm the champion wrestler of the Thirteenth I must practise all day to uphold the honour of the Legion. And . . . because I'm hung like the Colossus of Rhodes, I stud all night to get a little extra money. For what? The money I earn does me no good because I never have a chance to spend it and I don't know what to spend it on.

'The stingy bastard didn't know I paid myself while he wasn't looking. If this chain is gold and if the jewel on the pendant is real it should fetch at least 500 *drachmae* so perhaps the evening was not entirely wasted. I should have held him up for more. One arm round his fat neck and he would have shelled out all his *drachmae* for fear of being choked to death. They always promise so much at night and then in the morning they cannot get rid of me fast enough. Here, son, take this little bag of money and get out, and before you've a chance to count it, you're out in the street, and when you open the bag, you find a hundred lousy *drachmae*. I did better than that when I was a child back in Smyrna. Remember the night the old Arab gave me five *perals*. But I was only a kid then and I didn't know all the tricks of the trade. Now, by Isis, there's not much I don't know. I can satisfy them all – men and women. I know at that first gasp, when I take off my clothes they are going to be satisfied. Oh! Zoticus, darling! Oh shit! How they all gurgle and gasp and pant for those extra few inches.

'Tonight it's my regular night with young Aperankhu the Egyptian Prince. He's decent. Lets me sleep after the first round and always pays me well. Besides, he's young and clean and nice to look at – soft skin, not like that old crocodile of last night. What was it the old bastard said had happened in Antioch. Caracalla is dead – had his throat slit by a soldier. Well, it's no skin off my ass. Caracalla never did anything for me. They say he wanted to be a soldier. Imagine an Emperor of Rome wanting to be a soldier. And now old pussy cat, Macrinus, is going to be Caesar and the first thing he'll do is to cut the army's pay. Who cares? If I had to live on a legionary's pay, I'd starve to death but fortunately Isis was good to me and gave me those extra few inches and a way to make a living. I wonder if it is the biggest in the world. Everyone says so. Even the Tribune called me over to him the time my breech clout fell off and wanted to finger it to see if it was true.

'What else did that old crocodile say? They don't think Macrinus will be Emperor long – some bastard son of Caracalla's who lives in Emesa will take the throne. The Syrian said he had seen him and he is the most beautiful boy alive. Sleeps with a different soldier from the Emesa Legion every night. Just my luck to be stationed here in Alexandria. Now, if I had been stationed in Emesa and that boy had slept with me, he'd forget all about the other soldiers and I'd have a steady job at the palace. By Isis! If I was husband to Caesar I'd be Caesar myself. Live in the palace, slaves to wait on me, fine clothes to wear. Hey, there! Off with his head! I'm Caesar's husband. To the cross with that Senator. He stepped on my toe in the baths. String him up! What's a senator compared to the Emperor's husband?

'How can I get transferred to the Legion in Emesa? Got to think about it. Who do I know? Aperankhu? No, he's nothing but a little prince with no influence. The old Syrian from Antioch? No, he's already missed his gold chain and I dare not return to him. If I could just get my hands on that boy in Emesa – just once. Just once for just one night! I'd have him so completely in my power he'd do anything I wanted. Isis, help me! Don't let these days of my youth pass without my accomplishing something. You were generous in your gift to me – almost too generous. Now let me make something out of it. The gold chain from the old crocodile to your temple if you will help me get to Emesa.

'What, sentry? Yes, I'm Aurelius Zoticus, the wrestler of the Legion. Publius Aemilianus? Why does the Tribune wish to see me. I'm not absent without leave. Not due to muster for another hour! Very well, I'll report to him at once. Up yours, boy! But you couldn't take it. You'd be split in two. Oh no? You'd like to try it some time. Ah, sweetheart, it would cost you more for an hour than you make in a whole year in this lousy army. I don't give it away for charity. For love? Soldier, what's that? Take my advice, don't do it for love.

'I'm off to see the Tribune. Perhaps he thinks he's going to get a free night. But no, he's not that way. Maybe his wife has heard about me and wants a little sample. That would be all right too. It might get me to Emesa.

'Aurelius Zoticus, 10th Cohort, Thirteenth Legion, reporting on order of the Tribune, Publius Aemilianus. Yes, my lord. A transfer from Alexandria? To the Legion at Emesa! Yes, my lord Tribune, I can be ready in half an hour. My Lord, a tiny favour? May I have permission to stop a moment at the Temple of Isis as we leave the City. Thank you, my Lord.

'Oh, Mother Isis, you work fast.'

'Mama, Mama, Mama! Oh Mama, what am I going to do
now? I'm here in this strange place with all these other men
snoring around me. I want you, Mama. Why did old Marcus
Salvius have to die and why did we have to be sold? Why
couldn't we have been bought together? Why did we have to
be slaves? Oh, Mama, my heart was breaking when they led
you down from the block. I hope that old man from Neapolis will be good to you. I didn't even have a chance to kiss
you as you passed me – you stepping down from the block, I
stepping up. In a way it was easier for me for you were not
there to see me sold. There were not too many bidders. I
don't suppose anyone wants a boy of eighteen even if he has
curly hair. I'm too old to be a minion and too young to be a
worker even if I have good muscles.

'An old man starting bidding on me. He looked like a
farmer from some such place as Pannonia in his rough
brown tunic and his leather leggings. But he didn't bid very
long and I was glad when he stopped. Then the agent for the
Florus Estate started bidding against the manager of the
Greens. For a while I didn't know whether I'd be herding
goats in the Campania or driving a chariot in the Circus
Maximus but the Greens won and now I'll be driving the
chariot. Well, it's better than washing dishes in some kitchen.

'They tell me I start training tomorrow. Takes about
three months, the man told me. I don't know his name and I
don't know anyone here and oh, Mama, I'm so homesick
and so lonely. Why can't we be back in the villa again, with
you heating some warm milk for old Marcus Salvius. After
we had put him to bed, we always had such good times together, playing draughts, reading and talking about the day
when I became a man and how I would earn my freedom
and yours. And Fabiola? I don't suppose I shall ever have a
chance to know another girl. I wonder where she was sold?
She came after me.

'Oh, Mama, I can't go to sleep for thinking about you and

Fabiola and the doves and the rabbits and all the good times we used to have at the villa. The men here are rough but one of them was kind to me tonight. He showed me an empty cot beside his own and got a blanket for me. He's a young fellow too. Only been here a month so he has not driven yet in public. I don't know his name but he's snoring away as if he didn't have a care in the world. You always used to come and pull the blankets up around my neck and kiss me good night and say "Hierocles, some day we shall be free".

'Maybe I'll be a great charioteer, the leader of the Greens and I'll make so much money on wagers that I'll be able to buy myself and then I'll come to Neapolis and buy you. I'll have to work hard because I must be the best – the best charioteer in Rome. "Live good, my son," you always said "and good will come to you." I'll try, Mama, I'll try but oh, I miss you so much tonight. It wasn't so bad in the slave pens where I could see you and Fabiola every day but now, I feel I shall never see either of you again.

'Why are some of us slaves and others rich and prosperous? I know, I know what you would say. Even the rich ones are not always happy. Look at Caracalla. He was Caesar and he was killed, so they were saying in the barracks tonight. Even being Emperor did not help him.

'I must go to sleep. We get up early here they tell me. Some day I shall be free, Mama. Some day I shall buy your freedom. Oh, I need you tonight. I need someone to love me. Someone. Goodnight, Mama. Goodnight, Fabiola. Goodnight poor little doves and rabbits at the villa. I wonder who is feeding you now. Good night.'

7

VARIUS PAUSED, HIS head thrown back, his hands drawing airy circles and his eyelids fluttering. He posed for a moment in the doorway of his bedroom, determined if possible to make a grand entrance. He had stolen into his mother's wardrobe and filched one of her gowns, together with the jewels of his choice. Soaemias's long Persian robe of pale green silk came only to his ankles for Varius was tall for his age but the breeze that swept through the doorway plastered the thin silk to his skin and moulded his young body provocatively. He wore a diadem of emeralds and pearls and had contrived to fasten Soaemias's earrings to his own ears by thin cords. An intricate necklace of gold and Egyptian turquoise encircled his neck and his fingers were heavy with gems. Dark lines of antimony enhanced the beauty of his eyes and his lips were encarmined with cochineal. As he stood languorously in the doorway he surveyed the room, then relaxed the grandeur of his pose with impatient disgust as he saw that Gannys was the room's sole occupant.

'What does this mean? Are you alone?' Varius was annoyed and angry. The careful preparations were entirely wasted on Gannys.

'Alone? Why yes, Varius.'

'But my guard? Where is he? Didn't Comazon send anyone tonight?'

'No, not tonight.'

'Then go at once to the slave quarters. Fetch me the young slave who bathed with me only the other day. What is his name? No, stop! I do not wish him tonight. I wish someone new and different, someone who does not know me and has never seen me before. Tonight I would be a real woman, soft and feminine, seductive and mysterious. Tonight I desire to be wooed tenderly and lovingly. Send to Comazon! Have a messenger start at once and say that Varius demands a guard tonight – one who has not been here before. Up, lazy Gannys and sit not there with that silly smirk on your face. Tonight I must know exactly how a man makes love to a woman.'

Gannys did not stir. He crossed his legs leisurely and fanned himself with his handkerchief.

'You might as well take off your mother's dress, Varius, although I shall tell you in passing that it becomes you well.

Indeed you are beautiful in it. Any man would fall madly in love with you.'

Varius tripped into the room, smoothing the folds of the silk with delicate fingers.

'Do you really think so, Gannys? But why, if I am so very beautiful, must I take off the dress. I went to a lot of trouble to get it. It's new and Mother has never worn it.' He paraded the length of the room, stopping before the silver mirror to admire himself. 'Oh, you hateful Gannys! You're trying to spoil my pleasure. You know how I hate to be disappointed and I had planned so much on this evening. Comazon had said something about a Nubian even handsomer than mother's Gigex, whom she will not share with me. Tonight I had planned to be mother and the Nubian would be Gigex. Oh, you are mean, Gannys and I've a mind to whip you. No, that would give you too much pleasure. Tomorrow I'll send you to the public whips. I will, I will, I will! And I'll go along to see you squirm. It won't be any make-believe whipping like I give you. I'll have him put a pattern of criss-cross welts on your back that we can play games on.'

'Oh, stop talking silliness! You know you wouldn't send me to the whips. What would you do without me? No, Varius, neither Nubian, slave nor soldier for you tonight or for some nights to come. Instead there is a message from Zenotabalus.'

'That tiresome old man! What does he want and why should he deprive me of my pleasure? When I become High Priest I'm going to banish him to some little temple where he'll have to do the rites alone. Does he forget that I am Caracalla's son now? Mother says that I shall soon be Emperor of Rome. Caesar! Does he know that?'

'He does, Varius,' Gannys was patient, 'but before you become Emperor of Rome, you must become High Priest of Elah-ga-baal. That is expedient. 'Twill win you favour in the East. As Emperor, you'll be Pontifex Maximus of Rome but you'll be a Priest of the Sun too.'

'Well, what does the old ninny want?'

'We did not tell you this, Varius, for fear you would be

66

frightened but tonight you are to appear at the temple for a very special ceremony. It will not be a pleasant one. It will be very painful and you will suffer.'

'Then I shall not go. Who would dare to make me suffer?'

'You are a man now. You must become one, and according to the rites of your God you must sacrifice your foreskin this night. The astrologers have set this as a propitious time. The sacrifice will be welcome to Elah-ga-baal.' Gannys stood up, walked across the floor to where Varius was primping in front of the mirror and laid his hand on the boy's bare shoulder. 'I fear the pain for you, dear Varius, but it is not too bad. It only lasts a moment and then they put a healing balm on that takes the pain away. It is done with a sharp knife, quickly, in one quick slash, so do not be afraid.'

Varius threw himself into Gannys's arms. 'Oh, Gannys, dear, dear Gannys, couldn't they cut off more than that useless bit of skin. Couldn't they cut it all off? I've heard about the priests of Syrian Attys and Greek Adonis. They emasculate themselves like Attys himself did and then they become as women, with beautiful round breasts. That's what I would like, dear Gannys, to be a girl.'

'Hush, Varius. 'Tis a hundred times more painful than the little clip you are to undergo, and dangerous too. Many die. Besides it is very bloody. Remember how the blood of Attys flowed out on the ground and caused violets to spring up. You hate blood, Varius, but even more you would hate never being able to satisfy yourself again. All you could do would be to satisfy others.'

'But that is all I really care to do, Gannys.'

'So you think now. But I have talked with eunuchs. Theirs is a sorrowful life with all the desires of a man and no way to satisfy them. But come, we must get ready for your trip to the Temple. You are to be there at midnight. The sacrifice will take place an hour after. Zenotabalus is sending an honour guard of priests for you.'

Gannys unhooked the gold clasps of the Persian robe and let it flutter to the floor. He picked it up, folded it carefully and then detached the jewels from Varius's ears, removed the diadem and the other jewels. Divested of his garments, there was no doubt about Varius's manhood and he turned to regard it in the mirror. He frowned and covered it with his hand, smiling to himself at its absence. Slowly he removed his hand and regarded the rapid tumescence approvingly. His fingers pinched the fold of skin which he knew he was about to lose, toyed with it and then reluctantly relinquished it as Gannys approached with a short white tunic on his arm.

Varius snatched the tunic away from Gannys, fingered the linen and flung it to the floor with anger. Since an early age he had refused to wear anything but silk, claiming that linen scratched his skin and that wool provoked a rash, but patient Gannys picked up the garment and in spite of Varius's screaming protests, he slipped it over his head. Varius twisted and turned, exaggerating his annoyance with fretful words, but Gannys proceeded to dress him. He slipped on long golden sandals of soft leather which reached half-way up Varius's thighs and laced them together with gold cords. He bound Varius's long hair back from his brow with a fillet of white wool and pinned a small, gold-rayed sun in the centre. He stepped back to appraise his work.

This simple costume, devoid of any ornament except the small rayed sun, increased Varius's beauty far more than the elaborate robes of coloured silk he usually wore. It completely erased the soft effeminacy of his face and gave him the look of a young athlete. His face seemed stronger, with the classic beauty of Greece predominating over the soft sensuality of Syria. His nose, descending in a pure line from his brow seemed chiselled with a perfection that minimized the wide, mobile nostrils. The slightly thickened lips seemed thinner and less sensual.

With a damp cloth, Gannys wiped off the white paint that overlaid the golden hue of Varius's skin; erased the black lines from around his eyes and removed the crimson from the lips. Bereft of his paint, his jewels and his clinging garments, Varius emerged as a boy, tall, slender and muscular. Again he turned and viewed himself in the mirror. He became Narcissus, in love with his reflection, and after studying himself for several moments, he leaned forward to implant his lips on those reflected in the silver.

'I look like a charioteer, dear Gannys.' His finger traced the lines of his cheek in the mirror. 'Oh, how handsome I am. And I shall be a charioteer. In spite of all that mother says to the contrary, I shall be one. I shall drive for the Greens in Rome because Green is my colour.' He leaned backward, the imaginary reins in his hand. In his thoughts he was already driving in the Circus Maximus, circling the dangerous track and hearing the plaudits of the Roman crowd. Varius's imagination knew no bounds and his fertile mind no limitations. Suddenly the expression of victorious joy changed to one of cruel vindictiveness. His eyes blazed with fury.

'And for a change, Gannys, I shall hitch the most beautiful girls in Rome to my chariot instead of horses and drive them around the Circus. Naked, every one of them! And they will pant and scream as they feel the whip. Their white skins will run with blood and I shall stand in the chariot and the crowds will scream "*Ave* Caesar".'

Gannys held up his hand for silence. The knock on the door was repeated. With his hand on the bronze latch, Gannys whispered, 'Do not be afraid, Varius. Zenotabalus will make a lot out of this, for you know, he loves ceremonies, but there is only one quick slash of the knife, one moment of pain. Do not be afraid.'

He opened the door and eight priests, dressed in white, their heads covered with white cloths through which two eye-holes stared, entered the room. The men advanced slowly, the black holes that marked their eyes staring blindly at Varius. Instinctively he recoiled from their relentless march towards him. They surrounded him silently, waiting for one of their group to speak. Although he was obviously making an effort to disguise his voice, Varius thought he could recognize the quavering accents of the old priest Zenotabalus.

'Are you Prince Varius Antoninus?'

'I am if you say so.' Varius was surprised at the name.

'Hitherto I have been known as Varius Avitus Bassianus. Now that I am the son of the divine Caracalla, I suppose my name becomes Antoninus.' Varius had somewhat regained his composure but he still feared the staring black holes that regarded him so impersonally.

'Then tonight I divest you of all names and titles. You become a common slave. You belong to the Sun God Elah-ga-baal. Consider yourself as his property, body and soul. It makes no difference tonight whether you are Bassianus or Antoninus. All are equal before Elah-ga-baal. Your body belongs to him and we shall do with it as we see fit. Bind him, men!'

Varius ducked low and tried to escape from under their arms but the circle closed in on him. From under their robes, the priests whipped out bands of white linen and before Varius could protest further, they had bound his hands close to his sides. Two more were kneeling on the floor, rolling the bandages around his legs. In a moment, he was securely trussed like a mummy, completely incapable of moving. They had neither blindfolded him nor gagged him – his eyes flashed defiance. Never before in his pampered life had anyone laid hands on him except those whom he had suborned to do his will. But, in this nightly abandonment of himself to his soldier companions, he was only playing a game – a game of his own femininity being mastered by their virility. He had always known that at a word from him, were the play to become too rough, it would stop. Now, he was helpless in the power of these unknown men. Perhaps, the thought suddenly flashed through his mind, perhaps after all they were not priests but hired assassins of Opellius Macrinus come to murder him.

He screamed, 'Mama, mama, mama!' His voice broke with fright. 'They are going to kill me! Grandmother, rescue me. Gannys, attend me. Why do you stand there, you stupid idiot, doing nothing while these men seize me?'

'Neither your mother nor your grandmother will intervene, Lupus,' the nameless voice spoke.

'Why do you call me Lupus?'

'Tonight you are known as Lupus. That is your name. You are the slave, Lupus.'

Varius twisted about. He saw Gannys, standing in the background, outside the ring of men.

'Good Gannys, come with me. I would see one familiar face among these sheeted figures with their baleful eyes.' He addressed the spokesman. 'May my slave attend me?' Suddenly he was humble – pleading.

'The slave Lupus has no slaves of his own. However, there is no reason why Gannys should not come.' The man leaned over to see that the bandages on arms and legs were secure. 'Take him, men, and conduct him to the temple.'

'I go to the temple, then?' Varius was reassured. If he were to go to the temple this was just another of Zenotabalus's ideas of ritualistic mummery. Well, he would act his part along with them.

'The slave Lupus is willing to sacrifice before the great God Elah-ga-baal tonight.' Varius spoke humbly.

'Yes, the God is dying and requires strength to bring him to life so that he may shine in all his glory in the heavens tomorrow. Tonight it is you who will give him that strength. Tonight you will sacrifice your manhood to him.'

'All of it?' Varius remembered the conversation he had had with Gannys before the priests arrived.

'Not all of it. Only a small part. Elah-ga-baal does not desire eunuchs in his service. Only men can serve him.' The robed figure leaned over and whispered in Varius's ear. 'Fear not. We shall not castrate you, Varius.' He signalled to the others and they hoisted the boy on their shoulders, three on a side. One led the procession and one came behind. Gannys followed.

The entire palace was deserted. Varius saw nobody as he was carried along through the empty corridors and courtyards. Once outside the gates, he was placed in a litter, the curtains drawn around him, and hustled through the dark streets. Upon arrival at the temple, which was entirely in darkness, he was lifted out and carried through a vast crowd of men, soldiers, freedmen and slaves, through the temple portals and the vast hall which was now empty of worshippers and from there, through a door of gold plates into the holy room behind the high altar where the most secret and holy rites were performed, for here was the sacred stone, descended from heaven – the mighty phallus of the sun.

Varius had been to the temple at night before and on his previous visits he had always seen it crowded with men who wandered its dim and unlighted reaches, searching for the companionship of the priests who were there to serve them. These services were not free but they depended on no set price. A single copper penny could buy them because nobody could be turned away. The Sun God needed many sacrifices to restore his life and speed him on his journey across the skies. Naturally those who had more to offer had the services of the younger and handsomer priests – those with the single copper coin had to be satisfied with the tired attentions of the older priests.

But, money was not a necessity at the Temple of Elahga-baal. The god was voracious, requiring and demanding all the strength he could obtain. Those who had no money but were desirous of earning some would be paid. These were the men who each night mounted the raised gallery around the sacred black stone and spent thereon their own libation, so that by morning the stone would be wet and glistening with the vital fluids of hundreds of men. This, as well as the services of the priests outside in the great hall, insured the sun's morning resurrection.

Tonight the temple was empty and the crowd of men outside the gates clamoured in vain for entrance. The steps of the hooded men echoed across the marble floor, returning from the high reaches of the pillared roof. When the doors to the holy of holies were opened and then shut again, their bell-like clanking died away only gradually. Tonight the inner room was seemingly empty. Varius could see no circle of men on the gallery around the black stone. There was only one dimly lighted spot instead of the hundreds of lamps which usually shone brightly in this room, in contrast to the darkness of the great hall outside. Here, where each man made his own solitary sacrifice, light was an incentive. Outside, where men and priests were coupled in strange embraces the darkness was welcome. One paid for privacy – one was paid for display.

Varius was deposited on his feet between two bronze standards, each of which supported a solitary lamp. It was the only illumination in the room and the black stone, strangely dull, loomed ominously in front. Gannys, Varius could see, had not been admitted. He was alone with the eight hooded men. It was a relief when he saw one of the priests lean over, untie the wrappings from his legs and unwind them. At the same time, he felt the pressure on his arms relax and in another moment they were free. He stretched them out before him, moving his hands and fingers to start the circulation, at the same time stamping his feet on the bare pavement. They paid little attention to him, letting him rub his arms and legs until he felt them return to normal.

Six of the priests divested themselves of their long robes, although they retained their hoods and, naked, they mounted the winding bronze stairs that led to the gallery that surrounded the stone. They bore tapers that they had lighted from the lamps below and as they circled the gallery above, they lit the almost continuous row of lights that circled it. Now Varius could see that the room was not empty. Far from it. The entire priesthood of the temple, released for one night from their regular duties were elbow to elbow, encircled around the balcony, gazing down with rapt, fanatical scrutiny at the menacing black stone below which now, under the bright illumination, showed the dried and scaling incrustations of former libations. Somewhere outside the room a gong was struck and continued in a slow, monotonous metronomic beat, to which the priests matched the movements of their hands. Gradually it increased in tempo and with it the movements until it reached a frenzied staccato beating. Mingled with it and rising above it were the moans and hoarse pantings of the priests in their labour.

Varius watched closely, feeling the excitement light a fire

in his own body, and as the tempo of the flashing hands increased and the maniacal moans intensified, he was suddenly grabbed from behind. Strong hands forced the upper part of his body backwards, his arms outstretched to the sides, his weight resting against the bodies of the men who held him. His head, unsupported, fell backwards and he could not see what was happening in front of him but he felt his tunic being pulled aside and another strong hand grabbed him. Then he screamed, as a sudden searing pain, so violent that he nearly fainted, took possession of him and convulsed his body. The fire of the pain abated a moment later and although he was still conscious of it, it became bearable.

The strong hands which were holding him lifted him to a standing position and he was free. The hooded figure before him pressed a bloody fragment of skin into his hand and he gazed at it dully, scarcely realizing that only moments before it had been a familiar part of his own body. The howling of the circle of priests above the black stone increased and the accelerated beats of the gong now filled the entire room with a sound so solid and violent it paralysed the senses. Already the stone was wet and glistening, becoming more and more bespattered as each fanatical zealot reached his climax.

'Throw it on the stone.' The hooded figure had to yell to make himself heard. 'If it remains on the stone we and you are blessed. If it falls, we are all cursed.'

Varius, glad to be rid of the bloody fragment in his hand, raised his arm and flung it at the stone. With one mighty crescendo, the howl from the priests arose, then froze on a high note. The gong stopped. An awful stillness followed and some of the priests on the gallery fell, swooning in hysteria. The baleful black stone glistened and the fragment of skin adhered to it, but started to slip and then continued slowly down, down, down. It fell off and landed at the base.

'Cursed are you and cursed are we.' The hooded figure grabbed Varius. 'The slave Lupus has brought disgrace and dishonour on all of us this night.'

Varius, still half-crazed by pain, shook off the clutching

hands. He made a grab for the creature's throat, clutched it in both his hands and hung tight. The talon-like fingers of the old man stretched out, frantically clutching at the thin air until they slowly contracted and the body slumped at Varius's feet. He turned, facing the assembled priests.

'Keep your hands off me! Come nearer and I'll strangle you one by one. I'm not Lupus. I'm no slave, purchased at the market to make a bloody sacrifice for you. You've had your will with me. I care not whether the sacrifice stayed on the stone or fell. Now, touch me not. No man lays a hand on me without my permission. I'm Varius Avitus Antoninus and I'll kill the first man who touches me.'

The priest who had held Varius's arms came forward slowly.

'We know who you are, Prince Varius. We will respect your person. What we have done is only in accordance with our ancient rites to fit you for the high place you will soon occupy. He who is to be High Priest must sacrifice thus. But the curse is already working. See, you have murdered Zenotabalus.' He reached over and drew back the hood from the recumbent figure.

Varius leaned over the priest. He regarded him, as he did all old men, with distaste.

'He still breathes. He is not dead. Carry him to his apartments. Tell him I did not know it was he whom I strangled. I shall make amends.' Varius straightened up. In his blood-stained tunic, he was, for the first time, a man. He spoke and acted like a man. 'Tell Zenotabalus I am sorry. Many times in my life I have begged to be forced to do something which I very much wished to do. But I do not ever wish to be forced to do something I do not wish to do again. Open the doors! Bid my slave Gannys who accompanied me to attend me. Prepare bandages to stop this bleeding.' He turned and walked to the already opened doors.

Despite the pain, he was smiling. His spoken words were only for himself.

'They obeyed me! When I spoke they cringed before me. They feared me. That is how it will be when I am Caesar.

Ah, 'tis a good feeling. I like to command.' He walked a few steps across the hall, hearing Gannys's steps behind him. He smiled. 'But there are times when I like to be commanded.'

8

VARIUS'S HEADY PLUNGE into authority, as the son of Caracalla, and his newly found power to command, as the presumptive Caesar, kept the entire palace in a frenetic uproar for some weeks after his initiation at the temple. That he suffered some pain from the operation was apparent but that he must force everyone in the palace from his august grandmother to the lowest kitchen slave to his demanding will was something entirely out of proportion to the extent of his invalidism. Julia Maesa began to wonder if she had misjudged the lad. With his present physical inability to handle the nightly parade of legionaries, he was bored and frustrated, slipping out of her authority and showing that he had a mind of his own.

Everything was tried to amuse him and keep him quiet. Eutychianus Comazon brought the Nubian he had been keeping in reserve and the Nubian reacted most admirably to Varius's manipulations. For a few moments, he purred like a cat in his pretence that the Nubian was Gigex and that he was Soaemias but the excitement those few moments produced so increased his pain that the Nubian was sent flying from the palace and nothing could be found to satisfy Varius.

The wily Gannys tried every kind of diversion he could invent to divert Varius's mind from his suffering but nothing succeeded. Gannys combed the bazaars for new scents, new pomades and new unguents but a mere sniff was all that Varius would devote to them. He had been hurt in his most vital spot – that from which he derived his greatest pleasure and excitement. Neither the new robes that Soaemias had made for him; the important papers that Maesa brought to him to sign; or the jewelled crowns that old Zenotabalus carried to the palace for his coming elevation to the priesthood accomplished any results. He did derive some momentary pleasure out of seeing the white woollen wrappings around old Zenotabalus's injured neck and the cringing attitude of the priest, but it was purely temporary. There was only one thing he wanted. If he couldn't have that, nothing else would suffice and if he couldn't be happy, he was absolutely determined that nobody else would be. Without his nightly amusements, Varius was bored.

After having tried all the nostrums and ointments known to the priests of Aesculapius, it was finally found that applications of snow, which in sun-baked Emesa was even more precious than gold, brought Varius some relief from his pain and, strangely enough Alexianus, who was unwillingly dragged to the sick room as a last resort, provided a poor substitute for other entertainment. Alexianus had been carefully coached in his new role and for the first time in his life, he managed to do nothing to offend Varius, nor to take offence at anything the other did. Varius, feeling somewhat more comfortable with the cold snow to alleviate his pain, discovered a new-found interest in his young cousin as a result of the efforts they were both making to achieve harmony, a certain community of interests was discovered – namely chariot racing.

Through some strange quirk in his character, Varius had always been attracted to the races. Perhaps it was because chariot racing had become the life and breath of the Roman people, or even more likely because the handsome charioteers were the idols of the populace. There was still some lingering trace of masculinity that neither Maesa nor Soaemias had been entirely able to crush. Varius was determined that he would learn to drive despite the danger and he found that Alexianus shared this desire with him.

Varius, incapacitated as he was, made no aggressive move towards Alexianus and gradually the younger boy overcame some of his distaste of the older. Their companionship ripened to the extent that Varius was only too willing to discuss the riper moments of his encounters with his soldier companions, and these the less experienced Alexianus countered with his reports on Apol and his progress with the slave girl as well as his own throbbing desire to learn of such an experience first hand.

Although Varius tried hard to convert his cousin to the delights of male companionship, he found that Alexianus would not agree with his assertions that woman, a vile creature governed by the moon, was unclean and not to be desired, whereas man, under the dominion of the Sun was always strong, clean and glorious. The exotic delights that Varius pictured had no appeal to Alexianus, and although Alexianus's desire for the young slave girl did not interest Varius, nevertheless, he recognized his cousin's need and through Gannys as intermediary, he smuggled the girl into his room one afternoon and when Alexianus arrived, he proudly presented her.

The boy, nothing loath, proceeded then and there to demonstrate before Varius how delightful a thing a woman could really be. Varius watched the entire process closely and found it most disgusting until he mentally pictured himself in the slave girl's place and then developed an interest.

Fortunately the snow kept him from becoming too excited. When the demonstration was over, which was almost before it had begun, and Alexianus quite satisfied that it was an improvement over manual methods, they spent some time comparing notes. Alexianus was grateful to Varius and Varius was able to understand his cousin a little better. A tentative *rapport* had been set up between them. It was never to grow to any degree of intimacy but as time went on, it developed into a programme of mutual sufferance. They had, at least, chariot racing in common – it was all they ever would have but it served its purpose.

Despite Varius's hypochondriacal enjoyment of his invalidism, the wound healed and he was able to dispense with the snow but a lingering tenderness still precluded the possibility of nightly companionship. At the end of two weeks, with the prospect of his entry into the priesthood on the morrow, Varius was nervous with frustration and the increased energy resulting from his abstinence.

When Gannys woke him, long before dawn on the day of the ceremony, Varius was in a fretful temper. He relaxed somewhat when he saw the robe of flowing gold, the gems and the jewelled sandals he was to wear but then, while Gannys was trying to dress him, all hell broke loose. The diadem was too heavy, it pinched his head; the gold robe scratched his feet. He ripped the robe with petulant curses and threw it at Gannys, then followed it with the diadem which struck Gannys with a glancing blow on the cheek and felled him. Blood started to trickle from the wound on Gannys's head and Varius, now completely at the mercy of his distraught nerves, stood in the centre of the floor, stark naked, stamping his feet and screaming wildly.

Old Maesa, barefooted and half-dressed, her silk himation dragging on the floor, came running in, thinking that the boy was being murdered. Soaemias, her face partly painted and a long line of black antimony on one side where her slave's brush had slipped, followed her. Neither of them could calm the frenzied Varius who now, with an audience, stamped and yelled the more. Still screaming, he took to throwing things, causing his dignified grandmother and his mother to duck most unbecomingly behind the furniture.

It was up to Mamaea, attracted by the screaming of all three to set things to rights. She advanced on Varius with a determined look in her eyes that froze his hand in mid-air with the small bronze statue he was about to fling at her. With her bare hand, she delivered a fulsome blow on his pink rump which he returned with a vicious slap across her face. He had always hated his aunt, but when he saw the vivid red mark that his fingers had left, he was instantly repentant and fell on his knees before her, his hands clutching at her hips. His screams gave way to uncontrolled sobs of contrition and by the time he was lifted to his feet, led to a chair and seated, with another application of snow, this time to his reddened eyes, he had become almost rational.

With a great display of penitent affection, he went to the

79

supine Gannys, knelt over him with endearing words and applied what was left of the snow. Gannys was finally revived and the flow of blood staunched. That was the signal for Soaemias to start quarrelling with Mamaea for daring to strike her darling Varius. Mamaea went into her usual harangue about Varius's upbringing until they were both close to blows. It was then Varius's turn to pacify *them* and at length old Maesa, her himation sufficiently hitched up to hide her sagging breasts, pushed them, spitting like cats, out of the room and left Varius to the ministrations of the now revived Gannys.

This was but a foretaste of the long, exhausting day. Once arrived at the temple, Varius squirmed and wriggled on his high throne, complaining that the incense made his eyes smart, the cushions were too hot, the throne too high. He was annoyed by the long processions; impatient at the interminable pauses when Zenotabalus droned his endless invocations; bored with the long paeans of praise to the sun and exasperated by the flutterings of the effeminate priests. He was hungry, thirsty, tired, and sick of the whole pompous ritual which was due to drag on all day from sunrise to sunset. His mind was set on one thing – the coming of darkness and the delights that it promised.

As the sun continued to mount in the sky until it reached its meridian, the songs and invocations were loud in their praise of the Sun God's power and strength. The youngest and fairest of the priests, trained through intense concentration, sat naked in the courtyard, staring straight into the sun, self-hypnotized into such a state of ecstasy that, by the power of mind only, their votive libations spurted forth in honour of their deity. This caused a passing interest to Varius and he leaned forward on his throne to watch, but relaxed into tired boredom as the young men, temporarily blinded by the light of their god and weak-kneed from their exertions were led away.

During the long afternoon, as the sun was declining, the joyous anthems changed into wailing dirges at the approaching death of the orb and when it had finally sunk redly behind the flat plains, the priests wept, tore their hair and lacerated themselves with thorn branches in their grief and sorrow.

With the final setting of the sun, the long day of solemnity and exhausting pomp drew to its weary close. Varius was led, in his glittering robes of gold, out on to the steps of the temple, to be cheered by the thousands who were gathered there; among whom was the entire complement of the Emesa Legion, many of whom had known Varius intimately and all of whom had received his generous donative. They led the cheers which greeted him and Varius knew, from the spontaneous warmth of the greetings and the vigorous shoutings, that he had won the army, at least the Legion stationed in Emesa. For a half an hour while he stood before them, resplendent in his robes and his beauty, the plaudits continued without abating and even as he turned to re-enter the temple, there was a swell of voices which called him back, just to have the pleasure of looking on his face.

This was their boy – their beautiful priest and master. He was no stranger. They had all benefited by his generosity. They loved him and wanted him to know it. Their boy! The same whom their hands had fondled, their lips had kissed, whose body they had enjoyed. Now he was High Priest of this strange Syrian God, Elah-ga-baal and soon, it was whispered, he would be Emperor of Rome. He was the son of their idolized Caracalla who had done more for them than any other Caesar.

Varius re-entered the temple with the shouting still in his ears and passed through the vast but now deserted hall, beyond the closed golden doors that sheltered the sacred stone and out through a hidden back door to the quarters of the priests. Here Gannys was waiting in a darkly cool room. He stripped off the stiff robes and the cumbersome jewels, gave him unwatered wine to drink and food, then led him to a couch whose silken sheets felt cool to the boy's sweaty limbs. He was asleep almost before Gannys had adjusted the pillows and there he slept in a drunken stupor, exhausted from

81

the gruelling ceremonies of the day until Gannys awakened him, with difficulty, an hour before midnight and led him to the now deserted baths.

In the *caladarium*, with its steaming hot water, he sweated out the alcohol in his body. Followed a cooling off period in the *tepidarium* and a quick plunge into the cold pool of the *frigidarium*, which restored him to sobriety. Now, fully back to his senses, he was ready for the lengthy manipulations of Gannys's hands with their perfumed oils and precious ointments. Once again, he was dressed in the short white tunic and the long golden sandals with their thigh-high straps. The door opened slowly and Zenotabalus entered.

'Tonight, once again, you shed the name of Antoninus and become the slave Lupus that you may wander in the great hall with the other priests, no greater nor no less than any of them. Here you will fortify yourself in strength and vigour which will be transferred to the great god who has died and must be revived. You can refuse no man. You can have no preference. As long as he holds a coin in his hand, be it gold, silver, or copper, you must take it and satisfy him, be he even the lousiest beggar in the market place, stinking from his oozing sores. Only by your efforts as a priest, can the sun be revived to shine tomorrow. If a man approaches you penniless, do not turn him away. Instruct him to knock seven times on the gold doors and they will be opened unto him. He can gain ten *denarii* by joining the sacrificial ring around the sacred stone and his sacrifice will be acceptable.'

Varius had been anticipating the evening all through the long day and he well knew what was in store for him without the prattlings of the old man. Who didn't in Emesa – and not only in Emesa but throughout the breadth of the Empire. Men travelled from the far-off reaches to this city and this temple, and many who had made the long journey preferred to live out their lives in Emesa. But Varius, although accepting the instructions in apparent humility, had already made up his mind that should any ancient approach him, even though he held a bag of gold in his trembling hands, there would be no Varius waiting to receive him. He would have silently slipped into the shadows and the old voluptuary could find some other victim.

Zenotabalus led him back into the great hall of the temple and abandoned him. There was no light in the hall, except the silver moonlight which crept through the arches and wanly illuminated those half-moon sections of the mosaic pavement which were not shadowed by the walls. Through these doorways, men entered from the street and, hidden behind each dark pillar, a twittering group of white-tunicked priests awaited them. Those who ascended the steps of the temple, upright in their strength and vigour were quickly claimed by the young priests, but the old men, who came puffing up the steps with shuffling steps and tapping canes were wont to stand long in the doorways until some aged priest, whose devotion to duty had outlasted his days of pleasure claimed them.

Varius was just another white-clad priest with little to distinguish him from the others except his exuberant step and the fleeting glimpse of his beauty as he stepped into the circles of dim light. In his desire to pick the right one, he lost two or three good chances as personable prospects came up the steps because the other priests were too quick for him. Varius was waiting to see the face: through long practice, the priests judged by the walk and bearing. Varius did know enough to shrink back into the shadows as two old men in dragging togas came in and were reluctantly claimed. One by one the priests who were around him found companions until Varius was finally left alone. The hours were passing and he began to fear that his first night would be entirely wasted and this he resolved must not happen. After his two weeks of enforced continence, if no likely subject appeared, he would join the circle of paid sacrificants around the stone.

The first influx of patrons was over and Varius peered out anxiously from behind the shadow of his pillar. The minutes dragged by and his eyes became strained from scanning the empty courtyard. The latch of the bronze gate clicked and Varius took heart. He saw a lone figure walking across the courtyard and ascending the steps. This one would be his, he vowed, and he was glad he had waited for the man appeared young and handsome and he walked with the springy step of an athlete. His shoulders were broad and he wore only a short pleated skirt of some thin white stuff, secured at the waist with a broad leather belt. Varius could see the play of moonlight on the rippling muscles, and the dancing highlights as the moon caught the metal buckle.

The unknown started the ascent of the steps and Varius took no chances on losing him, but ran to the top of the steps to welcome him. There he stood, with the bright light of the moon on his face and body, his arms outstretched. The stranger came up the steps slowly and halted one step below Varius and, tall as Varius was, their eyes were nearly on a level. They stared at each other silently, each enraptured with the physical beauty he beheld.

Varius was overwhelmed by the complete embodiment of masculinity that stood one step below him. He gasped at the swarthy beauty of the Levantine face with the slightly aquiline nose, the flashing eyes veiled by sooty lashes, the moist lips which parted to show a row of gleaming, white teeth. His hand ached to reach out and touch the skullcap of tight black curls.

The stranger smiled and Varius smiled back, allowing his rapt gaze to travel down the column of the neck with its throbbing vein to the broad shoulders and the wide chest with its copper discs of nipples to the flat belly and the slender hips. He wondered what the short pleated skirt concealed and if the hidden mystery could possibly compare with what he had already seen.

Zoticus was similarly enamoured. Never before had he seen such beauty. For a moment he almost forgot his mission. But then he remembered the reports of Varius's beauty. Could this be he? Could this beautiful boy be the one for whom he had made the long journey from Alexandria? Praise be to Isis if he were. In spite of the reports he had received, he had half anticipated some snotty-nosed lad.

Varius was too dazed to move. Zoticus ascended the last

step, a piece of gold in his outstretched hand. Mechanically, Varius reached out his hand to receive it but before Zoticus laid the money in his palm, he heard the hoarse whisper.

'Are you he whom I seek – the Antonine?'

'I am he,' Varius managed to stutter.

'I come from the Tribune Eutychianus Comazon seeking you alone.'

'Why has the Tribune never sent you to me before?'

'Because only today I arrived from Alexandria.'

'And your name?'

'Aurelius Zoticus. And you are Varius Antoninus.'

'I have been called that but tonight I am the slave Lupus.'

'The slave Lupus? I do not understand.'

'The slave Lupus, already the property of one Aurelius Zoticus from Alexandria. You have purchased me with the piece of gold you hold in your hand.'

Zoticus placed the gold piece in Varius's palm and his fingers touched the boy's hot, moist flesh. Varius was trembling, his knees buckled under him. Zoticus picked him up in his strong arms and carried him into the dim shadows of the temple. They embraced each other with a mutuality of desire.

Varius's hands sought. He gasped. It was true. All the beauty and strength he had seen in the moonlight was as nothing to what his questing hands now encountered. Surely it must be the god himself for no mere human could be so splendidly accoutred. This was no man. This was the godhead himself. Elah-ga-baal!

Zoticus would have borne him to the floor but Varius extricated himself from the enveloping embrace.

'Not here, Zoticus, my lord, master and god,' he panted. 'Not here. Let us go back to the palace where a soft bed, bright lights and perfumes await us. Let us reap the full pleasure of this night and not spend ourselves like temple catamites on the hard, cold floor. But first, this gold piece to the treasury and a prayer to Elah-ga-baal for having blessed me by showing himself to me.'

With Zoticus's protecting arm around Varius, they walked

the long length of the shadowy hall. They passed many couples in strange embraces in the shadows and they stumbled over others on the floor, who stopped their writhings only long enough to curse them for their clumsiness. Varius deposited the gold coin in the box beside the doors leading to the inner shrine. With his hand in Zoticus's, he knelt on the pavement.

'Most high and sacred Elah-ga-baal, today I have been lacking in love and respect for you. I scoffed at your rites and I ridiculed your priests and now I am sorry. Tonight I know how great and powerful you are for you have come to me in all your magnificent greatness. From now on, great Elah-ga-baal, I shall serve you and love you. This wonder that you have delivered into my hands this night shall be a sign between us, always reminding me of your magnificence and your love for me.'

He stood up and once again he sought the warm shelter of Zoticus's arms.

'To the palace, my lord Zoticus. Your slave, Lupus, commands it. Get a litter, the fastest you can find. Let us hurry before you vanish from my sight to begin your morning journey across the skies.'

'Yes, let us hurry little Antonine ...'

'Lupus!'

'Lupus, then, but let us hurry although you need have no fear that I shall vanish. This flesh of mine is all too solid. I am as anxious as you to seek your bed. For over a week I have been travelling, and during that time I have lain with neither man nor woman.'

'And I, master, have been travelling all my life, waiting to arrive at this moment.' Varius's hand tightened. 'Promise me you will never leave me.'

'I shall never leave you, little Lupus.'

'Never? Not even if our path leads to Rome?'

'Least of all there, little Lupus. You will need me to protect you. See, my arm is strong.'

Zoticus was jubilant. Things were working out better than he could have dreamed. This would not be a difficult task –

86

'twould be a pleasure. He was as loath to release Varius as Varius was to leave his arms but he bethought himself of the soft bed in the palace. Once in that bed, he would see to it that he never left and besides, it was better than the hard mosaic floor of the temple. If only he could last until they arrived. He plucked Varius's hand away. Perhaps after all, in spite of his scoffing, there was such a thing as love. Possibly it had come to him. He hoped it would be profitable.

But to Varius, hurrying through the dark hall beside his god, there was no question. He knew that love had come to him.

9

VARIUS WAS MORE than willing to leave the diplomatic moves, the involved intrigues and the carefully laid plots which were to bring him closer to the throne, in the able hands of his grandmother, Comazon and his mother. He was quite uninterested in politics and the methods that were being employed to make him Caesar. Being Caesar meant nothing to him except that it would give him the opportunity to do exactly as he pleased without opposition. Who could oppose Caesar? Not even Caesar's stern grandmother or fluttery mother, least of all his sour-faced aunt. From now on, he was determined to rule his own life exactly as he pleased. He gave warning to all his family and to Comazon and Gannys. No more restraints! Let them not cross him! He was willing to be Caesar and when that time came they could rule Rome as they pleased but he would rule the palace and himself. His first edict was that Aurelius Zoticus should remain in the palace and receive the highest rank next to himself.

Julia Maesa scented danger. It was one thing to have Varius amused nightly by a constantly changing procession of soldiers. They came and went and there was neither permanent attachment nor influence, for Varius was all too anxious for the next night to pay much attention to the one who departed in the morning. It was a contact of bodies not of minds. They served a double purpose in that they kept Varius entertained and at the same time were being won over to his side. But, it would never do for Varius to have a permanent lover. Oh no! As time went on he would rise to an ascendancy of power and subordinate Varius to his own will, regardless of what the family desired. It would mean sharing authority over Varius with a stranger and from what Julia Maesa had seen of Zoticus, he seemed a most undesirable stranger. She was not blinded by love. Under the glossy beauty of the man, she saw his cunning, his crafty designs and his cruelty. No, Aurelius Zoticus must follow the path of the other soldiers – in for a night and out in a morning. Varius thought otherwise. Zoticus must stay.

Soaemias also was far from happy about the arrangement. She had heard glowing reports of the fabulous Zoticus from Alexandria and was determined to have him for her own and not share him with her son. Gigex was a poor comparison to this paragon and besides, Gigex was losing his ardour and it was time he was replaced by a fresh recruit. She knew Varius well enough to know that he would not share Zoticus and moreover, she did not want half a loaf. No, far better to get him out of the way for the time being and let Varius forget him. Then, she could get him for herself later. Her suggestions, however, fell on deaf ears. All her hints amounted to nothing. Zoticus must stay.

Gannys, whose influence over the young Varius had always been paramount, sensed a lessening of his power with Zoticus in such close attendance, and he too used his influence to discourage the permanent installation of this – what he termed – fortune-hunting wrestler in the palace. His propaganda was subtler than that of Maesa or Soaemias who had emphatically forbidden and nothing else. Gannys pointed out to Varius how quickly one could tire of the same person and the far greater thrill of the unknown – that titillating anticipation of something new and different every night and the excitement of variety. Varius would not listen. He was convinced that nothing could possibly exceed what he already had. Varius was far too infatuated, too completely satisfied with what the Sun God had tossed into his bed. Gannys was all for sending Zoticus back to the Legion and finding something better. Varius thought otherwise. Zoticus must stay.

Zoticus, now sure of his hold on the boy, was as determined to remain as Varius was to have him. He did not find his duties arduous. He too was infatuated, perhaps not as whole-heartedly as Varius, but he found the boy's beauty compelling, and certainly life with Varius was far pleasanter than his former frequently unhappy encounters with whomever had the money to pay for him. He remembered the fat, unsatisfied wives, the scabrous old men and all the other thrill-seeking undesirables who had to pay to be desired. That had been a labour of constant pretence, a nightly effort which had been slowly wearing him down. With Varius, he did not have to pretend. The boy himself was sufficient inspiration. In his own way, Zoticus loved the boy but he loved the ease and luxury of the palace more. More important still was the prospect of the ultimate power and authority that would become his. The pretty little Antonine was to be Emperor of Rome. Everyone said so. And . . . what better position was there in the whole Roman Empire than to share Caesar's bed permanently.

So Zoticus remained, although the Tribune Comazon pointed out that Zoticus was a soldier and the penalty for desertion was death. If he did not return he would be a deserter and the cross awaited him. Varius pooh-poohed the silly law. Comazon as Tribune could give Zoticus a leave of absence. The loss of one legionary would not affect the army but the loss of this particular legionary would certainly affect Varius's happiness and well-being.

Soaemias was willing to bribe Varius with the offer of her own Gigex if he would but relinquish Zoticus but Varius saw through his mother's transparent generosity and declined. Gannys went into raptures over a slave from the Sudan which he had seen in the market and whom he was sure would be far more satisfactory than Zoticus but Varius was not interested. Finally, Julia Maesa advanced the crowning argument. Zoticus could have no official position in the palace if he remained. He was not a slave – he was a freedman. He was a Plebian. Therefore he could neither mingle with the slaves who were below him nor the Patricians who were above him.

The Bassianus family was not in the habit of taking a mere freedman into their bosom and now that Varius was an Antoninus in addition to being a Bassianus, there was certainly no place for Zoticus in the palace unless he were to be retained as a servant, and a freedman could not be a servant as he was not a slave.

The various social classifications seemed so much idle folderol to Varius but he found a way to stop his grandmother's nagging. He reminded her that according to the stupid Augustan law of Rome, he must eventually marry. What status then would his wife have? Why ... regardless of whom she was, she would immediately be raised to imperial rank. That satisfied Varius. If the woman whom he married would be raised to imperial rank, the man whom he married would be equally high. Maesa had been unwittingly forced into a corner and she could have bitten off her tongue but the words had been spoken.

Varius, seeing his advantage, proceeded. Ergo! He would marry Zoticus. The only difference was that Zoticus would be his husband instead of his wife. Once having propounded the idea, Varius was immediately in favour of it and in spite of his family's vast and tiresome objections, he insisted on going through with it.

Old Zenotabalus, who saw a chance to regain Varius's favour was the only one on his side. The old priest delved back into the ancient archives of the Sun God and found that in times past, many of the High Priests of Elah-ga-baal had been married to the godhead. Even the stiff-necked Jews had been known to marry their Jehovah. As Varius insisted that Zoticus was an incarnation of Elah-ga-baal, Varius would only be marrying his god.

Zenotabalus informed the fuming Maesa that this would indeed be a true marriage and would negate any marriage to a woman which might come later, which marriage was strictly forbidden to a priest of Elah-ga-baal. With Varius first married to Zoticus, and through him to the Sun God, any other marriages would be merely to satisfy the demands of Roman Law. If Zoticus were to be Varius's first spouse, he would not be tainted by the ensuing marriage to a woman. At length even Julia Maesa had to yield, albeit unwillingly, to the preponderance of sacred authority which Zenotabalus, with an eye to binding Varius more closely to him, either discovered in his musty tomes or invented on the spot.

So, much to her chagrin, despite Soaemias's jealousy, Gannys's annoyance, and Comazon's better judgment, the marriage was solemnized in the temple, with Varius in the diaphanous red draperies of a bride and Zoticus stalwart in white linen. Having found Zoticus in the temple, and having been indissolubly bound to him there, Varius became more than ever convinced of the power of Elah-ga-baal. Had not the Great God granted him his greatest happiness on earth? From then on, his fanatical love for his God occupied third place in his affections. First, himself, second, his husband Aurelius Zoticus and third his God, Elah-ga-baal! He worshipped all three to excess and he became dominated by his own effete neuroticism for himself, his lover and his God.

He was intensely jealous of Zoticus. If the wrestler so much as glanced twice at another person, man or woman, Varius immediately went into a fit of violent anger, dark despondency or fretful petulance. He would have had Zoticus infibulated but Zoticus had been circumcised in Egypt and there was no foreskin to hold the *fibula*. He instituted a careful system of espionage throughout the palace whereby every moment that Zoticus spent away from his side was reported back to him. Zoticus belonged to him and he was unwilling to share him with anyone else.

He did, however, insist that Zoticus keep up his training as a wrestler. His glorious physique could not be endangered by a life of inactivity. One courtyard in the palace was refurbished as a gymnasium for Zoticus's morning exercises. For a time Varius worked with him, intrigued by the novelty of physical exertion. He found, much to his disgust, that the rounded and feminine softness of his arms and legs was beginning to disappear under a hard coating of muscle and he did not want that to happen. Although he relinquished his attendance, he made sure that Zoticus was well guarded during these long hours of absence away from him.

However, great as his passion for Zoticus was, Zoticus could not entirely satisfy him for Varius was an insatiable little satyr. He began to miss both the variety and thrill of the unknown, exactly as Gannys had predicted. Although he was determined that Zoticus would have eyes for nobody but himself, he saw no reason why he could not add a little variety to his own life by resuming his adventures with the army, unknown to his husband. These, however, would have to take place during Zoticus's morning practice instead of at night, which he was willing to devote to his spouse, as any legitimate wife should. Other married women took lovers, why not he? It would only make him more sure that he was truly married, if he were to carry on some interesting intrigue, hidden from his husband. All wives did.

To have a legitimate excuse to absent himself from the palace, he decided to devote these free hours to the service of Elah-ga-baal, and as soon as Zoticus was off to his practice, Varius hied himself to the temple to dance before his god. Attendance by the soldiers was encouraged, and after the ritualistic dance, which was obscene enough before Varius embroidered the steps with further obscenities, there was always the private room behind the altar where Varius could entertain those who had been chosen from the audience by Gannys. As time went on and news of the rewards that awaited promising and co-operative young legionaries spread through the camp, a line of ten to twenty would form before the door of the private room, to be called in singly, in pairs or in dozens depending on Varius's idea of entertainment for the day.

Zoticus, sweating at his practice, knew nothing about these

morning gambols and believed, as he had every reason to believe from Varius's impassioned love-making at night, that he was the only one. He was secure in the knowledge that he could not be replaced. There was none other in the Empire so equipped as to replace him. He was secure in Varius's affections and he was supreme in the palace. His assumption of the incarnation of Elah-ga-baal and the sacred rites that bound him to Varius were such strong ties they could not be broken.

While Varius was conducting his petty intrigues, keeping his jealous watch over Zoticus and arranging for his outside revels in the temple, Julia Maesa, with the help of Comazon was slowly pulling the necessary strings to get Varius on the throne. In this she found her ablest ally to be the utter stupidity of Opellius Macrinus who now called himself Caesar, confirmed as such by the Senate and upheld by his own legions.

Egged on by Maesa and Comazon, King Artabanus had declared war on Rome and Opellius Macrinus was forced to accept the challenge. He was so ignominiously beaten that he had to meet the strict terms that Artabanus laid down – complete freedom for Parthia and a huge indemnity of money. The Roman Legions were not accustomed to defeat, nor were they accustomed to the half pay and half rations under limited service which Macrinus imposed upon them to gain the wherewithal to pay the stiff demands of Artabanus. Discontent had become rife in the legions. If they were to be idle, they wanted to be home, not quartered in Syria. Their adored Caracalla had been murdered and they were left at the mercy of his murderer. the penny-pinching Macrinus.

Then, having so foolishly stirred up discontent and near mutiny in the army, Macrinus made his fatal move. He sent two of the legions to Emesa to go into winter quarters there. This was playing directly into Maesa's hands. She already possessed one legion faithful to Varius, now she would have two more to work on and once again her coffers of gold were thrown open, and the line outside Varius's door in the temple lengthened. The soldiers were never allowed to forget from whom their bounty came. It was given to them by Antoninus, the son of their beloved Caracalla.

To these men, loveless, half-fed, discontented, homesick and bored with the grey monotony of camp life, the exotic figure of the beautiful boy, dancing to the lascivious measures of flute and harp in the sensuous beauty of his own face and his transparent robes, became a constant reminder that this was Antoninus, the son of their Caracalla. The thin silks and bright jewels of the boy were a colourful contrast to their drab tunics. The beauty of his painted face and the clean lines of his young body were far more enticing than the scrawny, stinking whores who followed the camp.

The soldiers came in scores to the temple to watch and worship and while they watched and desired, the tall, the strong and the handsome were culled from the crowd and led to the baths behind the temple. There they were bathed and clothed in clean, new uniforms and then led forth to wait in ever-lengthening lines at the door of the room behind the high altar where they were to meet this glorious child of destiny in embraces that would dispel their solitary lovelessness.

When they departed, satiated, clean of body, clad in new uniforms, with a pouch of gold at their belt and the assurance that they had brought honour to this strange god, they were all the more willing to acclaim this passionate Antoninus, extol his sensuous charms and display their newly found riches. Every soldier who had not previously been chosen was hoping that his turn would come on the next day, and as word was spread by the fortunates even the great hall of the temple became too small to hold them all, and Varius must dance on the steps outside so that all could see him and admire him and come to love him for the colour, romance and joy he brought into their empty lives.

Eventually of course, Zoticus heard about it. Word of the temple activities penetrated even to his carefully guarded courtyard, but Zoticus took a broad-minded view of the proceedings. He was satisfied that no one person could supplant

94

him – why be jealous of an army. He had also come to realize that with Varius's satyric nature, no one person could ever satisfy him. He knew his own hold over the boy and he was still infatuated with him. But jealousy would only estrange them, and he was not so blindly enamoured that he did not realize full well the value to Varius's prestige that was being enhanced daily. Winning the army was a stepping-stone to the purple and that was the direction Zoticus desired to go.

To keep his dignity as a husband, however, he concocted a dramatic little scene, during which he threatened to kill himself if Varius didn't love him. Tears and mad protestations of love and fidelity from Varius were allowed to convince him that suicide was out of the question. For the first time in their relationship, Zoticus refused himself to Varius until Varius came crawling to him across the floor, begging for his favour. With a great show of relenting he took Varius into his arms and forgave him, reluctantly admitting to the necessity of Varius's morning temple dancing. All during his magnanimous forgiveness of Varius, he was mentally determining that two could play the same game. Zoticus too had been accustomed to variety. The cuckolded husband could have as many intrigues as the errant wife. With Varius's coffers always open to his greedy hands, it would not be too difficult to outbribe if he could not outwit Varius's spies.

Now, with three legions at her command, Maesa, able general that she was, felt that the time had come for decisive action. Early one morning, a procession formed in the palace yard. First in rank was a resplendent chariot of gold and ivory, whose six white horses were driven by Zoticus. Varius stood, clad in the imperial purple with the simple golden laurel leaves as a coronet. In the next chariot, driven by Gigex, Julia Maesa rode, accompanied by the full-bosomed Soaemias, and behind them stretched a long line of some twenty carts. Each cart was heaped high with iron-bound wooden coffers, gold vessels and silver statues – the vast fortune which Julia Maesa had spent a lifetime garnering for just this occasion. They drove through the city, stopping only long enough for Varius and Zoticus to sacrifice at the temple of Elah-ga-baal, then on to the camp of the three legions where they were met by Eutychianus Comazon and the Tribunes of the two new legions. Every soldier who watched, and they were all detained to the camp for just that purpose, saw his idol, the new Antoninus, son of Caracalla, driving into the camp and although they were not sure who the old dame in the second chariot was nor the identity of the high-breasted whore beside her, they were certainly not unaware of the long line of treasure wagons. Their cheers mounted as Varius, his purple robes and his golden crown making him look more like a man than the flowing Syrian robes and elaborate jewels ever had, ascended the steps of the hastily erected platform.

There was only one thing left to do and the cheering, shouting, joyous soldiers did it. They deposed the pretender Opellius Macrinus and unanimously elected Varius Emperor of Rome under the title of Marcus Aurelius Antoninus, Antoninus Filius, Severi Nepos, Augustus Pius, Felix. Varius had insisted on the name Aurelius, not out of deference to his distinguished ancestor, but to signify his marriage to Aurelius Zoticus. From that day on, Varius insisted that he be called Antoninus. He was never Varius again. Although unconfirmed by the Senate, unacknowledged by any except three legions and a usurper in the eyes of the State, Varius was Emperor of Rome – Caesar. Varius was no more. To all the world, he was Antoninus, except to his husband to whom he still preferred to be known as Lupus, the slave of Elah-ga-baal.

Immediately the camp was closed and fortified and messengers sent off to Antioch, demanding the surrender of Opellius Macrinus. Other messengers were dispatched to all the legions of the East and to the August Fathers of Rome. The Antonine House was back on the throne – let Opellius Macrinus recognize it. But this, Opellius Macrinus was not willing to do. He underestimated the popularity of him whom he called that 'hermaphroditic idiot' but he had at least begun to think. He dispatched his Praefect, Ulpius Julian, with a large body of troops to Emesa with orders to take the camp of the mutinous legions, slay the would-be Antoninus together with his family and his stud, Zoticus, and return to Antioch with the Antonine's head.

Julian covered the hundred and twenty-five miles between Antioch and Emesa but when he arrived, his troops were so wearied from forced marches that he foolishly gave them leave to retire behind their lines at sunset and prepare for battle on the morrow. Therein he erred. During the night, certain of the Emesan legionaries stole into the camp of Julian's legions, spreading the news of the wonderful new Antoninus and liberally distributing his gold. When morning came, they had departed to their own camp but the rising sun outlined the tall slender figure of Antoninus, standing on the walls of the camp, dressed in his imperial robes, bulwarked by his treasure chests behind him. He stood there boldly and proudly, even bravely for he was in danger of death from any arrow hastily shot from the bow of a legionary loyal to Macrinus. No arrow was shot nor spear thrown. The cheers of his own legions were echoed by those of the invaders, who threw down their weapons and refused to battle against the idol of the army – all except the Praefect Julian and a few officers who were still loyal to Macrinus. These managed to flee but were soon hunted down and the head of Julian, no longer needed to command his legions, was severed from his body.

Comazon gave instructions that the head be carefully wrapped in costly stuffs, sealed with Julian's own signet and that it bore the notation 'From the victorius Praefect Julian to his August Emperor, with greetings'. It was then dispatched to Antioch and when Macrinus opened it, he was shocked to see the features of his faithful Praefect instead of the softly sensual features of the 'hermaphroditic idiot' which he had anticipated. The news spread and four more of the Antioch legions deserted to Antoninus. Macrinus had only his Praetorians and a small army left.

When news reached Emesa, Antoninus gave the order to

his faithful legions to march to Antioch and as they proceeded along the road, their strength was augmented by the garrisons of the towns and cities through which they passed. The news of their triumphal progress reached Antioch and Macrinus was forced out of his lair and with his usual stupidity, he decided to take command himself. Antoninus had by then arrived at Immae, only twenty miles from Antioch and Macrinus resolved to trust his Praetorians and go out and meet the Antonine in battle. As always, he did the wrong thing. The jubilant forces of Antoninus, fighting now for their adored favourite and the son of their own Caracalla, were invincible. At their head was Antoninus, suddenly transformed into a man and a soldier, at least to all appearances. He galloped into the ranks of the invaders, sword in hand, acting a most convincing part in his role of masculinity. As he advanced, the proud Praetorians fell to their knees, shouting '*Ave* Caesar'. By nightfall every soldier who had supported Macrinus was willing to recognize Antoninus as Emperor and that night Antoninus was the true and only Caesar, lacking only the confirmation of the Senate. But that was a mere formality. That vacillating, fawning body of six hundred old men were only too willing to be on the winning side. Macrinus, as ignominious in defeat as he had been in power, fled disguised as a woman. By some strange deific justice, the roles were reversed. Antoninus was now Emperor and Macrinus had become the 'hermaphroditic idiot'. Opellius Macrinus had never made a right decision. His utter stupidity was the main reason why he was the only Roman Emperor never to rule in Rome.

The triumphant army of Marcus Aurelius Antoninus, Almighty Caesar and Emperor of Rome, entered the eastern imperial city of Antioch, the second largest in the Roman Empire. Marcus Aurelius Antoninus, Caesar, Emperor of Rome, Pontifex Maximus, High Priest of the Sun God Elahga-baal, the greatest man in the Roman Empire, was still only a fourteen-year-old boy. That night, when the lamps were extinguished in the strange room in the Palace of Antioch, where only the night before Opellius Macrinus had slept as Caesar alongside his flat-breasted wife, the little Antonine gladly conferred his title of Emperor on the wrestler, Zoticus, in whose love he sought sanctuary, fully content to be Empress rather than Emperor – to be the slave Lupus rather than to be Caesar.

10

ANTONINUS PACED THE cold floor of his bedroom in the draughty old Palace of Nicomedia with short nervous steps. The charcoal braziers seemed to do little to dispel the chill. He hated Nicomedia with its grey days, so different from the sun-drenched heat of Emesa. He hated Nicomedia; he hated this crumbling palace; he hated his family; he hated Gannys and now he hated Aurelius Zoticus. The long lash of silk-covered steel wire on the little jewelled whip which he held in his hand, snapped out at everything he passed – the stupid bronze sphinxes which upheld the arms of the chairs, the table of rare citron wood by the bed, even the marble statue of Antinuous, the beautiful boy whom the Emperor Hadrian had loved. He looked up at the cold marble eyes, the soft lips and the rounded cheeks.

'You were Caesar's wife,' he shrilled, 'and I am Caesar's wife. Your husband drove you to suicide and so will mine.' His whip wrapped around the sleek marble legs and he waited for it to uncoil and then stalked to the bed, lashing the silken sheets in his frenzy. That bed, oh that abominable bed which had witnessed Zoticus's perfidy of only last night, when he had held Antoninus in his arms and made him believe that he loved nobody else. The liar! Now, the couch which had been the stage upon which so many rare and pleasurable dramas had been enacted was an odious thing – something to be cursed, hated and avoided.

He stopped his frantic lashing long enough to reach down under the pillow and make sure that the damascene dagger was safely hidden. He withdrew it. It was needle pointed and razor sharp. A quick draw of the hand and he could cut Zoticus's throat and that is exactly what he would do – exactly! Or . . . should he cut the traitor's throat? Perhaps he should despoil Zoticus of that of which he was most proud, his greatest distinction to fame. Oh, no! No! He couldn't kill Zoticus nor could he mutilate him. He must not forget that Zoticus was the incarnation of Elah-ga-baal. Oh, he loved him so much. He wanted him so much. Even now at this very moment, knowing of his lying disloyalty, he wanted him, wanted him, wanted him. Nobody had ever satisfied him like Zoticus.

But, if he didn't kill him, he could scare him. Yes, he could frighten him by pretending to kill him. That would bring Zoticus to his knees, begging for forgiveness and pleading not to be sent away.

Everything had gone wrong since they were forced to halt their overland journey to Rome in this miserable Nicomedia. Why hadn't they stayed in Antioch? Antioch could just as well be the capital of the world as Rome but no . . . his grandmother must go to Rome, his mother must go to Rome, Zoticus must go to Rome, Gannys must go to Rome and Comazon must go to Rome. Well, they were going to Rome but they were not going by ship. In that Antoninus had been adamant. Elah-ga-baal was going to Rome with them so that every Roman knee would bow to his omnipotence. And he was not going by ship because water was death to fire. The black stone phallus of the Sun God was being transported from Emesa to Rome along with the fleshly one that hung pendant from the god's incarnation, Zoticus, and it was going overland.

Zoticus again! Curse him! Whatever he thought about, his thoughts always returned to Zoticus. His husband and his Emperor! In all the months since he had been married, he had had no cause for complaint until tonight and now Gannys had told him that Zoticus was unfaithful. Gannys had seen him. Dear, good, faithful Gannys who was always looking out for his little Varius, no, his Antoninus. Yes, Gannys had seen him, coupled with some filthy woman and in the pantry of all places. In the pantry! Well, Zoticus was the son of a cook, probably he felt at home there. But . . . with a woman, an unclean beast! How could Zoticus be Elah-ga-baal if he desired a woman when it was strictly forbidden?

Gannys had not recognized the woman. What a pity! Antoninus would have had her killed, crucified, fed to the beasts, thrown into a pit of snakes. He would have her ugly fat breasts sliced off. Fat, floppy tits! How he hated them on women but how he longed for them on himself. Zoticus would be forced to tell him who she was. He'd hold the dagger to Zoticus's throat, pricking just a little so the blood would flow and Zoticus would squeal out the name – her name. Even if it were his own mother, he would have her killed. To think that Zoticus would abandon him for a woman!

He knew that Gannys was waiting in the small robe room where he had commanded him to stay. But now, he could not understand why Zoticus did not arrive. He had commanded him to be here at this hour. Zoticus was nothing but a peasant at heart. He was a wrestler, crude, boorish and common. That oily smile and those too perfect teeth! Those huge peasant's hands! Common, that's what Zoticus was but oh what a man! Yes, he was a peasant, but Antoninus would not have him otherwise.

There were footsteps in the hall outside and a mumbled word to the guards at the door. This would be Zoticus. He always wore heavy sandals which made a ringing noise as he strode along the floors. Naturally the guards would not question him as he entered. Yes, it was Zoticus. The door opened and he stood on the threshold a moment, the thick hanging of Babylonian tapestry raised in one hand. With his head cocked a trifle to one side, he grinned at Antoninus, then sucked in his breath to expel it in a whistle of admiration. He winked, slowly drawing one eyelid down.

'You're beautiful tonight, *domina mia*! Something has caused your cheeks to flush, little wife, and the red stain becomes your paleness. But then, you are always beautiful.

That is why I married you.' He dropped the tapestry and held out both arms, expecting Antoninus to come running to him.

Antoninus did not move. 'It is you who have caused my cheeks to flush tonight. And call me not your wife, Aurelius Zoticus. I have made up my mind to divorce you. I shall not be married to you longer – you are an unfaithful husband.' His lower lip trembled and tears started to well up in his eyes. He fought them back. He did not know whether he was weeping from anger or sorrow.

Two steps brought Zoticus nearer. His manner was confident. This was only some new melodrama that Antoninus had hatched up. 'Come come, little wife. You accuse me of being unfaithful and yet you denied me entrance to your room tonight until this late hour. Whom were you sporting with?' He indicated the rumpled sheets, 'And how many?'

'None! At least not tonight. And I do not "sport" with other men. I only follow the demands of my god.'

'How fortunate you are to have such a god. But even Elah-ga-baal does not demand that you prostitute yourself to the army in the morning while he is strong. Night is the time for that and I am always here to make any sacrifice you wish.' He came closer to Antoninus. 'Think you not that I am jealous, little wife, when I picture you, wasting your love and kisses on those worthless soldiers while I sweat and groan just to keep this body of mine strong and powerful for you?'

Antoninus backed away from the outstretched arms. He had managed to control his tears.

'You filthy, lying Smyrnan! You obscene son of a whore-mongering palace cook! Gannys was right when he told me never to trust a Smyrnan. I suppose you were sweating and groaning for me this morning in the pantry. You were sweating and groaning, but not for me. Did you choose the pantry because you were reared in one? Tell me now, who was she?'

'Who was what she?' Zoticus dropped his arms. 'By the

thousand tits of Isis, what are you talking about now? Sometimes I think you are crazy.'

'Yes, crazy with love for you.' Antoninus backed towards the bed. His outstretched hand told him that he had reached it and he fumbled underneath the pillow, holding the dagger in his hand. He saw the quick look of anger on Zoticus's face but it was immediately erased by a smile.

Zoticus laughed, brushing aside Antoninus's remarks as a joke and once again opened his arms and walked towards Antoninus. When he was but a few steps away, Antoninus sprang forward, the dagger clutched in his hand, but Zoticus, a trained wrestler, automatically reacted to the attack. His hand caught Antoninus's and his strong fingers doubled tightly around the other's wrists. Slowly Antoninus's fingers opened and he dropped the blade, but he was upon Zoticus, clawing, screaming and biting. For a moment, one fleeting second, Antoninus was the aggressor, then Zoticus pushed him away and held him at arm's length. Antoninus glared at him, but Zoticus deliberately clenched one fist, and with his eyes staring straight at Antoninus, let him have the full force of his fist in the face. The force of the blow knocked Antoninus back on the bed and he lay there weeping and kicking his heels in utter frustration.

Zoticus feared he had gone too far. He had not meant to hit the lad so hard. He stepped to the bed and laid a restraining hand on Antoninus's shoulder.

'Now let's get this straightened out, little Lupus.' His words were soothing. 'When did Gannys see me and where and with whom?'

At first Antoninus could not answer but finally he managed to gasp through his sobs. 'This morning, an hour after I had left for the camp and I don't know with whom but it was a woman.'

Zoticus sighed with relief. For once, most fortunately, he was truly innocent. He had had women, whenever it had pleased him. He had even had Soaemias. But this morning he had had no woman, and he had a witness to prove it. All the morning he had been with the young Alexianus, teaching

103

him to wrestle. He knew that Antoninus had little love
for his cousin but he also knew that Antoninus respected
him.

'Whose word would you take against mine, little wife?
Would you take the word of the slave Gannys who hates me,
and has always hated me, because he knows that you love
me? Or would you take the words of your cousin Alexianus
who, although he dislikes me, is not in the habit of lying?'

'I – I – I – would believe Alexianus. I have never known
him to lie.' Antoninus was getting some control over himself.

'Then send for him. Have him routed out of bed and
brought here. Tell him not what you want of him. Do not
prepare him for the question but when he arrives, ask him
only one thing, "What was Aurelius Zoticus doing this morning and *all* the morning?"'

Antoninus thought the matter over carefully, checking his
sobs. He summoned a slave and sent for his cousin and when
the boy arrived, rubbing the sleep from his eyes, Antoninus
questioned him in the same words that Zoticus had used.

'What was Aurelius Zoticus doing this morning and all
this morning?'

Alexianus's answer was prompt and unpremeditated. 'We
were together in the public baths in the further courtyard
and we were wrestling. Why?'

'That is enough, I believe you. As to *why*, know you not
that nobody ever asks Caesar for a reason? Now back to
your bed. Know that I trust you. You are not like the rest of
the family.'

When the door had closed behind Alexianus, Antoninus
went to the other smaller door across the room. He opened it
to find Gannys crouching behind it. The slave's face was
livid. Evidently he had overheard.

'Come out!' This time it was Caesar commanding. It was
neither the boy Varius nor the Antonine, nor yet the soft
and pliant wife of Zoticus. Antoninus could be imperial
when he wished.

'A few hours ago, you made certain accusations to me against Aurelius Zoticus.'

Gannys had overheard enough to know that he could not retreat. He must use his nimble wits to brazen it out.

'I still do accuse him. I say that he was with a woman in the pantry yesterday morning an hour after you left to sacrifice before the sacred stone of Elah-ga-baal in the camp.'

Antoninus walked slowly across the floor and picked up the dagger. Gannys's eyes furtively followed the movements of his hands.

'You did not say *yesterday*, Gannys, you said *today*.'

Gannys essayed a weak smile and fluttered his hands. 'I did? How stupid of me! I must have been confused. But then, time means nothing when one is with you, my master. Moments speed by so quickly when one is in your glorious presence.'

'Stop it, fool! Even if you did mean yesterday, you were wrong,' Antoninus was stern, 'because yesterday after I left for the camp, I decided to go to the baths on my way and see Zoticus. He was a-straddle a man, straining to pin the man's shoulders to the ground, which is something different from trying to straddle a woman in the pantry.' He balanced the blade in his fingers. 'You are lying, Gannys. Why do you lie about Zoticus?'

Gannys started to edge towards the door that led to the wardrobe. Once barricaded behind that, he felt he would be safe until Antoninus's anger had passed. Zoticus noticed the movement and flanked him, standing in front of the doorway. Gannys looked wildly around the room, seeking some escape. He saw Antoninus slowly advancing towards him, dagger in hand. He sank to the floor, and when Antoninus reached him and stood over him, he became a fawning suppliant. Although he didn't believe that Antoninus would actually kill him, he realized that the dagger was sharp and that it could wound severely.

'Yes, I lied, Varius. I call you Varius because you will always be Varius to me.'

'There you are wrong. I am no longer Varius. I am Caesar.

'I lied, great Caesar, because I love you and I wanted to free you from this monster,' he looked over his shoulder at Zoticus standing behind him. 'All Rome wishes to free you from him. Through him, you are losing the love of your soldiers. They resent his evil influence over you. Who is he to be Pro-Consul of Bithynia? Free-born Romans resent paying their taxes to this cook's son. Why should he have access to your treasure, to dip his greedy hands into your gold and buy off your spies? Why does he have the power to wreak his vengeance on innocent men? He had you put Nestor to death and Fabius Agrippinus because they dared speak up against him. He had Pica Caecilianus killed merely because he did not bow low enough to him. Through him, you executed your good friend Castinus the Tribune, merely because Castinus tried to warn you that the army did not approve of your marriage to Zoticus. Oh, Caesar, this Zoticus will ruin you and I but sought to save you, to break up your odious relationship.'

'Close your foul mouth, Gannys. I shall not answer your stupid accusations. You are only a slave, how dare you accuse Caesar.'

'Caesar? I am speaking to Caesar, for you are Caesar and not he.'

'There you are wrong. To the world I may be Caesar but here in my bedroom, Zoticus is Caesar and I am Caesar's wife.' Antoninus, his eyes still on Gannys, transferred the dagger to his left hand. His right hand sought the rim of the low table which held the perfumes and ointments with which he was wont to lubricate himself during the night. His seeking fingers slid over the smooth surface of the polished wood until they encountered the handle of his little whip. He clenched it tightly and as Gannys, who crawled crablike across the floor on his knees, approached him, he lashed out suddenly and caught Gannys a downward glancing blow across the face. The thin wire lash cut deep into the flesh, so deeply that Gannys's cheek lay open with a bloody flap of flesh. Without thinking, he hurled himself at his master.

'Curse you, Varius! The whip I like, but only on my back.

Now see what you have done, vile creature that you are. You and your stud, Zoticus, have ruined me. From now on, I shall no longer be beautiful. And see what he has done to you – already your eye turns black. Did he hit you? Would that he had killed you. You miserable boy! After all I have done for you.'

'Stop it, stop it, I shall hear no more.' Antoninus brought down the lash again.

'You will hear more, you will, you will! I've taught you everything you know; waited on you; pimped for you; painted you and coached you in the way a woman makes love. Now you turn on me and ruin me.' In his rage of pain and anger he grappled with Varius and pushed him violently against the table. It overturned, sending the bottles and jars crashing to the floor. For a second they both struggled to regain their balance but fell backwards on the bed, Gannys on top of the struggling Antonine.

Zoticus leaped to the rescue, pulling at Gannys's legs but the slave, weak and womanly as he was, displayed that strength that comes only with rage. He was beyond the bounds of thinking and his hands clenched tightly around Antoninus's neck, forcing the boy's head back over the edge of the bed. Antoninus's face became livid, then empurpled and he gasped for breath while Zoticus, with the full strength of his mighty arms, belaboured the maddened Gannys. With a vice-like grip, he managed to bend one of Gannys's arms back, giving Antoninus a chance to catch his breath and in that brief moment of respite, Antoninus slowly bent his arm, bringing the dagger towards him point up. Zoticus with a mighty heave, lifted Gannys up as Antoninus straightened the dagger; he slammed Gannys down on the steel, the dagger entering the slave's throat. There was a gush of blood which encarmined Antoninus's face, a bubbled gasp from Gannys and he lay still, sprawled over his master, one foot twitching as his life flowed out over the boy whom he had served.

Zoticus lifted the body and flung it to the floor. With a corner of the sheet, he wiped Antoninus's face and lifted him to a sitting position. Antoninus looked at the body on the floor, thrown there like a broken doll.

'Oh, my Gannys!' He slipped off the bed and embraced the bleeding corpse. 'Gannys, dear Gannys, what have we done to you? Wake up, Gannys. Speak to me, oh speak to me. What have I done to you?'

Zoticus kicked the body with his heavily shod foot. 'Done to him? You've killed him, that's what. And why not? He threatened you. He would have choked you in another moment had I not been here to save you. I've saved your life but 'twas no more than any husband would do when he saw his wife being strangled by a slave. But I forgot, mayhap you are no longer my wife – you were going to divorce me.'

The tears and blood on Antoninus's face had smeared the white lead and rouge with which Gannys had so recently painted him. He looked up at Zoticus and with one hand still on Gannys's body, he inched over the floor, looking back at Gannys for a fleeting second and removing his hand reluctantly.

'I shall never divorce you Zoticus.' He flung both arms around Zoticus's knees and lowered his head to kiss the rough sandals, then raised it, running his cheeks against the glabrous legs, smearing them with blood, paint and tears. 'You did save my life. You did, mighty Caesar, otherwise the miserable slave would have strangled me.'

His seeking lips came higher and higher. Zoticus placed his hand on the boy's head and held it close. His fingers tightened in Antoninus's hair and suddenly he pulled the boy's head back so that he could look down at him. Zoticus had come back to earth, his feet were firmly planted in reality.

'Why did you stop me? Why, oh, why?' Antoninus stared up at him with baffled desire.

'I saved your life, little Antonine. Had it not been for me, you would be there, lifeless on the floor, instead of that bastard Gannys. He tried to force us apart, divide us. He invented lies about me so that you would send me away. See what happened to him? And see what nearly happened to you. So perish all enemies of Zoticus, for I am more than a man.'

'You are the god Elah-ga-baal,' Antoninus admitted as he tried to disentangle the hand that held his hair, but the grip did not relax, instead it pushed his head farther back.

'Stop, Zoticus, and let me finish!'

'All in good time. I saved your life. Does that mean nothing to you?'

'I am trying to repay you, Zoticus, trying to show my love for you if you will but let me.'

'There is a better way of showing me your love, my little wife.'

'No better way that I know of.' Antoninus was half pleased, half resentful of the hand that clutched his hair.

'There could be gold, as much gold as this miserable carcass weighs.'

'Double the weight if you desire. Poor Gannys was thin, he didn't weigh much. Yes, double the weight if you but let me finish.'

Zoticus relaxed his grip and the heavy hand which had clutched at Antoninus's hair now became softly playful as it patted the tousled curls.

'You may. But first a promise, beloved spouse.'

'A promise, darling Zoticus.'

'Promise me that you will never believe a bad report about me again. And no more talk about divorcing your Zoticus. Promise me on Elah-ga-baal. Swear before me, there on your knees, both as my slave Lupus and as Emperor of Rome. Swear that if you ever doubt me again, you pray that the Great God of the Sun will strike you dead.'

'I swear, I swear, I swear! May Elah-ga-baal strike me dead if I ever doubt you again.'

'And the gold?'

'Tomorrow when the treasury opens, it will be yours.'

'And an official appointment as *concubinus* at five gold talents a year?' *

* A talent was worth about £12,500.

'At ten, dear Zoticus, and confirmed by the Senate if you will but let me finish.'

Zoticus's hand drew Antoninus's head closer. He sank to his knees to the floor, Antoninus in his embrace. Gannys's lifeless foot was beneath them. He released Antoninus only long enough to push the offending flesh away. Surely Antoninus would be satisfied now. He would demand nothing more of Zoticus this night and Soaemias would be waiting. Ah, there was a woman! How few men could serve two Augustas of Rome in one night, be husband to them both and yet remain Emperor in everything but name.

11

THE LONG DREARY winter at Nicomedia dragged wearily on and Antoninus awaited the advent of spring. He had refused to wear wool and as a result had shivered through most of the winter in his thin robes with their chilling embroidery of icy gems. But he was obstinate. He maintained that wool scratched his tender skin and he refused to wear it. This obstinacy extended even to the life-sized portrait which was being painted of him, to be sent on to Rome in advance of his arrival. It was to be hung in the Senate above the statue of Victory, and each high-born Roman senator would be compelled to bow before it and scatter a few grains of incense on the altar beneath it, as an acknowledgement of the divinity of Caesar.

The idea of the portrait had originated with Antoninus and Julia Maesa had not seriously objected but she had insisted that Antoninus sit for it, garbed in the Roman toga, austerely without ornament, except for the simple garland of gilded laurel leaves on his brow. Whereupon ensued another palace tempest. No Roman toga! Antoninus stormed and raved and tore the offending garment to shreds, choosing instead his most elaborate Syrian robe of emerald-studded gold cloth, his highest and most fanciful tiara which was composed of tier after tier of jewels in filigreed gold, and a profusion of gems which dripped from his ears, neck, wrists and fingers.

The argument had raged for three days with all the palace against him. Even Zoticus had tried to convince him that his female role was quite acceptable in the bedroom but might be displeasing in the company of the August Fathers. But the picture was painted as Antoninus wished. When it was completed it was so flamboyantly feminine that it looked more like a painted Assyrian harlot than a Caesar, even though that Caesar was a handsome boy. However, the very vulgarity of its flamboyance seemed to please Antoninus and it was sent off ahead of him to prepare Rome for the coming of the new Emperor. Prepare them it did! All of Rome who could get into the Senate House flocked to see it, viewed it with stunned awe, genuflected before it and then scuttled to their homes to giggle and gossip about it.

The Praetorian Guards, those self important bully-boys of Rome who were instrumental in choosing the emperors they were afterwards supposed to guard, were loud in their denunciation of the portrait and it was the cause of their voicing critical opinions of Antoninus himself, although these opinions were not expressed publicly. If this were Caracalla's son, he certainly had come a long way from his soldier father. But . . . was he Caracalla's son? Ah, that was a question nobody could answer. At any rate, Caracalla was dead and so was old Miser Macrinus but, by all the gods, what had they put in their places – a painted whore, a queen, a Syrian Cleopatra!

Zoticus behaved with propriety all through the winter at Nicomedia. His one quarrel with Antoninus, which had resulted in the death of Gannys, showed him that this capricious boy must be handled carefully or Zoticus would be just another legionary again without his pleasant bed companion and his huge annual stipend as *concubinus* to the Emperor. He was undoubtedly influenced in his action by the fact that Soaemias, who had been so avid for him at first, now treated him coolly. She had felt that Zoticus was all she wanted or desired, but the physical pain and incapability of action she was wont to undergo for several days after a session with him was hardly worth the price of her pleasure. Somewhat reluctantly she returned to Gigex, who during the interval that she courted Zoticus, had managed to store a reservoir of potency to indulge her in a more painless ecstasy.

A new slave had to be found to replace Gannys and after a search of the slave markets of Alexandria, Antioch, Byzantium and Delos by Zoticus's agents, a Greek youth, by the name of Cleander, was discovered and purchased who combined the necessary qualifications. He was young, as beautiful and as feminine as Antoninus himself, nearly as well endowed as Zoticus and perhaps most important still, he was well versed in the art of hairdressing and the intricacies of the *toilette*, for he had been a personal slave of the Queen of Parthia and had learned all the secrets of her dressing room.

Antoninus adored him, berated him, teased him, scolded him, scratched him, bit him, whipped him, ravished him and made his life hell, then in the next moment kissed him, petted him, forgave him and indoctrinated him into the camp where Cleander daily competed with his master in whoring. Instead of resenting his new slave's popularity, Antoninus enjoyed it for it meant someone to compete against and afterwards to share his experiences with.

Their daily wagers as to their ability to achieve numerical superiority added zest not only to Antoninus's participation but to that of the soldiers, who laid wagers on the side and eagerly supported their partisans. Antoninus and Cleander adopted the colours of the Roman racing corporations, Antoninus as a Green and Cleander as a Blue. Soon, to make the sport more interesting, Zoticus recruited two soldiers who were willing to trade the rough life of the barracks for the greater comforts of the palace and these two additions were known as Red and White.

In addition to Zoticus, whom he considered his husband, and his slave Cleander, whom he called 'sister', Antoninus also made a confidant of one Aurelius Eubulus who was also from Emesa and had all the vices of an Emesene. This Eubulus Antoninus dispatched to the furthermost ends of the empire to recruit promising youths who could compare with Zoticus. To this end, he carried a gold and ivory replica, which was to be his standard of measurement. Eubulus was to meet Antoninus in Rome with his raw levies and this was another reason why Antoninus was particularly anxious for the winter to pass.

The pink drifts of almond blossoms were covering the barren hillsides when the long procession, part imperial, part sacred and part military, finally started out from Nicomedia overland to Rome. Antoninus rode in his big chariot, driven by Zoticus, with Cleander crouched on the floor beside them. Then came the high wheeled covered Roman carts which separately carried Soaemias, Julia Maesa and Mamaea with Alexianus. Comazon rode next on horseback, followed by the mounted Praetorians with the sun flashing on their gilded uniforms. The lumbering wagon, drawn by ten white mules, which bumped along behind them contained the sacred stone phallus of Elah-ga-baal, and finally the dusty line of foot soldiers, four abreast, heavily shod but in light marching armour. In the rear were the baggage trains, the camp followers, hucksters, whores and the general rag-tag and bob-tail which followed the army. Advance units with baggage trains were ahead so that camps could be prepared in advance for the night.

Whenever the route took them through towns or cities, the most imposing palaces and the best houses were always set aside for the imperial family's use, and sometimes surrounded by this temporary peace and comfort, Antoninus insisted that the stay be prolonged several days to which all willingly agreed. The roads were not the paved military roads of Rome and were either ankle deep in dust or mud, depending on the weather; as the high-wheeled carts were unsprung each mile covered was an agonizing ordeal.

Each night the shrine to Elah-ga-baal was set up in the centre of the camp, but many nights Antoninus was far too exhausted to participate in the nightly sacrifices which he willingly abandoned to a coterie of priests from the temple in Emesa who accompanied them. The long days in the chariot, under blaze of sun or pelt of rain, were so tiring that Antoninus, contrary to his usual practices, oftimes desired nothing more than a rub-down with a steaming towel and a quick anointing of his tired limbs by Cleander, before seeking instant slumber in the protecting arms of Zoticus.

The days, however, were not entirely without pleasure or excitement. The great charioteer, Gordius of the Greens, had been drafted from Rome to teach Antoninus, and under his expert tutelage, Antoninus became a proficient charioteer. Every day he transferred from the big, commodius travelling chariot to a lighter racing one and, in competition with Zoticus or some volunteer from either the guards or the army, raced over the roads. Antoninus was fair in his racing as he was in everything else, unless he was possessed by one of his malicious rages. Although he always wanted to win and was disappointed when he didn't he would not accept challengers who allowed him to win just because he was Caesar. It had to be a hard fought race and, if he lost, he was more than happy to reward the winner with a substantial purse of gold or any valuable ornament which he happened to be wearing.

The long caravan progressed over the hills and mountains of Thrace, across the fertile valleys and hills of Moesia, through both upper and lower Pannonia and finally into the boot of Italy. Antoninus's reputation and preferences had preceded him, and at every stopping place there was some prepossessing volunteer, publicly acclaimed by the town fathers as a local champion to rival the world famed Zoticus. Often Antoninus availed himself of them and their willing services, but just as often he merely examined them to satisfy his curiosity, too tired to more than admire them, and turned them over to the voracious Cleander. None of them compared with Zoticus.

By July they arrived at Rome and the long journey was nearly over. Just outside the gates of Rome, a permanent camp was set up so that preparations might be made for an elaborate processional to enter the city. Here Antoninus received the August Fathers of the Senate and he proclaimed the most important pronunciation of his entire reign. He granted complete amnesty to all senators, officials and freedmen of Rome whether or not they had supported Macrinus. Such a magnanimous gesture was unheard of. Previously every Emperor had ruthlessly slaughtered the friends of his predecessor.

Rome rejoiced, and those who had feared they faced either death or exile came out freely in support of this new Antonine. This decree was the keynote of Antoninus's entire reign. It was to be a reign of peace throughout the Empire – a reign without wars or bloodshed. The *Pax Romana* extended to all corners of the Empire. Every Roman, from the white togaed Senators to the humblest freedman was able to walk the streets without fear, and to seek his bed at night with the certainty that he would awaken in the morning.

Antoninus abolished the hated corps of informers which had flourished under Caracalla. He trusted every man, granted immunity to all and asked only that the Romans love him and adopt a religion of love and understanding. Rome under Antoninus reached the peak of glory – a glory she was never to know again. Antoninus was the summit which had been reached by a long, weary road from the Divine Julius, and after Antoninus it descended through the tortuous paths until the glory of Rome was swept away by the invading barbarians.

The preparations for his entry into Rome were most elaborate, for Antoninus was determined that the reception would far exceed any triumphal procession that Rome had ever seen. Although the Senate had not voted him a triumph, it mattered little to Antoninus. He would have one anyway. He was the principal actor in a vast pageant and nothing should dim his stellar role. He took unto himself a list of fanciful titles which he did not bother to ask the Senate to confirm. He made himself Consul and Tribune of Rome, and appointed those whom he liked to important posts. Quadratus, a burly young freedman from Nicomedia, who nearly rivalled Zoticus, became Praefect of the Night Watch. Maxentius, an ex-slave from Moesia, one of the local paragons encountered along the way, was made Praefect of Sustenances, and Hellenus, who had been a dancer in the theatre of Antioch, became Praefect of the Palace. The absent Eubulus, still sending conscripts for Antoninus's pleasure army from the far reaches of the empire, was made Pro-Consul of Illyria, *in absentia*.

Strangely enough, these youths with nothing but their physical proportions to recommend them, proved themselves far more qualified to perform their official duties during Antoninus's reign than the grafting Romans who had purchased the offices by bribes under former régimes. The Roman worthies sneered at these new appointments but in their anxiety to please the new Antonine, they fawned at the feet of peasant, slave and actor.

It required a week for the preparations for the triumphal entry and to prepare the large donative which was to be given to the senators, their wives, the Roman plebs and the army. But the preparations were finally terminated and Antoninus rose early on the morning of July 11th to prepare himself. The road leading into the city, and the Via Sacra inside the gates, had been sprinkled with yellow sand in which gold dust was mixed to give it a sumptuous brilliance.

Antoninus was determined that he, his god and his lover would be the centre of all eyes. It was not only his own introduction to Rome but that of his religion and the man, Zoticus, who to him was the embodiment of his religion.

The procession formed in the camp and progressed in its triumphal march to the gates of the city, where it halted for its final arrangements under Antoninus's careful supervision. He descended from his litter, where he had been propped up rigidly on cushions so as not to disturb his robes or his jewels, that he might oversee the final details.

The recruits which Eubulus had garnered from the four corners of the Empire, together with the conscripts which had been added during Antoninus's journey, were to lead the march, each with a long brazen trumpet which would

116

proclaim the procession. That none of them knew the least thing about trumpets or how to play them made little difference to Antoninus – their physique was impressive, their short linen tunics were revealing and their voluptuous male beauty would easily offset the caterwauling which they produced on the horns. Surely they would set the Romans in a mood to appreciate what followed.

That which followed was Antoninus himself, starkly alone so that no eye would be able to miss him. But instead of walking forward, he had proposed to walk backwards so that his gaze would never leave the sacred stone of Elah-ga-baal which immediately followed him. It would be impressive. The Roman Caesar, supreme lord of all creation, walking backwards along the sacred way, looking neither to the right nor to the left, ignoring the plaudits of the crowd, his eyes riveted on the relic of his god and his god's incarnation. For Zoticus was to drive the chariot that held the sacred stone.

Antoninus had chosen a dramatic costume for himself and an equally dramatic one for Zoticus. Other Caesars might be content with the stark Roman toga or the purple robes of Empire. Not so, Antoninus! His long Syrian robe of thick white silk was heavily encrusted with rubies – the fiery stone of the sun. On his head, he wore a foot high diadem of tier after tier of rubies, and other rubies encircled his neck, his arms, his waist and his ankles. The weighty costume made it difficult to walk when one faced in the direction he was going. To walk backwards in this heavy mass of silk, gold and jewels was almost impossible but none could gainsay him.

Six white horses, harnessed abreast, drew the chariot with the sacred stone and Zoticus, as the driver of the chariot, represented the godhead. He wore only the scantiest wisp of gold tissue around his loins which left no doubt as to his qualifications for his world-wide reputation. The remainder of his superb body was gilded and on his head, he wore a resplendent gold helmet whose branching rays of beaten gold extended in a wide circle of flashing light around his head. The effect of the whole was barbaric and breathtaking – the backward walking Caesar in his flashing robes, the six milk-white horses, reined to a slow walk, the gold and ivory two-tiered chariot with the gleaming beauty of Zoticus in front and the grim black phallus of Elah-ga-baal on a raised platform in the rear.

All this had been Antoninus's personal contribution to the triumph. What followed after had been left to Julia Maesa who rode with Soaemias in another equally resplendent chariot. Then came Eutychianus Comazon with his gold-armoured Praetorians, the new officials that Antoninus had appointed, and behind them rank after rank of legionaries all in spotless new uniforms and shining armour.

But even in the most carefully organized plans, there is always some insignificant thing that remains unforeseen and this happened during Antoninus's backward march along the Sacred Way. Instructions had been given that every inch of the way should be thoroughly raked and swept and spread with sand, that not the smallest pebble remain. Antoninus had insisted on wearing the fragile, high-heeled sandals which were worn by Syrian Priests at their ceremonies and he was aware of the difficulty of walking in them, especially walking backwards. Burdened by his heavy robes and the towering diadem, not being able to see where he stepped, Antoninus of course encountered the only pebble on the path. He stumbled, vainly tried to regain his balance as the heavy diadem slipped forward over one eye. He would have fallen in a struggling array of silk and jewels, had not a strong hand reached out to save him. This strong hand supported him until he was safely back on his feet, the diadem once more in position and then, for one fleeting second, before he resumed his backward march, Antoninus had the opportunity of seeing who had saved him.

Antoninus considered himself, and rightly so with his experience, a connoisseur of male beauty. He had already had a rare opportunity to make a comprehensive study of handsome men for he was in daily contact with Zoticus, Cleander, Quadratus, Maxentius and Hellenus – men who had been carefully culled from all the Empire and represented the epitome of masculine beauty. Furthermore, Antoninus had had the flower of the Legions that were stationed in the East; he had the representatives of the various towns and cities through which he had passed and but recently he had examined and passed comment on the company of personal guards which Eubulus had rounded up. But in that one fleeting second that he looked at his rescuer, all his former conceptions of male beauty were swept away.

No antique Greek statue nor even the marble replicas of Hadrian's beautiful Antinuous could compare with what Antoninus saw. The golden curls were in a careful disarray which tempted his hands to ruffle them even further. The smooth white skin was softly tinged by the gold of the sun but not enough to hide the underlying rose of the cheeks. The eyes of dark violet were large and ingenuous – eyes that inspired confidence and trust. They were eyes that lighted a flame of love in Antoninus's heart. There was a chiselled perfection in the Grecian nose, the subtle bow of the lips and the firm roundness of the chin that seemed almost unbelievable. The whole face, so frankly open, so honestly appealing and yet so boyish was a direct contrast to the sensual, almost obscene beauty of Zoticus. Here, mingled together were the youthful beauty of Apollo, the boyish charm of Eros, the forcefulness of Mars, the strength of Hercules, the lithe fleetness of Mercury and the grave intelligence of Jupiter, all heightened by the gleaming radiance of Elah-ga-baal.

Had not the eyes of all Rome been on him, Antoninus would have stopped the procession, merely to ascertain the identity of this golden youth and where he could later be found. But, the procession was advancing, the horses were coming nearer and Antoninus was powerless. He fastened his eyes on the blond youth as long as he could distinguish him in the milling crowd, neglecting his adoration of the sacred stone in the chariot and the driver who had always been paramount in his affections. The eyes stared back at him, and Antoninus fancied he saw the same strange longing in them that he knew must be so readily apparent in his own.

For the rest of the way, the pomp and ceremony of the procession became nothing more than tinsel to him. He could not forget the face he had seen. When the trumpeters ahead had finally reached the Palace and had halted before the towering entrance, Antoninus showed himself for only a moment on the uppermost step, accepting but briefly the plaudits of his subjects, then disappearing into the shadowy reaches of the palace.

Alone he walked the porphyry halls, alone he ascended the broad marble stairs, and alone he stood on the marble-pillared balcony that surrounded the *perystilium* below. Suddenly he realized where he was – he was in Caesar's palace, the Golden House of Nero. He was lost, he did not even know, in this vast labyrinth of marble and ivory and gold, where his own apartments were. Apparently he was alone in the palace. No one had come to attend him. He spied a large brazen gong and beat upon it with a hammer. Soon there was a sound of running feet, and several slaves came running towards him. They must have recognized him from his elaborate robes for they knelt upon the pavement.

'I am Caesar,' Antoninus whispered, still dazed by his experience in the procession and awed by the vast magnificence of the palace. 'Where are my apartments?'

An old man got up off his knees and advanced with bowed head.

'If the great Caesar will precede me.'

'Nay, he will follow you.' Antoninus brushed aside formality and trailed the old man down the stairs, through other halls, courtyards, rooms and pillared porticoes until they at length arrived at a pair of massive double doors of black ebony, with hinges and latches of gold. The man struck the doors and they slowly parted. Antoninus entered, cheered by the familiar face of Cleander that greeted him.

The slave came running across the room to flutter around Antoninus.

'How beautiful you look, great Caesar. The robes become

you and the new carmine I used for your cheeks has just the right glow. Your bath is waiting, shall I undress you?'

'I tire of being Caesar, my sister. The bath can wait. There is something else far more important. Tell me, whom do we know who is well acquainted with Rome.' He took off the weighty diadem and tossed it on the bed. 'Quick, think fast. Who among my train is not a stranger here?'

Cleander shook his head. 'Quadratus is from Nicomedia, he knows not Rome. Neither does Maxentius nor Hellenus. Your Zoticus entered Rome today for the first time. If only Eubulus were here.'

'But he isn't. He is in Britain. Think, you whorish slut. Use your head for something else besides your pleasure. There must be somebody in the suite of the Emperor of Rome who knows this accursed city.'

'I have the answer. Gordius! He who came from Rome to teach you to drive a chariot. He is the favourite of the Greens. He must know all Rome. He should be here now, down in the stables, for he was to drive your racing chariot in after the procession was over.'

'Run, Cleander, fetch him at once.'

While Cleander was gone, Antoninus paced the room. He could not forget the blond curls and the classic face of the youth who had kept him from falling. He must have him. At once! He burned for him. Those lips! By Elah-ga-baal what a man this blond stranger was! His delirious phantasies occupied his thoughts until Cleander returned with Gordius.

The charioteer walked across the floor, his heavy sandals ringing on the stones. He was short, squat and muscular with a face prematurely aged by his broken nose and a body marred by scars.

He bowed. 'You desired me, Great Caesar?'

'You know Rome, Gordius?'

'Every stone, from the Palatine to the Suburra.'

'Then you must find someone for me. I know not his name or who he is or where he lives. But, you must find him. Employ those whom you wish in the search. If you locate him, I will reward you amply but find him and find him today.'

'But whom shall I look for, Great Caesar? You say you know him not, neither his name nor where he lives.'

'Look for the most divinely beautiful youth in Rome. His age would be eighteen or nineteen, even twenty. He has hair as blond as summer wheat that curls all over his head and catches the light as if it were beaten gold. His eyes are as blue as the violets that sprang from Attys's flood and regard one from under a veil of dark lashes. His face is more beautiful than anything Phidias ever imagined. His body is like that of Hercules,' Antoninus sighed and looked up at Gordius. 'Alas, it is a poor description of him. No words can do him justice. I would have thought him a god come to earth but he has one tiny imperfection that proves he is mortal. On his left cheek, about an inch below his eye, there is a tiny brown mole, an absolute perfect pinpoint of darkness which adds to his beauty. Just now I recollect it.'

A strange look passed over Gordius's face. Fright, surprise and consternation mingled there for an instant but it was erased before Antoninus noticed it.

'Did you by any chance see, Great Caesar, if he wore a slave collar?'

'By the Sun, he did. It was there. I saw it. Do you know him Gordius?'

'No. I but asked to find out if he were slave or free. It would narrow the search.'

'He is a slave. By the gods, I am fortunate. Now I can purchase him. Go, Gordius! The owner of such a slave must be proud to display him. Seek him in the baths, carrying the towels of some rich Roman. Seek him in the front rows of the Circus Maximus where he will be armed with a fan to keep the flies off his master. Seek him in the palaces of the Palatine where he will be the *concubinus* of some mewling Patrician sprig. Seek him wherever you can but seek him. Go, Gordius, go and when you return with him, I will fill your hands with so much gold you will not be able to carry it.'

'I shall try, great Caesar,' Gordius bowed low as if to hide his face. 'I trust I can find him.'

Antoninus motioned to Cleander to open the door for Gordius. As the charioteer passed him, he drew several gold bracelets from his arm and tossed them to the man who caught them and mumbled his thanks. After he had gone, Antoninus looked after him, puzzled.

'The man should have smiled, Cleander. The bracelets were worth a fortune. Instead he looked worried and unhappy.'

'Perhaps he fears you will order him killed if he does not succeed. Gordius is a slave, you know, the property of the Green Corporation.'

'So he is. Run after him, Cleander, and tell him his life is not forfeit if he fails. I could not hold it against him if he cannot do the impossible.'

He listened to Cleander's soft footsteps running along the portico. No, he would not kill Gordius if he failed but surely if he did fail, Antoninus could not live. He could not pass another day until he had satisfied himself that this glorious person really existed. Would that Eros's dart had penetrated the other's heart also. Then he would seek Antoninus in the palace, for no power on earth could keep him away. In his musing, Antoninus spoke aloud.

'Regardless of what his tunic hides, I would abandon Zoticus for him. If he will but love me. I can buy what Zoticus has but I cannot buy love and even without knowing him I love him and I must have him. I must.'

He heard voices other than that of Cleander in the portico. A look of resentment spread over his face as his pleasant phantasy was interrupted. The door opened and Cleander bowed in his mother and grandmother. There was a girl with them, a girl a little older than he. Antoninus looked up in annoyance.

'Caesar does not grant an audience to strangers now.'

Julia Maesa took the girl's hand and advanced to Antoninus. Her face was set in a determined smile. 'This young lady, my dear grandson, will soon be no stranger. She is Julia

Cornelia Paula, the daughter of my good friend Julius Paulus and she is to be your wife.'

Antoninus stared at the girl. Without saying a word he came closer to her, so close that he could reach out and touch the finely pleated amethyst-coloured silk of her stola. He circled her, sniffing and fingering the fabric of her dress.

'My wife? Get her out of here. She reeks of saffron and it is a perfume I detest. She stinks! And that gorgeous dress she wears – tell her to take it off and give it to me. Away with her, away!'

'But, Varius . . .' his grandmother laid a placatory hand on his arm.

'I am not Varius, Augusta. I am Antoninus. I am Caesar. Now, get the slut out of here before I order the guards at the door to drag her out. And as soon as you get her out of here, strip her and send the dress back to me. Get out! Get out! Get out!'

He undid the gold cord that held his robe and started lashing at them and wisely they beat a fast retreat. When the door had again closed, Antoninus started to laugh.

'She looked like a rabbit, my dear Cleander – a startled pink and white rabbit. And she stank under her reek of saffron, a sickly smell of woman which nauseates me. Oh, how ugly she was but what a pretty dress. I must have it. Run after her and demand it. I would don it tonight in case Gordius finds my man of gold. Go, Cleander, go.'

12

'I WON'T MARRY the cursed wench and there is nothing you can do to make me. She stinks!'

Antoninus's little whip was constantly flicking away at Julia Maesa's multitude of treasures – antique Greek Tanagra figurines, delicate vases of opalescent muhrrine glass, portraits of the family in tinted wax, and vials of costly perfumes. 'So there!' He stamped his foot to emphasize the point.

'You shall marry her! There will be no more discussing the matter. You shall marry her and that's an end to it. It will be an occasion for a donative to all Rome and it will make you popular. Besides, the Augustan law requires that you marry.'

'The Augustan law! Pouf! Who was Augustus? A Caesar. Well, I am Caesar and I'll make another law which says that I am already married to Zoticus. I do not intend to marry any woman. With her clothes off, she would look like un-baked dough, white and disgustingly soft. How could I stomach her after the smooth hardness of Zoticus. Disgusting! Do you hear me? I am Caesar.'

Julia Maesa walked across the floor and took the whip from his hands. Lifting her knee, she placed the ivory shaft across it and broke it. The pieces she flung on the floor. Antoninus started to howl with rage but she grabbed him by both shoulders.

'No more noise out of you! For once you will do as you are told. You marry Julia Cornelia Paula. You say you are Caesar. Did you ever hear of Caligula?'

'Of course! He was Caesar too!'

'And he had his throat slit by a soldier; and Claudius was poisoned by a dish of mushrooms fed him by Agrippina; Nero was stabbed by a slave; Domitian was stabbed in the groin; and Commodus was strangled by a wrestler. They were all Caesars. Need I say any more?'

'Are you threatening to murder me, grandmother? Tell me, what would you use, poison or a knife-blade?'

'Either if necessary but neither if you behave yourself.' She looked at him grimly. 'But if you think you are Caesar, think again. You are nothing but a painted doll to hang clothes on.' She hit her chest with her clenched hand. 'I am Caesar! I rule Rome and I rule you too. Don't forget it. I put you where you are and I can take it away. I can be indulgent in many things, but not in this. This girl is what we need. We are upstarts, Varius. Nobodies – descended from a priestly house of Emesa who were called kings by courtesy only.'

'But Priests of Elah-ga-baal.' Antoninus was not ready to dismiss his birth so lightly.

'And what is Elah-ga-baal in Rome? Nothing but a dirty black stone. Listen! This girl is a Cornelia of the great Cornelian gens – Roman patricians when we Emesenes didn't even have a clay pot to pass water in. She's stupid – too stupid to interfere in politics but sufficiently pretty to appear at public functions as an Augusta. In other words, she is a complete nonentity except for her name and that will connect us with the great of Rome.' Her voice lowered and became conciliatory. 'You don't have to live with her, Varius, or sleep with her.' She started to laugh, 'By Venus, neither one of you would know what to do with the other. But marry her you shall.'

His grandmother's laugh banished Antoninus's rage. His moods were always ephemeral. From a blind, screaming tantrum, he could pass into affectionate docility in a moment. He flung his arms around his grandmother and laid his head on her ample bosom.

'She need not be disappointed on her wedding night, dear grandmother. I'll allow her a taste of Zoticus.'

The old lady frowned. 'She may still be a virgin, if there is such a thing in Rome. He'd kill her, as he almost . . .' Her words trailed off. She had almost said 'Soaemias' but caught herself in time.

Antoninus did not notice. 'But how she'd love it! Oh, by all means, grandmother, let us have the ceremony soon, and I shall go now to design a new robe to wear and new jewels to wear with it, but tell this Cornelia not to scent herself with saffron.' He kissed his grandmother and danced through the door.

A small litter of light cedarwood, upholstered in yellow silk with a frivolous canopy of the same material, was waiting outside her door. Before entering it, Antoninus stroked the legs of the two Nubian litter bearers, and when he had sufficiently titillated them to produce the effect he desired, he stretched out on the litter and ordered them back to his apartments. Distances were so great in the Golden House that Antoninus never walked, especially as he had insisted that his own rooms be as far removed from those of his family as possible.

As he was carried along through the oppressively ornate and seemingly endless corridors and open porticoes, his thoughts were already with the new robes and jewels he would have made for his wedding night. But, Antoninus's thoughts never dwelt long on one subject, and particularly in these days when they were wont to revert time and time again to the beautiful face under the blond curls which he had seen the first day he had entered Rome. Two weeks had passed and in spite of Gordius's searching, no trace of the sun-crowned Apollo had been found. Gordius reported to him every morning but always with the same negative answer. He had combed the baths, the Circus and the servants' quarters of the big palaces on the Palatine. He had, or so he said, sent men into the eating places and the wine shops of the Suburra, searched the brothels, both male and female, with no results. Gordius took the gold Antoninus always gave him but he had produced no results.

Had Antoninus been able to locate the fellow, he might have forgotten him after one brief session but the mere fact that he had been thwarted in his desires to see this golden boy, to know him and satisfy himself with him, magnified his desire until it had become an obsession. Even Zoticus had been almost forgotten. In spite of Zoticus's endowments, Antoninus was beginning to tire of him. Yes, he loved him. But Zoticus was becoming tiresome. Perhaps he could dispense with him. Well, not entirely, because he knew that as long as he lived there would be times when nobody but Zoticus could satisfy him and, of course, Zoticus was the incarnation of Elah-ga-baal. But . . . he could send Zoticus off to Bithynia – he was supposed to be Pro-Consul of Bithynia anyway. No . . . Bithynia was too far away. Well, he would think about it later. If someone could only locate the Sun-boy. Perhaps he would rival Zoticus. Oh, what did it matter? He was tired of *colossi*.

The bearers put the litter down in front of the twin ebony doors that marked Antoninus's apartment. At a knock they swung open, and Antoninus walked the few steps inside the room and waited for the doors to close.

There were to be ten races this afternoon – bitterly fought contests between the Greens and the Blues. It was the one sport that Antoninus loved and the only one. Not for him were the gladiatorial contests and the killing of wild beasts. He loathed the sight of blood, and when he was forced to attend such displays, he concentrated his eyes on the food which he insisted be served him. He was bitterly criticized for it for the Romans loved their games, but they loved their races too and in that he would join whole-heartedly. He found himself sitting excitedly on the edge of his ivory chair when the first chariots were lined up. Although the leathern helmets which the drivers wore hid their faces, he knew that one of the drivers for the Greens was Gordius. He could tell by the short, squat body, the immense arms and the profusion of scars. Gordius was the only one he could identify – the others were merely so many hairy or hairless arms and legs, all bulging with muscles and all exciting to look at.

The first race started and they had made six complete circles of the *spina*. There were four more golden balls to be dropped on the *metae* at each end. Two of the chariots had already been eliminated. One had smashed a wheel and had been ground into splinters as the others passed over it. The driver, now a mass of bloody pulp, had been removed. The other chariot had crashed up against the centre *spina* but the driver had managed to cut himself loose and jump out unhurt to cling to the stone masonry with his fingers until rescued.

Antoninus sank back in his chair as the chariots thundered past. He noted that Gordius still held the lead and the sight of Gordius brought his mind once more, as it did so often, to the Sun-boy. He watched the chariots round the *spina* and saw another golden ball drop. They raced up the other side where he could not see them, but his eyes were on the next turn, prepared to meet them as they came into view. They came, Gordius still leading by a nose, but the chariot of the Blues was gaining on him. Another driver, the long green streamers flying from his helmet, gained on the Blue, coming up abreast of him, with the intention of cutting him off before the turn so that Gordius would have an unobstructed field. Gordius turned his head slightly, saw his ally of the Greens coming to his rescue and forged ahead. Just as they were passing the imperial *podium*, the Green and the Blue locked wheels.

The cheer that mounted in Antoninus's throat was cut short by the deafening crash. There was a tangle of horses, a maelstrom of turning wheels and splitting wood and one of the chariot wheels flew up spinning in the air, nearly landing in the imperial box. Antoninus ducked instinctively as he saw the spinning wheel, laid his head on the wide marble railing and covered it with his arms. The wheel fell short of the box and clattered to the ground, but what Antoninus saw as he looked down was far more important to him than the danger he had just escaped. The driver of the Greens had been thrown from his chariot and had landed head first against the imperial *pulvinar*, his feet high up on the rounded kerbstone, his head, bared of its helmet, rolling in the sand and his yellow curls glistening in the sunshine. It was! By all the gods of Rome and Greece and Egypt and by holy Elah-ga-baal, it was the Sun-boy, he whom Antoninus had been seeking for the past month.

He stared in thrilled bewilderment for a second, unable to move, then quickly, without even a word to Zoticus or Cleander, he leaped out of his chair and ran out of the door at the rear of his box. He glanced around the marble paved *vestibulum*, ignoring the door he had always used, seeking a smaller one which he knew led downward to another door that opened out on to the sand of the Circus. It was through this that drivers summoned to the imperial box could enter.

Antoninus raced down the narrow stone stairs, pulled the huge bolt which fastened the lower door and stepped out into the sunshine of the Circus. Without a thought of the chariots which might be rounding the *meta* at any moment, he ran alongside the *pulvinar* to where the figure of the Sun-boy was lying and knelt beside it on the sand.

Immediately the Circus became more alive than it had ever been before. The oncoming chariots were flagged, the drivers pulling hard on their mounts to stop them. Various attendants raced to the splintered wreckage and surrounded Antoninus who had now managed to pillow the charioteer's head on his lap and was wiping away the sweat and blood with a section of his tunic which he had torn off. The racing chariots had ground to a stop not far off and Gordius jumped out and ran over to Antoninus. His first look was at the figure on the ground. He saw that the driver was breathing. Only then did he look at Antoninus.

'You have found him, great Caesar.' Gordius spoke as a man facing certain death.

'I have found him, Gordius. Call the stretcher bearers. Have him moved, but gently.'

'To the infirmary?'

'No, to the palace.'

Gordius turned to issue the necessary orders which sent attendants running. As they waited, the blond head still on Antoninus's lap, Gordius knelt beside the two.

'I lied to you, great Caesar. I knew whom you wanted but I lied when I pretended I could not find him.'

'But why, Gordius, when you knew I wanted him so much?'

'Because, great Caesar, I wanted him too. You see, I love him.' Gordius reached out a grimy hand and laid it beside the Antonine's on the driver's face.

Antoninus looked up to see tears in the big man's eyes. 'Your tears have saved you, Gordius. I know that you love him. What is his name?'

'Hierocles, great Caesar.'

'Hierocles.' Antoninus spoke the name and the eyelids of

the driver opened slowly. 'Hierocles, there are two people here who love you – the driver Gordius and myself. Perhaps you cannot make the choice now but you belong to one of us. Which one shall it be? I would not claim you if your heart is somewhere else. I could take you and I could force you to love me under threat of death. But that is not what I want. From the moment I saw you on the day I entered Rome, I have wanted you Hierocles. I think I love you.'

The eyelids opened wide and the glazed blue eyes looked up at Antoninus. They saw, but they saw but dimly. 'And I you. But a slave cannot aspire to Caesar.'

'No, Hierocles, but a Caesar can aspire to a slave. Now, speak no more, conserve your strength.'

'Gordius! Do not harm him, great Caesar. He loves me well but I do not love him.' The eyelids closed. Antoninus reached a trembling hand under Hierocles's leather cuirass. He felt the warm flesh, soaked in sweat, but his eager fingers told him that the heart was still beating. 'Oh, Elah-ga-baal, save him for me. Do not let me lose him just as I have found him.'

The stretcher bearers had arrived but Antoninus would allow nobody but himself and Gordius to place Hierocles on the litter. Gordius, after a moment's hesitation, said: 'I shall go to the Praetorians and give myself up, great Caesar. Do with me as you see fit. I am not worthy to be his lover or your subject.'

Antoninus smiled wanly. The thousands of spectators in the Circus were cheering him as he walked along but he heard them not. He turned to Gordius.

'I cannot punish you, Gordius. I would have had any other man crucified who betrayed me as you did and yet I know why you did it. Your tears told the truth. You loved him. I would not have wanted to lose him either. I would have done the same thing so I cannot blame you for doing what I would have done. You are free, Gordius.'

'Then may I return and prepare for the next race?'

'Hardly. My new Praefect of Sports does not indulge in chariot racing himself. That is only for slaves.'

'But I . . .'

'You are no longer a slave, Gordius, nor are you a chariot driver. Rome will miss you for you have driven the Greens to victory many times. I need a Praefect of Sports. I need men I can trust. Even though I take away from you that which you love most, it is not I who take it away. You heard what he said.' He nodded at the figure on the stretcher.

'That he did not love me. I knew that, great Caesar. I knew he never loved me, but I loved him.'

'Then methinks you are punished enough. No, Gordius, report to the Praetorians if you must but report as my Praefect of Sports. This,' he stripped off a plain gold ring from his finger and handed it to the driver, 'this makes you a freedman and a Roman knight. Go in peace, Gordius, and be my friend.'

They had reached the entrance to the stables which opened on to the Circus. Gordius took the ring and slipped it on his little finger. He knelt before Antoninus and kissed the torn hem of his tunic.

'Today, great Caesar, you have won a lover in Hierocles. Since the day he first saw you, he has spoken of nobody but you. He is capable of great love, Caesar, for he has never loved before. Do not accept his love and then make sport of it. Yes, great Caesar, you have today won a lover worthy of you and in your great joy, do not forget, you have also won a friend, the humble Gordius.'

13

HIEROCLES WAS CARRIED back to the Palace in Antoninus's own litter, borne through the endless halls to Antoninus's apartments and gently bedded in Antoninus's bed. The tall ebony doors were closed and bolted within and sentries posted outside to see that nobody approached. *'Allow no one to enter unless authorized by Caesar!'* That was Antoninus's command.

Zoticus protested, pleaded and threatened outside the ebony doors but the guards had had strict orders. For two weeks, the only persons to pass through the doors were the priests of Asclepius with their healing nostrums and the Greek chirurgeon who was attached to the court. Antoninus did not show himself either in the palace, the Senate or in the hall of justice. A hastily signed decree gave Julia Maesa and Soaemias full authority to represent him in the Senate and once having done that, he cast the government of Rome from his shoulders and devoted all his thoughts, actions and endeavours to saving the chariot driver, Hierocles.

Until he was certain that Hierocles would recover he never left his bedside day or night except when, exhausted from lack of sleep, he would doze on a cot alongside the bed, delegating Cleander to watch while he dozed. He never rested for long, but was up again assiduously attending to the wants of his Hierocles. He nursed him, fed him, kept cold compresses of snow on his head and when there was nothing else to do, sat silently beside him, loving him, feasting his eyes on him and fanning him to keep off the stray flies. No Caesar was ever waited on with such loving care as the charioteer Hierocles received from his Caesar.

Fortunately Hierocles was not seriously injured. There was an egg-sized lump on the back of his head, where he had struck the masonry, divers cuts and bruises on his legs and body and two deep gashes on his wrists where the leather reins had cut into the flesh. He had not had time to slash the reins with the dagger that every charioteer carried in his belt for such an emergency, and as a result of being dragged by the frightened horses his wrists and upper arms were torn and mangled. The Greek chirurgeon had washed the wounds in vinegar and his skilful hands had patted and patched the flesh together. The priests of Asclepius then bound them with folds of much washed linen and a special healing ointment, all while Hierocles was in blissful unconsciousness. From his death-like coma, he had slipped into a fevered delirium, during which he talked incessantly while Antoninus sat beside him, greedily piecing together the stray bits of information which Hierocles disclosed, and thrilling to the sound of his name occasionally mentioned in the boy's wanderings.

'Mama! Mama! Why don't you come to me? Why don't you come and comfort your little Hierocles as you always do? I need you, *mama mea* and I want you. And bring the young Antoninus with you, mama, because I want him too. Oh, Antoninus, I saw you today. For one brief heartbeat, our eyes looked into each other's and I loved you. I loved you. Yes, mama, I loved him. Don't you know who Antoninus is, mama? He is Caesar. Go fetch him and bring him here. Tell him Hierocles calls for him and he will come.'

Antoninus sat quietly by and marvelled at this love which had come so simultaneously to both of them. Tenderly he would lean over and wipe the strings of drool from Hierocles's lips, smooth the sweat-damp tendrils from the forehead and wash the livid cheeks with snow-cooled rose water. Oftimes he would slip his hand gently between the damp curls and the hot pillow and try to comfort the boy with quiet, reassuring words.

'Your Antoninus is here, Hierocles. Were you to call from the ends of the earth he would hear and come to you. Were you to call even from the fields of asphodel on the other side of the Styx, your Antoninus would hear and come to you. Could you but open wide your eyes and see, you would see Antoninus sitting here by your bed, as anxious as any peasant wife about her husband. Yes, Hierocles, I am here.'

But the ears of the charioteer did not hear. His lips would twitch and he would rave on.

'Alas, you are good to me, Gordius, but I cannot return this love you so greatly desire. No, Gordius, I could not love a man like you but I could love a boy, some soft skinned handsome stripling whom I could master but I would have to be the aggressor, not the pliant recipient you wish me to be, Gordius. Oh, Antoninus, my Caesar. I could love you, Caesar. I do love you. Caesar! Great Caesar! What would you say if you were told that a slave loved you? Me, a Carian slave, a charioteer, something to make the crowd cheer when I win

134

and something to be carted to the Putrid Pits when I die. Gordius, I cannot do it, I cannot . . .'

As Antoninus sat beside the bed, during the long watches of the night, while Cleander slept, his hand often itched to slip under the sheet and discover what it might encounter. At length, when he had tortured himself sufficiently with dread and curiosity, he resolved to make the crucial test. It must be made sometime – it was inevitable. Better to make it while Hierocles was in his delirium than to wait until he was conscious. Antoninus checked to see that Cleander was sleeping soundly and then tiptoed across the room to bring all the lamps together around the bed.

With an unsteady hand on the sheet, he hesitated then, prepared to encounter even the worst, he closed his eyes and flung back the sheet exposing the charioteer's nude body. For a moment he was afraid to open his eyes, but when he did, he was glad he had taken the fateful step. His fears had been groundless. It was all too evident that Hierocles would never compete with Zoticus. Here was no phenomenon that would be heralded from Mesopotamia to Britain. Yet, on the other hand, what he saw needed no *apologia*. This Hierocles could well be an object of envy among all men, were one to rule out such rare exceptions as Zoticus, Quadratus, Maxentius, Hellenus and some of the pleasure legion which Eubulus had already recruited.

As he looked, Antoninus became aware that there was more to real love than he had ever before realized. He understood now, that, regardless of what the down-flung sheet had disclosed, it would have made no difference.

On the third night, the fever left Hierocles. His sheets became wet with sweat and the fevered ravings stopped. He slept naturally throughout the remainder of the night. Antoninus noticed the change, and when he had called the waiting priests of Asclepius to confirm his discovery, they assured him that the danger was past. Now the wrists would heal and Hierocles would live. In his utter exhaustion, Antoninus slept but awoke as the first streaks of the morning sun glowed behind the purple linen curtains of the room.

Hierocles opened his eyes slowly and dimly saw the Antonine's face bending over his own. Their eyes met momentarily and then Hierocles closed his tightly only to reopen them immediately. His gaze wandered from the face above him to the walls of grained marble, the furniture of gilded bronze, the pillars of alabaster that framed the softly moving curtains and then back to the silken sheet that covered him. Once again, he looked up at Antoninus.

'You are Caesar?' There was a trembling panic of fright and disbelief in his voice as he tried to lift himself up by his bandaged arms but the pain caused him to fall back on the bed.

'The world calls me that, Hierocles.'

'But, if you are Caesar, I do not know the correct way to address you. Oh, this must be another dream such as I have been having. I thought that in my dream, Caesar came to me and that his hands were cool as he placed them on my forehead but that his lips were hot as he pressed them against my own. Where am I? Why do I dream thus?'

Antoninus supported Hierocles's head a few inches above the pillow. 'You dream thus, dear Hierocles, because you love Caesar. You confessed it in your dreams. But fear not, you do not, cannot, love Caesar half as much as Caesar loves you.'

'Then I am not dreaming?' the blue eyes questioned in wonder. 'This is not a dream, that Caesar leans over me and that I am in Caesar's palace. But again, I say I know not how to address Caesar. I fear I shall say the wrong words and you will condemn me for the ignorant slave that I am.'

'Were I not Caesar, Hierocles, and were you not a slave, but we were simply two people, one not be-purpled and the other not be-slaved, how would you address me?'

Open-eyed, his gaze steady now, Hierocles considered the question for some time without his eyes leaving those that looked at him. Once or twice, his lips formed soundless words but no voice gave them meaning. Tears appeared in the corners of his eyes and rolled down his cheeks. When he did speak, he spoke with effort.

'I would address you as *beloved*.'

Now it was Antoninus's turn to weep and he buried his face on Hierocles's chest. He was crying from sheer joy – the miracle had happened. Now, he knew for a certainty that this love of his was returned. These were conscious words – not the ravings of delirium.

'Then never address me otherwise, Hierocles. I do not know – I do not understand what has happened to me. Only this. I know with a certainty that of all things I hold most precious, you are the most precious of all. From the first fleeting moment I saw you, I have thought and dreamed and desired nothing else but you. Since you have been here I have let my eyes look at nothing but you, and I have never tired of what I saw. Yes, *Carissimus*, this love I have for you is a wondrous thing.'

Hierocles moved his head back and forth across the pillow, shaking it from side to side in doubt and negation.

'But tell me not this, beloved, if you do not mean it. I had rather get up and crawl away from here now, knowing I would never see you again, if I thought your protestations were not true. You are Caesar, great Caesar, mighty Caesar, and I am a slave, a charioteer, purchased on the block for less money than one of the horses I drive. You have the power to command my love and I must needs accept on your terms whether it be for a night, a week or a month. But, beloved, that is not what I desire.'

'Nor I, Carissimus.'

'All my life I have longed for love but now, if I find it only to lose it, I shall be more miserable than before. Believe me in one thing, beloved, believe me. I do not love Caesar, with all that that love might bring me. I love you, and I ask for nothing more.'

Antoninus's cheek rested softly against the other's. Then he raised his head and without taking his eyes from Hierocles's, he slipped from his chair and knelt on the floor beside the bed. His hand slipped under the sheets.

'Here in Rome, it is the custom that when one man gives a pledge to another, he grasps the other's hand to make the pledge binding. In the east, where I come from, we have yet another way of binding a pledge. 'Tis very ancient and even the Hebrews used it, and it is mentioned in their holy book where their patiarch Israel made his son Joseph to swear with his hand upon his private parts. Even our Latin word *testiculi* and *testes* also mean to testify or swear for that was the ancient significance of these organs whereby men swore their most solemn oaths. As I cannot take your poor hand in its bandages, Carissimus, I shall use the ancient pledge of the east and swear on something far more sacred to me than your fingers. On this!' Antoninus clutched Hierocles under the sheets. 'And my covenant with you, Carissimus, is this, that if we ever separate through any fault of mine, I pray that my god, Elah-ga-baal, will strike me dead.'

'Then pray the same for me, and that will be my covenant with you, beloved,' Hierocles smiled up at Antoninus and he lifted his head as far off the pillow as he could to kiss the lips above him, 'but, oh beloved, if you continue this pledge much longer, I cannot answer for what is going to happen.'

Antoninus took his hand away. 'As I perceive, and that will be a pleasure we shall defer . . .'

'But why and for how long?'

'Until you are better. You are too weak now. The fever has but left you and I would not want to bring it back.'

'And now I hunger for food.'

'Which is a good sign.'

Antoninus clapped his hands and Cleander rose from his cot and came across the room, rubbing the sleep from his eyes. He saw at once that Hierocles had regained consciousness and he ran to the side of the bed, to kneel there alongside Antoninus.

'He has awakened?'

'Not only awakened, Cleander, but now I know he loves me as much as I love him.'

'Praise be to Roman Elagabalus and Grecian Zeus!'

Antoninus indicated Cleander with a nod of his head to Hierocles.

'My slave, Cleander.' He prodded Cleander with his elbow.

'Run to the kitchen and have them prepare a meal for Hierocles – something soft and nourishing that will stay his hunger but not put too much of a strain on him. Go, Cleander and hurry the lazy cooks. Watch them while they prepare the food and taste it yourself.'

Cleander got up from his knees and ran to the door. Antoninus arose and drew a chair closer to the bed. For a long time they were content merely to look at each other. There were a million words that each wanted to say – there was so much for each to know – all the details of their separate lives up until this moment to be discussed, compared and understood but these words were not necessary now. It was enough that each pair of eyes should behold the beloved features of the other, that Antoninus's fingertips should rest for a fleeting second on Hierocles's cheek and entwine themselves in his hair, and that the warm smile each one gave the other should be answered.

Hierocles broke the silence.

'We must start this love of ours with complete understanding, beloved.'

Antoninus nodded, waiting for the next words.

'We must make it endure,' Hierocles was emphatic.

'I want it to last as much as you, Carissimus.'

'Then I must confess to you, Antoninus, I do not come to you as clean and unsoiled as I would wish. I wish that I could tell you I am a virgin, unspoiled by either man or woman, but that I cannot in all truth do. I have been with one other.'

'Gordius?' Antoninus hoped the answer would be *yes*. He did not fear Gordius.

'Yes, Gordius.'

Antoninus breathed a sigh of relief. 'And only Gordius.'

'Only Gordius! When the Greens bought me, I was entirely ignorant of life. I had never been separated from my mother before. How I suffered from loneliness. The first night in the Greens' barracks I wept, alone in the darkness and Gordius, who slept beside me heard my weeping. He left his cot and came to mine and stretched out beside me holding me in his arms throughout the night. I came to love

Gordius but not as I love you, more as a father or a brother. But that love was not enough for Gordius, he wanted more.'

'And did you give him what he wanted?' Antoninus anxiously awaited the answer.

'The things that Gordius wished me to do, begged me to do, I could not, even though I cared for him. But in the end I accepted certain conditions. Now I wish I had not. I wish I had kept myself for you alone, Antoninus.'

Antoninus was silent. He saw the long, endless procession of faceless bodies pass before him – bodies that he had used and enjoyed often without looking at the face. Only the bodies! Oh, how countless many to compare with Hierocles's one timid experience. For the first time he regretted them – the slaves, the priests, the soldiers, the paragons of manhood whom he had caused to be assembled so that he could prostitute himself. Nubians, Egyptians, Arabs, Syrians, Smyrnans, Greeks, Gauls, Britons, Spaniards and every other tribe and nationality. His face burned as he remembered the nights he and Cleander had spent, be-wigged and be-painted, in the lowest bordellos in Rome, competing with each other to see who could garner the most *denarii* from the pot boys, hostlers, sailors and gladiators. How each would brag of his fistful of silver the next morning! He blushed to think of the lusty orgies in the camps when a hundred men had felt his hands in the course of a morning. But even more, he tormented himself with the nights he had given to Zoticus and the manner of things they had invented. He hung his head to hide his shame, trying to control his voice as he spoke.

'Would that my confession might be so simple, Carissimus. Where you regret the lone Gordius, I would have to regret thousands. If you reproach yourself for having been soiled by one, how can you accept the fact that whole armies have sported with this body of mine?'

'The past is past, Antoninus. Let us have a future where there will be nobody else but you and I.' Hierocles was pleading now.

'And how I wish I could promise you, Hierocles, but my

140

promises would be written on water. I know not what demon there is inside me that drives me to such horrible excesses, but demon there is and drive me it does. Always I have tried to think it was my god and that what I did was good and necessary in his sight. I felt that I was acting for him, strengthening him, and bringing him daily to life but now I see I was not doing it for my god but only to indulge myself. But,' he lifted his face and looked at Hierocles, 'if you will be patient with me, I shall try. I shall not promise you that from this day on, only your body will satisfy me and then break my word to you as I know I most probably shall, but this only will I promise you. I will try and with your help, perhaps I shall succeed.'

'We shall succeed, beloved.'

'Then promise me this. Punish me whenever I fail, Hierocles. I have never been punished in my life and perhaps that is what I need. I shall not resent your punishment for I know it will be proof of your love for me. Then, Carissimus, after you punish me, forgive me but never leave me. There is much that suddenly needs to be changed and settled now that you have come into my life. It will require patience and understanding on your part. I must dissolve one marriage – my marriage with Zoticus – and enter into another briefly, that with Cornelia. Then that must be dissolved and I shall at length be free for you.'

'Settle both matters in an hour. Banish Zoticus and refuse to marry Cornelia.'

'No, Hierocles, I cannot hurt Zoticus. You begged me not to harm Gordius, now I beg your indulgence with Zoticus. True, he must leave me but the parting must be easy and painless for us both. Bear with me, Carissimus, and let me handle these matters for I have been raised in a palace and I know all the intricacies of palace diplomacy, whereas you . . .' He turned at the sound of Cleander's footsteps. The slave entered bearing a tray covered with a napkin. He came over and set it on a table by the bedside.

'Of all the foods here, I have tasted and prepared them myself. You have nothing to fear.'

'Then go, Cleander, for I have another errand for you. Somewhere in the slaves' quarters of this palace there must be a carpenter or mason – someone who makes little repairs when necessary.'

'Yes. Veio, the Mauretanian slave. You remember, he whom we both had the day he came to fix the hinge on the doors . . .' He stopped suddenly and looked from Antoninus to Hierocles.

'Your mouth will get you in trouble some time. I do not require this Veio's services now but seek him out and get me a file from his tool chest, a strong one. Bring it to me and do not dally with Veio or I shall have you whipped. On the way out, give my orders to the new guards who come on duty soon. Nobody, absolutely nobody is to be admitted except on the word of Caesar. Go, Cleander, and hurry.'

He uncovered the tray. Cleander had prepared a simple meal of eggs cooked in milk, ripe black figs, warm spiced wine and bread still hot from the bakers' ovens. Antoninus took a spoonful of the creamy eggs and conveyed them to Hierocles's mouth but the charioteer pushed the hand away gently.

'You were saying that you were skilled in palace life but that I . . . and then you stopped. Let me finish your words. You were about to say that I am only a slave and have always been one. Is that true?'

Antoninus plopped the spoonful of eggs into the open mouth and waited for Hierocles to swallow them.

'My words do not matter. What if you were a slave? You are no longer.'

Hierocles's head came down close to his chest and he caught the thin iron collar in the cleft of his chin. 'And this?' he questioned.

'Why do you think I sent for the file? My fingers, and mine alone shall free you. As the file eats through that iron collar, you will progress through every status that man holds in the empire. At the first bite, you are still a slave, at the second a freedman, at the third a knight, at the fourth a senator, at the fifth,' he hesitated that the full impact of the words might reach Hierocles, 'at the fifth, Carissimus, you shall be Caesar.' He disengaged the iron collar from Hierocles's chin and plopped another spoonful of eggs into his mouth. 'Yes, you shall be Caesar. The Senate will confer the title on you.'

'And you? What will you be, beloved?'

'I shall be Caesar's wife. The Divine Julius once said that Caesar's wife should be above suspicion.'

Hierocles grinned. 'Caesar's wife had better be beyond suspicion or Caesar's wife shall have two black eyes.'

Antoninus grinned back. 'Hear the man brag! With both his hands bandaged, Caesar's wife could still have time for playing if she wished!'

Hierocles stretched his long legs out straight under the sheet. The folds of the thin silk outlined more than his legs.

'Would that there might be some other pledge you might make to me, some other solemn oath you might swear at this instant, beloved.'

'You mean . . .'

'I mean that I think your eastern way of pledging one's word is most satisfactory, most pleasant and most necessary, particularly to a man whose hands are bandaged.'

Antoninus relinquished the spoonful of egg he was ready to feed Hierocles. He slipped from the chair and knelt once again on the floor beside the bed.

'There are a thousand pledges I could give you, Carissimus, which one shall I give you first?'

Cleander entered the room, the file clutched in his hands. The other two neither heard nor saw him. With the file still in his hands, he tiptoed out, closing the door softly behind him.

14

THE PRIESTS OF Asclepius were pleased to report progress in the healing of Hierocles's wounds but advised that the bandages should remain on for another two weeks, which opinion was confirmed by the Greek chirurgeon. Gladly would Antoninus have continued his role of slave, nurse and wife to the convalescing Hierocles but as much as he wished to disregard the fact, he was also Caesar.

Julia Maesa informed him of that fact when she finally managed to penetrate the guards at his door by bribery. As Caesar, he had certain duties to perform, notably his immediate marriage to Julia Cornelia Paula and its attendant ceremonies. Although Antoninus raged as usual over being forced to do something which he, himself, had not initiated, he remembered the threat that Maesa had made. Few Roman emperors had ever died a natural death, and Antoninus knew that either the knife or poison awaited him if he did not bow to Maesa in certain of her demands. Having won his reluctant consent, Julia Maesa, who had already prepared everything in advance except the bridegroom, announced that the marriage would take place on the morrow.

She had ignored the recumbent figure on the bed, propped up now with pillows, during her stormy harangue with Antoninus, but once having finished and having gained her point, she allowed herself a glimpse of this new threat to her power. Fortunately, in spite of her fears, Zoticus had never seriously imperilled her position. Zoticus did not care for politics. He was interested primarily in himself, keeping his superb body in condition and hoarding as much money as he could against the day when he would no longer be in favour – a day which he knew to be inevitable.

Julia Maesa brushed Antoninus aside as she advanced towards the bed and carefully surveyed Hierocles before she spoke to him.

'So, you are my grandson's new fancy boy who is going to play Zeus to his Ganymede. Well, you seem to have all the qualifications, except one which is hidden by the sheet. The Antonine chooses well – his Zoticus is a handsome devil but I believe you are even handsomer. Furthermore, you look honest, which is more than I was ever able to say about Zoticus. So, if you make any claims to being a man, and if you should be honest to some degree, see if you can't make something out of the Antonine instead of the silly, simpering harlot he tries so hard to be.'

Hierocles did not quail before the stern eyes of the old woman. He recognized her authority and he realized that she, not Antoninus, was the true Caesar, but he also realized that it was she, more than anyone else, who had made Antoninus what he was. Now that the iron collar had disappeared from around his neck, Hierocles felt able to speak freely. He was becoming conditioned to the purple, even an Augusta of Rome did not frighten him.

'Most gracious Augusta,' he inclined his head as far as he could to make a courteous obeisance, 'I ask of Caesar only one thing. That he has already pledged me. I want neither position, money nor power. I am not interested in politics, intrigue or conquest. I desire neither gold, jewels nor proconsulships. Perhaps you will understand when I say that I love Antoninus and not Caesar. Antoninus, not Caesar, loves me. I am not qualified to instruct anyone. I was born a Carian slave and I have been a chariot driver. However, there is much in Antoninus's life that we both regret.'

'Then you know of his disgraceful escapades?'

'I know that suddenly great power was placed on the shoulders of a fourteen-year-old boy who was ill-equipped to handle this power. I know that from his youngest days, he was taught to indulge himself in every sensual passion that could be taught him. I know that nobody has ever loved Antoninus for himself alone. You never loved him, Augusta. To you he was a means of power. His mother never loved him, as her love had been squandered on almost as many men as his has been. This Zoticus whom you mention has never loved him – he was only interested in feathering his own nest. Now, Augusta, Antoninus has someone who loves him, someone who would die for him if he but ask. Perhaps you will see a new Antonine. Who knows? Eros can work miracles. At least, he can be no worse than what you have already made him.'

Maesa bristled. 'Hold your tongue, young man. No ex-slave

speaks so to the Augusta of Rome.' Her mood seemed to soften and her words lost their bitterness in the ghost of a smile. 'Hola, the youth has spirit! Spirit can be dangerous, young man, but if what you say is true – that you will curb this young scamp – then I shall not oppose you. Make something that looks like a man out of the Antonine if you can, but keep him and yourself out of politics. That is my province. And, if you can persuade him to dress like a man and keep him from playing the whore in the Suburra, I shall be grateful.'

Antoninus was jubilant. 'You conquered grandmother! And I promise you, Hierocles, I shall go no more to Apollonia's or such places. I'll do more than promise you, I'll even pledge my word in the eastern manner.'

'Not so,' Hierocles grinned and moved his bandaged arms to cover himself. 'I know what your pledges lead to, and we but finished one of those sessions less than an hour ago. Remember, I'm a man and not an army.'

'So Zoticus always reminded me and now, I am reminded that I must see Zoticus. We have much to discuss, and I think it better that I discuss it alone. My palace diplomacy has been at work and the painless parting is imminent. However, Carissimus, if you do not desire, I shall not see Zoticus alone.'

Hierocles considered the matter carefully before he answered. 'It has been some weeks since you saw this Zoticus. Perhaps when you see him, the fascination which he has always exerted over you will return and you will forget your Hierocles.'

'Have no fear,' Antoninus's lips brushed those of Hierocles. 'I shall never forget you. The conversation that we shall have will be concerned with business only. Two people must be eliminated from my life – Zoticus and this lump of dough which they call Cornelia. I have made my plans very cunningly for one to remove the other. Zoticus will depart from my life willingly and painlessly, but Cornelia's departure will not be so painless. I am dismissing Zoticus for only one reason – because I love you. I go now to Zoticus's apartments.

146

Fear not that I shall not return.' He brushed Hierocles's lips again. 'Do you play draughts with Cleander until this afternoon, when, if you are willing, we shall renew our pledge.'

Antoninus walked across the floor without his usual mincing steps, opened the doors himself and stepped out into the corridor where, as usual, his litter was waiting. Today the glistening ebony limbs of the litter bearers had no fascination for him.

'To the apartments of the Pro-Consul Zoticus.'

Zoticus was pleased to see him and inwardly congratulated himself that Antoninus had not come a half-hour earlier. He glanced quickly towards the bed to check its appearance. The covering had been carefully smoothed and its unwrinkled surface did not betray the frustrated struggle which had so recently taken place there. The sweating slave had given up in despair and left, and probably even now was spreading the word that the mighty Zoticus was impotent – a dead and lifeless behemoth that resisted every effort and could not be revived.

Zoticus was aware of what had been happening in Antoninus's apartments. At first he had not feared the results but now he knew he was on the way out. His one claim to Antoninus's love had disappeared. Yet he was relieved. Living in Nero's Golden House reminded him of the old fable of Damocles who had lived under a sword, suspended by a single horsehair. Zoticus had always been conscious of the sword over his head and now the frail horsehair that had held it had snapped. However, he still cared for Antoninus even though he knew he had lost him. He spread his arms wide in greeting.

'My Lupus! Life begins anew for me at this moment.'

Much of Zoticus's magnetic charm still remained for Antoninus and it made the part he was to play easier. He rushed into the open arms and as always, his hands deliberately sought that which he had always marvelled at, but in spite of forceful administration, the greatness of Zoticus remained limp.

147

Zoticus shook his head sadly. 'I do not know what has happened to me, little Lupus. I've tried male and female slaves but neither has been able to rouse me. The one claim I had to fame has departed. I shall never be able to satisfy you again, little Lupus. I must leave you.'

Antoninus appeared to be weeping. He was a facile actor and now he put all his talents to work. 'Did you try drinking satyrion.'

'Goblets and goblets!'

'But, oh, my Zoticus, you cannot leave me.'

''Twill do no good, little Lupus.' He walked to the table of polished wood and poured wine from a gold flagon into a gem-encrusted goblet. 'Now I can only drink to forget my troubles.' He gulped down the wine and wiped his lips with the back of his hand. 'It was nice of you to remember me with the dozen *amphorae* of Falernian. Not only is it the most delicious wine I have ever tasted, but it showed me that you were still thinking about me. I've finished ten of the dozen already. One drink seems to call for another.' He filled the goblet again but Antoninus took it from him.

'Yes, it is the finest wine in all the Empire. Each *amphora* costs more than its weight in gold, Zoticus, but I wanted you to have it to console you in my absence. I felt that you of all people deserved it and so I had it sent to you, but drink no more now. This recent failure of yours is serious. Do you realize what it means to our relationship?'

'I do, little Lupus, I do. It has worried me more than all else. Now that I cannot serve you as a husband, I am worthless to you. Dismiss me, Antoninus, and let me go. You will not miss me, you have a new love, but tell me, little Lupus, is he more of a man than I am?'

'More of a man than you are today but less of a man than you were a month ago. Do not blame me, Zoticus for loving him. It is a strange feeling I have for him, different from what I ever felt for you. When you touched me every nerve and muscle ached for you. But when he touches me there is nothing but a strange, delightful peace. Let us not talk of him now, let us talk of you.'

148

'Do you intend to banish me, little Lupus?'

'Not banishment, Zoticus, never that! Listen! My father – not Caracalla, but the husband of my mother, was Varius Marcellus. He was a wealthy man, here in Rome, and while we lived here when I was a child, we had a magnificent villa on the Campania, more palace than farm. I have not had an opportunity to re-visit it since we returned to Rome but I remember it and all its delights. It supports some six hundred slaves. This, Zoticus, is yours and with it the rank of *Eques*, if you will but retire there, ready however, at any moment to attend my call to return to Rome. Your stipend as *concubinus*, your rank as Pro-Consul to Bithynia and your taxes therefrom will be continued. Perhaps, leading the life of a country squire, you will be able to regain your vigour.'

Zoticus sighed in gratitude. It was far better than he had ever hoped for. He put out his hand for the goblet of wine which Antoninus had put on the table but Antoninus reached for it at the same time and his hand encountered it first. He raised it to his lips and would have drunk but it slipped from his hands and crashed to the floor. Zoticus picked up the flagon to pour another drink but found it empty.

'I'll call a slave and have it refilled. We'll drink a toast to my new rank and my new position as a country knight.'

'Never mind, dear Zoticus. I have not drunk wine these many weeks. I doubt if I shall ever want to drink it unwatered again. Hierocles does not believe in drunkenness.'

Zoticus's smile was almost a smirk. 'A most admirable young man. And I suppose he is too pure minded to let you sleep in his arms at night.'

'Not at all! In some things he even exceeds you, Zoticus, for he has a more fertile imagination, but as for sleeping in his arms, that is a pleasure yet to come. Both arms are now bandaged and still very tender.'

'With both hands bandaged, he has been most fortunate to have you with him during his convalescence.'

'And I most fortunate too. But enough. Before you leave

for the Campania, I have business to talk over with you. A last favour you can do me.'

'Then I am not to leave today?'

'Neither today nor tomorrow but the day after. You see, Zoticus, I am being married tomorrow.'

'To Hierocles? Surely you do not wish the divorced husband to help you sacrifice to Hymen?'

'Exactly that, but not in the way you mean. No, I am not being wed to Hierocles tomorrow. We shall wait until after my divorce. The Senate might frown upon two marriages.'

'Your divorce from me?'

'No, stupid man, not from you, You and I were married before Elah-ga-baal by old Zenotabalus. Nothing can break that tie. Tomorrow I am to be married to Julia Cornelia who douses herself in saffron water. It will be a big ceremony, with all the fat old senators and their wives, and my own family and half of Rome besides. There'll be a big donative to everyone, but Maesa is arranging this one differently. Everyone will get a little ivory tablet with a number on it and the number will represent some sort of a prize like a new slave, a country villa, wine, cattle, money, many different things.'

'Now what do you want of me?'

'To take my place as a bridegroom.'

'What, me to marry the Cornelia?'

'No, no, no! I'll marry the bitch. But after the wedding when we are conducted to the red-draped bed in the new apartments which Maesa has had decorated for us, you will be there, hidden in the ward room."

'Yes, go on!'

'And when she is in bed, lo, you will appear and do the nasty job she will be expecting. Meanwhile I shall sit on the bed and watch you and her, particularly her. I want to know every little scream, every gasp, every twitching . . .'

'So that when the bandages are removed from Hierocles's hands, you can do likewise?'

'How did you guess, wise Zoticus? But . . . remember this. You are to show her no mercy. When morning comes Cornelia will want but one thing – to return to her home and papa and never see a man again. She'll flee from the palace like the frightened rabbit she is and then – why then, I shall have grounds to divorce her because she left me.'

'Most cleverly devised,' Zoticus said, 'but haven't you forgotten one important thing? If I couldn't arouse myself for you just now, nor any of the whores in the Suburra, or the priests of Elah-ga-baal, how then, little Lupus, will I be able to service the Cornelia so that she will never want another man again?'

'Drink no more of the wine I sent you, Zoticus. Taste it not again today or tomorrow, and when tomorrow night comes and you climb into my bridal bed, you will see that all will be well.'

Zoticus stood up quickly and flung Antoninus on the floor. 'Why you . . .'

Antoninus got up from the floor and smoothed the folds of his silk tunic. 'Never again drink wine, Zoticus, that a wife who wishes to marry a new husband sends you.'

Zoticus was relieved. His problems had been solved, and he was not the limp wretch he had thought himself to be. He gathered Antoninus in his arms and embraced him, but Antoninus slipped out of his grasp, the door closed behind him and Zoticus was alone. He clapped his hands and his slave entered.

'Tell me, boy, how many *amphorae* of the wine that Caesar sent me now remain?'

'But two, my lord and master.'

'Then send them with the compliments of Aurelius Zoticus, Pro-Consul of Bithynia to the chariot driver Hierocles who now resides in the apartments of Caesar.'

'To the chariot driver Hierocles? Yes, my lord and master.'

'And mark them "For your Wedding Night" and sign my name.'

15

HIEROCLES WAS BOTH surprised and pleased when Zoticus's slave arrived with the gift of wine. He had Cleander bring the two *amphorae* to his bed and hold them up before him that he might examine their dusty contours and the cobwebbed seals of green wax. He directed Zoticus's slave to thank his master, but as soon as the boy had left, Hierocles told Cleander to remove the *amphorae*, saying that he might either keep them himself or give them away. Hierocles never drank anything but milk and honey-water.

Cleander was overjoyed with such a rich gift and admitted that he would keep the *amphorae* and their precious contents for his own use. For the next few days he went about his duties with a worried expression on his face, and Hierocles overheard him telling Antoninus a most unusual experience – unusual at least for the concupiscent Cleander. Antoninus smiled, realizing the reason for Zoticus's sudden generosity, and his sage advice to Cleander was to give up wine, as he himself had already done.

Hierocles had a brief glimpse of Zoticus on the morn of his departure, the day after the festivities that celebrated Antoninus's wedding to Julia Cornelia. Zoticus and Antoninus had arrived back at the imperial apartments, after having spent the night sacrificing to Hymen on the nuptial bed. Hierocles could but admire his predecessor. Surely Antoninus could not be blamed for loving the fellow. He was indeed handsome in his suave, dark aquilinity and his reputation had been known even in the racing barracks. Even his name had become a part of the Roman argot. A man was described as being 'A regular Zoticus' or 'Not so much of a Zoticus'.

Cleander afterwards told Hierocles that Zoticus drove away from the pillared portico of the palace in a silver and tortoiseshell chariot, drawn by four perfectly matched Cappadocian horses, followed by six mule carts, piled high with heavy coffers and a train of some twenty slaves following on foot, bound for his villa in the Campania. Cleander also volunteered the information to Hierocles that later that same morning, a half-conscious, moaning Cornelia was carried out of the back door of the palace in a hired litter and taken to her father's palace on the Palatine. Hierocles never saw the Antonine's wife. She kept her title of Augusta for only eight days, whereupon she was divorced by Antoninus and stripped of her titles. She not only deserted him, he told the Senate, but she had a blemish on her body. After her brief and painful *regnum*, she never returned to the palace again.

After the day and night that Antoninus had spent away from him, Hierocles had no further cause for complaint for every moment that Antoninus could steal from being Caesar he spent with Hierocles. The days passed in a procession of sunlit hours of games and laughter, and the nights were purple caverns of love. Neither tired of the other, although Hierocles was still hampered by his injured arms.

Then, came the day when the priests of Asclepius removed the bandages, and the Greek chirurgeon examined the healed wrists. They were, he said, as good as new, except for the angry red scars which would soon be less prominent. That night was given over to a special celebration in Caesar's apartments. It was a dinner for two, served by the now fully recovered Cleander and the menu was one of Antoninus's own choosing – a first course of rare delicacies from the sea, swimming in garum, that special blue-green sauce the imperial chef had invented and which had become the envy of all Rome. Next, succulent oysters, raw and chilled with snow, with a sauce made of that rarest of spices, pepper, which, when combined with oysters was said to be a potent aphrodisiac. Followed then, the Empire's greatest delicacy, sow's teats, cooked in camel's milk with Lybian truffles, and served with a delicate border of fattened dormice, baked in poppies, and glazed with honey. Antoninus would have delighted in mulsum, that cup composed of white wine, roses, absinthe, nard and honey, but Hierocles forbade it and Antoninus seemed content with the honey water, beaten with raw eggs and flavoured with the juice of bitter oranges from Spain. To top off the feast, there was a decorated pasty from Neapolis, which opened to disclose a gift for Hierocles – a pair of massive gold bracelets set with onyx cameos, big as oyster shells, which bore twin profiles of Antoninus and Hierocles – with Hierocles in the foreground as befitted a Roman husband.

The pasty from Neapolis and the cameos, which were a speciality of that southern city, reminded Hierocles of his mother who had been sold into slavery to a man in that city, and when he mentioned it to Antoninus, along with his thanks for the bracelets, he begged that Antoninus send imperial agents to Neapolis to find his mother, free her from slavery and bring her back to Rome.

Antoninus did not want to disappoint Hierocles, but he advised against such a course. His experience with his own relatives had proved that they were a necessary evil and to keep as far as possible away from them. He wished they were both in Neapolis or even farther and certainly if they were he would never send for them. He also feared that with Hierocles's mother in Rome, he would have to share his lover's affection with another, but Hierocles pleaded so abjectly and when denied, threatened with mounting temper to withhold his favours from Antoninus that very night. Faced with that awful probability, for Antoninus had been anticipating this night of all nights, Antoninus relented. He would have summoned Pluto from Hades, rather than lose this night with Hierocles.

Consequently, at midnight, a detachment of the noble Praetorians was sent off to Neapolis, resentful of the fact that they were to find a slave, purchase her, outfit her as a Roman matron of a patrician house and bring her back to Rome. The Praetorians were angry but they had no choice – Caesar had commanded and they had to obey. With their leaving, Hierocles's angry mood vanished and that night, for the first time, Antoninus slept in his arms, and never again, as long as he was Caesar of Rome, which is to say until the day he died, did he ever sleep anywhere else.

And now, came the afternoon when Hierocles's mother would arrive and Hierocles dressed himself in gold armour, a tunic of white silk, and a long cape of fine purple wool, heavily banded in gold, with a helmet crested with the white plumes of the ostrich. Once again, he stepped into a chariot but this time, he did not touch the reins; his own slave drove the horses. A company of Antoninus's own guards, the agglomeration of Eubulus's distant searches, followed him. Antoninus had decided not to be present at this reunion.

Hierocles had only gone a few *milliae* along the Appian Way when he spied the company of Praetorians advancing, with his mother's tall and commanding figure in the chariot. Both groups stopped, a chariot length apart, and Hierocles took the imperial salute, for, true to Antoninus's word, he had been proclaimed *Caesar Honoralibus* by the Senate which entitled him to all the honours paid to Imperial Caesar himself. He descended from his chariot and walked over to that which contained his mother, offering her his hand and helped her alight.

It was a happy meeting, there in the bright Roman sunshine of the Appian Way. Dulcilla, Hierocles's mother, was a handsome woman, as she must needs to be to have birthed so fine a son, and the *stola* of fine linen, widely purple bordered, added to her beauty. She clasped Hierocles in her arms, kissed him, and tried to restrain her tears.

'My son! I do not understand all that has happened, only this . . . we are here together once more and from what they tell me, I am not only free, but you are a freedman also.'

'In one night, *mater mea*, I passed through all the stages that any Roman might have. I started as a slave, then I became a freedman, a Roman *Eques*, a senator, and I ended up by becoming Caesar.'

'Caesar?' She looked up at him, her fingers on her lips, shocked with fear. 'Marcus Aurelius Antoninus is Caesar. Hush, my son, or you will be overheard and arrested. You must not try to impersonate Caesar. It is death to do so. Oh be quiet, Hierocles, before the guards overhear you.'

'The guards, *mater mea*?' Hierocles laughed and unclasped her. 'The guards? Pfft! Are you familiar with the imperial salute, mother?'

'Why yes. Once I went to the games with our master, dear old Marcus Savius, and I saw the soldiers give the salute to the Emperor Caracalla. Something about the right hand high in the air and the words *Ave* Caesar!'

Hierocles nodded in agreement. 'Then watch this.' He turned to face the band of guards who were standing a respectful distance away at rigid attention. 'Centurion,' he called, 'attend me.'

The Centurion walked stiffly towards mother and son. When he was but a few feet from them, he stopped, raised his right hand and said in a loud voice, '*Ave* Caesar! How may I serve Your Imperial Majesty?'

'My apologies, Centurion, I have changed my mind. You may retire.'

Again the hand was lifted and the same words spoken. The Centurion stepped back.

'Well, mother,' Hierocles smiled to see his mother's eyes bulging in surprise. 'Do you believe that I am impersonating Caesar or that I am Caesar?'

'I know not what to believe. I had thought the Antonine was Caesar.'

'And so he is, but, mother, I am Caesar's husband.'

Dulcilla stepped back, her face contorted with horror. 'You are what?'

'Caesar's husband! Ay, look not so shocked, dear mother. The great Nero was married to his Pythagoras; Hadrian took Antoninus to wife. I am married to Caesar.'

'Would that you had remained a slave! I've heard of this infamous Antonine and his evil ways. 'Tis common gossip even in the slave quarters, that he impersonates prostitutes in the lowest bordellos of the Suburra; that he has lain with a thousand soldiers in one night; that he is a depraved monster, steeped in nameless vices, perverted in all the unnatural things that men do with each other.'

'*Was*, mother, not *is*,' Hierocles shook his head, 'and like all common gossip, grossly exaggerated. This is Rome, *mater mea*, and today in Rome nearly every man has a Roman wife whom he neglects and a Greek *concubinus* whom he loves. I am more fortunate. I have a wife whom I love who is also my *concubinus*. Look about you mother! Why are you here? Why are you dressed as a Roman matron of consular rank? Where is the slave collar which you always wore around your neck and why has it been replaced with a necklace of pearls? You made the journey to Neapolis in a farm wagon, why do you return in an imperial chariot with a Praetorian guard of honour. And . . . why do you hear your son, who was a slave, addressed as Caesar? Because the little Antonine loves me, mother, and because I love him.'

'Then he cannot be a depraved ogre, because if he were you could not love him.'

'No, mother, my beloved is a boy who has but recently passed his seventeenth birthday. He is a boy who has starved for love without ever knowing what love really is and now that he has found my love, he glories in it. He is a boy who has never been taught right from wrong, until I started to teach him. I am proud of my beloved, mother, not because he is Caesar, but because he is mine.'

'Then I shall try to love him too. Mayhap it will be difficult, but I shall try.'

'Thank you, mother. Now stand beside me in my chariot and we shall soon enter Rome. This Caesar and his mother, who were yesterday slaves, today have all Rome at their feet. See the crowds lining the streets to see the Lady Dulcilla pass. Lady Dulcilla! That's you, *mater mea*! Today you have a little house awaiting you that once belonged to Fadilla, the sister of the Emperor Commodus, located on the Esquiline Hill* and connected with the Imperial Palace.

* The Golden House of Nero began on the Palatine Hill, continued into the valley and then rose up the Esquiline in a series of connected houses and palaces.

There I shall leave you with your new household, but I shall return at the first opportunity. We have much to talk about, dear mother. And now, we enter Rome. Stand straight, Lady Dulcilla. Smile at the people as you pass for if I am an honorary Caesar of Rome, then you are an honorary Augusta. Bow slightly, dear mother, and accept the plaudits of the poor people for now you can afford to smile at the lowly plebs.'

They drove on through the crowded streets, for although wheeled vehicles were barred from the streets of Rome during the daytime hours, the imperial chariot was an exception. The little house of Fadilla was, as Hierocles had said, charming and Hierocles left his mother there in the care of slaves which had been purchased for her. After he had seen her safely inside and introduced her to her attendants he left her, still somewhat awed by her position, and drove off, urging his charioteer to lose no time in reaching the Golden House. Antoninus was awaiting him, and he knew the boy would be petulant and childish after his absence.

He leaped from his chariot at the front portico of the palace, ran through the long halls and corridors until he reached the now familiar ebony doors. The guards admitted him without questioning and he burst through the doors, his arms outstretched for Antoninus. The room was empty. There was no Antoninus.

Hierocles made a hurried tour of the apartments – the big reception room, the bedroom, the adjoining baths and the wardrooms, even the pantries where their meals were prepared when they preferred to dine alone. Antoninus was not in any of them, and Hierocles felt that sudden suffocating clutch of panic that comes from disappointment and fear in not finding a lovèd one. He returned to the reception room and stood there, puzzled and distressed as to the complete absence not only of his lover but the slaves who were usually in attendance. Antoninus had made him promise – the third hour after midday. He checked the water clock. He was on time! Where was Antoninus?

A door closed softly in the adjoining room and he ran to

where the sound came from. The wardroom door leading off the bedroom was slightly ajar. Whoever had closed it had not closed it tightly. So as not to make any noise, he tiptoed across the floor and opened the door. Once inside he stood quietly in the centre of the room. Nothing stirred. Then he detected a slight movement behind the silken gowns hanging along one wall and he plunged his hand between them. It encountered warm flesh. He took a firm grip and pulled. It was not Antoninus, it was Cleander.

'Why do you hide from me, Cleander, and where is Antoninus?'

'I do not know, I do not know.' Cleander's look of injured innocence was not convincing.

'Then why are you hiding?'

'I was but hanging up Caesar's robes.' Cleander tried to twist out of Hierocles's grasp, but Hierocles only tightened his hold.

'You lie, you little bitch.' Hierocles seized his arm and bent it behind his back. 'You lie! Something is going on here that I do not understand. Where is Antoninus?'

'You are hurting me,' Cleander was whimpering. 'Oh, but you are hurting me. I don't know, I don't know, I don't know! Oh, you will pull my arm out of the socket. Oh!'

'I'll break your arm,' Hierocles applied more pressure. 'Where is Antoninus?'

Cleander screamed in pain. 'Stop, oh stop! He will have me crucified if I tell you and you will kill me if I don't. Stop, stop, Hierocles!'

'Yes, I'll kill you and gladly.' In his rage, Hierocles gave the arm a vicious twist and Cleander only screamed the louder. With his other hand, he pulled the sword from his scabbard and held it against Cleander's throat. 'Now tell me, screaming bitch. Tell me, and if you tell me, I shall see to it that you are not punished, but if you don't, I'll slit your throat from ear to ear.' He relaxed the pressure enough to stop Cleander's howling.

'Loose me and I'll tell you. But you must promise me, no

matter how angry Antoninus is with me, that I shall not be punished. And put away that sword.'

'It is a promise.' Hierocles sheathed the sword, 'Now, where is he?'

'At the baths.' Cleander rubbed his aching arm. 'Yes, at the baths. He paced the floor from the moment you left. Every five minutes I had to run to the water clock to see how much time had passed. To pass the time, I had him try on a new robe, but he tore it to shreds, see.' He pointed to a heap of rags on the floor. 'Then he started his pacing again and finally he said he could stand it no longer. First, he said he was going to the Temple of Elah-ga-baal to make a special sacrifice for your return.'

'My return? I was no more than five *milliae* from the city.'

'Yes, but he was frantic with fear and worry over you. A wheel might come off the chariot and you might be killed.'

'Me – a chariot driver who has lost many wheels in the circus?'

'That matters not. He had worked himself up into such a frenzy, he could no longer contain himself. Then he decided to go to the baths.' Cleander looked up at Hierocles. 'You know what it means when Antoninus goes to the baths? It's his way of forgetting his worries. But this is the first time he has gone since he knew you.'

Without answering, Hierocles turned and ran from the room. Still running, he retraced his steps through the long halls and out through the front portals. A centurion was dismounting from a horse and Hierocles snatched the reins away from the astonished man and leaped into the saddle, heading for the great new baths which Caracalla had begun and which Antoninus had recently caused to be completed.

When Hierocles arrived at the baths many recognized the former chariot driver who was now almost Caesar, and made way for him. Some tried to restrain him with greetings, others to plead their cases, but he ignored them all and kept on, straight through the disrobing room where half of Rome seemed to be dressing or undressing. He skirted the *calendarium* and the *tepidarium* until he came to the *frigidarium* with its huge indoor pool, now crowded with men of all ages, for this was the popular hour.

Beyond the pool were a series of dimly lit, narrow corridors, with curtained booths, each with a couch, where bathers could rest after their baths. There was little rest, however, in these dim corridors. They were the most famous place of assignation in all Rome and the doorways, unless the curtains were drawn, were usually occupied by Roman youths, their bodies freshly oiled from the baths, their hair arranged in elaborate curls and their smiles set on their faces as they shook the curtains and rattled the rings that attached them to the brass poles, in order that they might attract the attention of the passers-by. Men prowled through these corridors, accepting or rejecting as their fancy pleased.

Hierocles did not slacken his pace as he entered the aisles. There was a great rattling of curtain rings as he strode along. Hands reached out to grab him, softly spoken invitations were whispered to him, nude bodies arched provocatively at him, but he hurried on. In the third corridor, he found that which he was seeking. Antoninus was standing in the doorway of his cubicle, be-painted like a harlot, his hair glistening with gold dust, his hand on the drapery. In the dim light, he did not recognize Hierocles as the helmet shadowed his face, but he did catch the glint of light on the gold armour and saw that its wearer was tall and strong. He rattled the curtain rings, and when Hierocles was a few steps away, he swung his body out towards him, a smile of invitation on his face.

'In here, soldier,' he whispered and simpered coyly. 'In here, you will find all the delights of Babylon, the entertainment of Egypt, the special arts of Greece. All for you.'

'And would I find the love of Antoninus?' Hierocles asked, trying to control his anger.

Antoninus recognized him. He stared at him, bewildered. 'How did you know . . .'

'Dress yourself!' Hierocles wasted no words.

'My clothes are not here, they are in the vestibule.'

'Then wrap your sheet around you.'

'Where are we going?'

'Home, if I can call that cursed marble labyrinth of a palace home.'

'And what are you going to do to me when we get there?'

'Wait and see. Come. Your sheet looks enough like a toga and we'll get a public litter at the side entrance.'

They passed from the dim light out into the sunshine and took a hired litter, whose greasy leather cushions were a far cry from the soft cushions of hare's fur which upholstered the imperial litters. Antoninus would have spoken during the ride, but Hierocles's unconcealed anger frightened him and they jogged along in silence. When they arrived at the palace, Hierocles directed the bearers to go around to the small door which led directly to their apartments. They ascended the stairs in silence. The ebony doors opened for them and they entered their own rooms. Cleander was standing there, wringing his hands, but Hierocles dismissed him before Antoninus had a chance to speak to him.

Hierocles carefully and slowly removed his helmet, un-buckling the strap that held it, taking it off and placing it on the table. He was fighting for some degree of calmness for he knew that in his present rage, he might kill Antoninus. To be safe, he took off his sword. With the same deliberation he unbuckled his greaves and his gold cuirass, threw off the cape and removed his heavy sandals. He stood before Anto-ninus, clad only in the short tunic of white silk. All through the process of removing his armour, he had never taken his eyes from Antoninus.

He advanced a couple of steps to where Antoninus was standing, the rough sheet still clasped around him. Antoni-nus shrank back, unaccustomed to the look of anger in Hierocles's eyes. He would have spoken but Hierocles silenced him with a gesture.

'Let us understand one thing. In spite of the fact that I hate you at this moment, I love you, Antoninus. That is the most important thing of all. Do you understand that?'

Antoninus nodded, 'And I love you Hierocles – I do.'

'No, you don't. Otherwise you would not have taken this love of ours and cheapened it by peddling yourself in the baths today. You love nobody but yourself. You do not care anything about me. I am just another passing fancy like your Zoticus was.'

Antoninus gathered courage. 'If Zoticus were here now, he would kill you. One swipe of Zoticus's hand and you would be on the floor.'

'I fear not Zoticus nor any other man. I love not Zoticus nor any person in the world but you. Again, I ask you do you understand that?'

Antoninus was ready to forgive and be forgiven. He dropped the sheet and came towards Hierocles, his eyes lowered in pretty repentance, his underlip protruding in a pretty pout.

'Then, if you love me Hierocles, forgive me for my foolishness and . . .' His hand reached up to unpin the fibula that held Hierocles's tunic at the shoulder.

Hierocles's hand descended, without mercy and with the full strength of the massive arm that had guided horses around the Circus. It caught Antoninus on the side of the head and jarred it sideways. A stain of white appeared on his cheek which immediately turned scarlet. Hierocles's other hand, equally strong and equally merciless, crashed against the other side of the boy's face and another mark appeared. Antoninus sank to his knees, screaming.

'I'll have you killed for this. Carian slave that you are! How dare you strike me? Guards! Attend me! Help!'

His words were choked off by the pressure of Hierocles's hand against his mouth. Hierocles dragged him squirming and protesting across the room, fell backwards into a low chair and forcibly bent the boy across his lap. The round, pink buttocks were beneath his free hand and he belaboured them until they too turned from white to scarlet to purple. Antoninus, gagged and helpless could but thrash his feet as the blows descended. Finally, more because his arm had tired than his anger cooled, Hierocles pushed the boy from him and Antoninus sprawled across the floor.

Hierocles then walked slowly over to the table and started to fasten the greaves around his legs, put on his sandals and slipped his body into the metal tortoiseshell of the cuirass and buckled it. Finally he put on the helmet and gathered up the purple cape and clasped the gold buckles that held it.

Antoninus watched him from the floor. 'Where are you going?' he mumbled through swollen lips.

'Back to the Barracks of the Greens, if they want to take me back.'

'You want to be a slave again?'

'I'd rather be the lowest slave in Rome than be a kept fancy man in this accursed palace. I stayed here because I loved you and in that knowledge I could keep my self-respect. But now I know that in spite of my love for you, I am nothing but a paid stud. Well, get your stud somewhere else. Go back to the baths and find one and bring him here and dress him up and call him Caesar if you wish. I don't care what you do. I'm finished.' He turned and walked towards the door.

'Hierocles.' Antoninus managed to put all the love he really felt into the name.

Hierocles stopped and inch by inch, Antoninus managed to pull himself across the marble tiles.

'Oh no, Hierocles. Don't go! Don't leave me. Stay but five minutes and in these passing moments, perhaps your anger will leave you and you will look down at this wretched person on the floor and you will remember that you once loved him and, regardless of what you think, he still loves you.' Antoninus had reached Hierocles.

Hierocles looked down at the boy. He was truly a piteous sight. One eye was swelling with a purple-green discolouration. A trickle of blood, mingled with saliva, hung from a corner of his lip. Suddenly Hierocles's anger left him and his hand, which had been tightly clenched at his side, relaxed and opened. Antoninus came even closer. He lowered his head and kissed the dusty tip of the rough sandal. Hierocles leaned over and the hand which had punished now became tender as it touched the gold-powdered hair.

Antoninus felt the touch and his sobs exploded. Gently Hierocles lifted him up, cradling him in his arms and walked the length of the room, into the bedroom, where he tenderly deposited Antoninus on the bed.

'When I was lying here ill, you once told me to punish you if you did aught that displeased me. You did displease me and I have punished you. Now I ask for forgiveness. Will you forgive me for using my strength on you, beloved?'

'Your beloved deserved it. But it will never happen again.'

When Antoninus could divorce himself from his official duties – sitting through the long speeches in the Senate, administering justice, receiving ambassadors and signing his name to new laws and decrees – he and Hierocles would steal away through the back entrance of the palace, out to the stables where they would hitch their *quadriga* of four coal-black horses to a plain, unembellished chariot, and go for long drives alone out into the country. Antoninus loved the rolling hills outside Rome and often they would purchase bread, milk and cheese from a farmhouse and, leaving the horses, walk across country to a pine-studded pool where they would eat, sleep on the fragrant pine needles and swim in the clear waters.

One day, on such a journey, they discovered a most idyllic spot. It was a tiny villa, hidden in the hills, inhabited by a kindly old couple who provided them with milk, cooled in the spring; freshly baked, crusty bread; and a stew which the old lady had made. They begged leave to eat in the little vine-covered courtyard behind the villa, and there, served only by the apple-cheeked old lady, who was entirely ignorant of their identity, they ate, lounged and relaxed for the rest of the afternoon in the dappled shade, with the sound of a brook dropping over a little waterfall into a pool below.

Later, after the sun had sunk, making sure that the old couple were safely occupied in the front of the house, they slipped off their tunics and swam in the cool, spring-fed waters of the little pool and dried themselves on the rocks, still warm from the sun, reluctantly dressing again and headed over the hills to where they had left the horses.

'Oh, beloved,' Hierocles held back the bushes as he made a way for them to pass through a hedge, 'would that all our days might be spent like this one. The rough stones of that little villa please me more than all the gold and ivory walls of our palace. The savoury stew that the old lady prepared tasted better than the imposing dishes of roast ortolans and camels' hooves which we have in Rome. How wonderful this afternoon – no calls upon you; no cringing, fawning office-seekers; no flattering sycophants; no long-winded senators. Didn't you enjoy it, beloved?'

Antoninus adjusted his steps to Hierocles's long stride. There was a change in the boy. His face, bereft of paint, his long locks trimmed, his flowing robes of silk exchanged for a simple linen tunic, had changed his whole appearance. The sun had tanned his arms and legs to yet a deeper bronze than those of his blond Hierocles, and his whole demeanour was far removed from the simpering catamite who had sold his favours in the baths and the Suburra. His natural beauty was enhanced, for now he was no longer hermaphroditic in appearance. He appeared as that which he was – a handsome youth, tall for his age with an engagingly open countenance.

'Yes, I was happy, Carissimus. Why is it that with you, long silences do not pall on me? We sit together, happy in the knowledge that the other is only a finger-tip away and words do not seem necessary.'

'No, because I know your thoughts and you know mine.'

' 'Tis true, Carissimus, and now I know what you are thinking. You wish I were not Caesar and that we did not live in the Golden House and that you and I might spend our days in this same sweet way always. How right you are! I tire of ostrich's brains and honeyed dormice. Sometimes I think we eat these horrid messes just because they are rare and expensive and not because they please us. Yes, Carissimus, the savoury stew and the cold milk and hot bread were delicious. But stay, Hierocles!'

Hierocles stopped. 'What now?'

Antoninus pointed to his chest. 'The cameo with your portrait. I took it off when we swam and left it on the rocks. I'll run back and get it. It is not far and do you walk slowly and I will catch up with you.'

'Nay, let me go, my long legs will cover the ground faster than those reedy stems of yours.'

'Reedy stems! After you have kept me squatting and rising day after day with weights on my shoulders! No, I insist on going and I shall run so fast, you will not reach the chariot before I catch up with you.'

Hierocles looked at him indulgently. 'Were it not that old Philomenus is probably eighty, I would suspect you of some intrigue but I saw no handsome young slave about that might have caught your eye, so I'll let you go.'

'Jealous!' Antoninus taunted him. 'Must you always be so jealous of me, Hierocles?'

'Would you have me otherwise, beloved?'

'Not for all the world.' Antoninus reached up quickly and pulled Hierocles's face down to his in order that their lips might meet in a fleeting kiss, then, before Hierocles could say more, the boy was through the hedge and running over the fields to the villa.

Hierocles walked slowly, looking back anxiously from time to time to see if he could catch a glimpse of Antoninus coming back across the fields, but he had reached the high road, caught the hobbled horses and harnessed them to the chariot before Antoninus appeared. His smouldering suspicions, increased by his anxiety, burst forth in quick-tempered words.

'Then there was some boy slave whom I did not see? Certainly it did not take you all this time to find your cameo.' Hierocles looked to where the jewel should be dangling on its chain. 'And you haven't got it on now. As a matter of fact, Antoninus, you didn't have it on this morning when we left Rome. I remember now. So . . . what devilry have you been up to? What kind of a filthy rendezvous were you keeping. I swear by Eros that as much as I glory in this love of ours, it has caused me greater moments of unhappiness than I have ever known before.'

'That's because you never trust me.'

'Trust you? How can I trust you? Five minutes out of my sight and you're off to rattle the curtains in the baths; you're fingering some new recruit that Eubulus has discovered; or you're getting some Numidian litter-bearer into a dark corner. Trust you? How can I. Get into the chariot!'

'I won't! I'll walk back to Rome.' Hierocles's spark drew Antoninus's fire.

'It's fourteen *milliae*. Get in, I tell you.'

'I won't! I'll start to walk, and the first farmer's cart that comes along, I'll hail for a ride and then, believe me, I'll make that farmer so happy, he'll leave his wife, his farm and his goats and come to Rome to search for me in the baths. That I'll do. I will! I will! I will!'

Hierocles picked him up bodily and threw him into the chariot, then jumped up behind, his legs barricading the struggling Antoninus so that he could not leap out. Antoninus tried to bite his leg but Hierocles drew back and kicked him. Antoninus howled and was kicked again.

'You bully!' Antoninus continued to scream as Hierocles kicked him again, 'You big muscle-bound bully of a chariot driver. I'll have you crucified. I'll have you fed to the wild beasts in the arena. I'll . . .'

'Shut up, or I'll kill you. I mean it.'

'Yes, you would. That's all I hear. My grandmother seeks to poison me; my aunt Mamaea stirs up the Praetorians against me; Pompianus seeks to start a revolution against me; and now you – the only person I love – threaten to kill me.'

Antoninus became strangely quiet and stopped his writhings. He stood up, between Hierocles's arms and the apron of the chariot. 'So, brute, you would kill me and why not? Your love is the only thing I have to live for and if it must always be like this, a thing of fighting and bickering, then, why live? I'd rather dash myself beneath the chariot wheels and be done with it.'

His hands on the apron gave him leverage and he sprang forward but Hierocles caught him and wrapped one of the leather reins around him. Antoninus did not struggle nor did he speak. Hierocles slowed the horses down to a walk, then a stop. He turned Antoninus round, disengaging the rein. They faced each other.

'Then tell me why you lied to me this afternoon. Why did you say you were going back to get the cameo? And what did you do when you got there? Whom were you with?'

'Will you believe me, Carissimus, if I told you I was with nobody? That I spoke only with old Philomenus and his wife Dorca? That I used the cameo merely as a pretext to go back to them? That I did so only because I wanted to surprise you? That I only wanted to surprise you because I love you? Would you believe me if I told you that?'

Hierocles gathered the boy to him. 'Yes, I would believe you. I cannot bear you out of my sight. I picture you doing all sorts of things with all sorts of people. I cannot think! I cannot reason! A red fire passes before my eyes and I want to kill anyone whom you touch or who touches you, and then sometimes I want to kill you.'

'It is not your fault, Carissimus. I do not deserve your love. I have given you reason to be jealous but, remember, I told you in the beginning, I could not promise to be true to you. And yet, marvel at this, Hierocles! The times that I have been untrue to you are becoming increasingly scarce. The last time I appeared in the Senate with two black eyes was three months ago and since that time, my hands have touched only you.'

'But the desire to touch others? You always have that?'

'Not so often, Carissimus. I live for your happiness. That is what I had in mind this afternoon when I left you. It was to be a surprise to you but now I shall tell you if you wish.'

'I do not wish to be told, beloved. This time I shall trust you. Prepare your little surprise.'

'But it will require that I shall be away from you two hours every morning.'

'With whom? No, I shall not ask you that. This time I shall trust you.'

169

16

FOR THE NEXT week, Antoninus was up early and gone before Hierocles awoke, and when he returned some few hours later, Hierocles, true to his promise, did not question, although his thinly veiled curiosity knew no bounds. At the end of the week, Antoninus woke him early in the morning; he was dressed in a rough linen tunic with sandals such as peasants wear, fastened with straps of leather which crisscrossed to his thighs. He indicated a similar costume for Hierocles, who dressed quickly. Antoninus picked up a canvas-covered roll on the floor, strapped together with a carrying strap.

'Say good-bye to these marble walls, Carissimus. We shall not see them again for a week. This is my surprise for you. Come, we shall leave the two Caesars asleep in their beds of down while Hierocles and Antoninus sneak down the back stairs with a travelling pack between them.'

'Where are we off to? And for a week? Caesar cannot be missing from Rome for a week.'

'The Court Calendar for today states that Marcus Aurelius Antoninus, Caesar, Emperor of Rome and all the other things he is, accompanied by the Caesar Honoralibus, has left the city to pass a week in meditation at the villa of Tiberius on Capri, and Cleander and Maxentius, dressed in purple robes and riding in closed litters have already left; thus the two Caesars have apparently gone. Come, let's get out of here. The very walls oppress me. I scent danger in them.'

Their chariot with the four black horses was waiting for them behind the stables but instead of allowing Hierocles to take the reins, Antoninus drove. They roused the sleeping sentries at the Appian Gate and sped out along the road, between the marble tombs which were just now being touched by the rosy light of the rising sun. They shivered a little in the delicious early chill of morning. Oh, how wonderful it was to stand side by side, under the blue Italian sky with Rome and the Golden House of Nero behind them.

Some few miles out of the city, Antoninus turned off the paved road and took a dirt cart-road that led up into the hills. There was a certain familiarity about the road to Hierocles. He felt he had passed this way before, and he became more certain when they stopped at a roadside tavern where he remembered they had hobbled their horses the afternoon they had spent at the farmhouse.

But, instead of stopping at the tavern, Antoninus kept going, and where there had previously been only fields there was now a road, hacked out of the farmland. It wound across the fields to stop in front of the same farmhouse they had visited. It was, yes, indeed it was the same farmhouse – the home of old Philomenus and his wife Dorca, but there was a new addition. Over the door Hierocles saw a stone lintel, carved with letters. He leaped down from the chariot to read them. The carved letters spelled out his own name.

Antoninus glowed with pride. 'Yes, it is yours, Carissimus. Now I can tell you why I fabricated the loss of the cameo. You loved this place so I came back and bought it from the old couple. Then, during the past week, I have had the road made and now it is all ours – the little vine-covered courtyard, the tumbling waterfall, the pool of water, the icy spring and all. It's ours, Carissimus, ours! It's the surprise I have been planning for you.'

Hierocles sat down on the threshold and buried his head in his hands. In his repentance, he could not face the dancing eyes of Antoninus. 'And this is why I beat you and distrusted you? Oh, beloved, can you forgive me?'

Antoninus pulled him up by the hand. 'Forgive you? There is nothing to forgive.' He led him through the door. Inside it glowed with a cleanliness that exceeded even that of old Dorca. There were only three rooms, plainly furnished except for the big bed with its embroidered cover which had evidently come from the palace in Rome. They examined it all then went through the tiny kitchen to the little courtyard.

Antoninus flung his arms around Hierocles. 'We have one week – one week to be here alone – you and I, Carissimus, with nobody to disturb us. Although you cannot see them, there is a company of my own guards encamped near here to patrol the borders of our little farm and see that nobody disturbs us.'

Hierocles returned the embrace. 'Then, let us make this week something we shall always remember, beloved. Let it be unspoiled by one angry word or gesture on my part. Let us live every moment of this week in such harmonious perfection that we shall always remember it. Here you are no longer Caesar.'

Antoninus released him. 'Come, farmer, there is work to be done! We have no slaves to wait on us and we cannot remain idle. You, to the fields, my man! The summer wheat is to be cut and stacked so that later we can thresh it. The chick peas in the garden are to be hoed, but before you start on your work you must cut me wood for my fire that I may prepare your food. And . . .' his fingers were carefully enumerating some mental listing, 'go to the garden and fetch me some leeks, and small white turnips, and a head of lettuce. I must start to prepare our midday meal.' He pushed Hierocles ahead of him.

Hierocles did not move. Instead he looked down at Antoninus with a patronizing smile. 'You cook, Little Caesar? What do you know about cooking? We'll die of starvation the first day.'

'And why do you think I have been getting up early every morning? I had old Dorca come to the palace, and every morning I have gone to the kitchens so that she might teach me. You talked about her savoury stew! Well, wait until you see what *I* prepare. Now, go! Leeks and turnips, and a head of lettuce for a salad. I have much to do. I cannot waste time talking to you.'

Hierocles left, grinning, and Antoninus repaired to the kitchen. He unstrapped the canvas roll and took out sundry

172

bags, boxes and packages which he distributed on the shelves. Then he set to work. Soon the fire was burning in the clay stove, dough was being kneaded on the broad table, an appetizing aroma was steaming from the iron pot. Antoninus hurried from stove to table. He set up a smaller table in the courtyard with rough clay plates and wooden spoons. He sped to the spring to fetch the milk that had been cooling there since the morning's milking of their one cow. As the sun reached its zenith, he went out into the field, yellow now from its golden harvest, to call Hierocles, who laid down his sickle and came running across the stubble to meet him. Beads of sweat covered his brow, his curls, as golden as the ripe wheat, lay plastered against his head and his damp tunic clung to his body. With a leap, he cleared the shocked wheat and arm in arm, they walked back to the villa.

It was cool in the courtyard under the vine, and Antoninus seated Hierocles, then proudly brought out his handiwork. The bread was as brownly crusted, the stew was as savoury fragrant, the milk as chilly cool as that which Dorca had served. They finished their meal with a dripping honeycomb and Hierocles leaned back in his chair, replete and satisfied. Antoninus flung himself on the floor at Hierocles's feet, his head resting in the other's lap.

For a long time they sat in silence, as the vine shadows shifted on the floor. It was an hour of utter peace. Like other similar hours they were to have during their week, it was something neither of them would ever forget.

Hierocles stretched and yawned.

'I am sleepy and sweaty. My belly's full of good food. I've worked hard this morning, little Antoninus, while you have worked too. Never did food taste more delicious.'

'Never before was it prepared by hands that love you so much.' Antoninus echoed Hierocles's stretching and yawning. 'Tell me, Carissimus, do farmers follow the pattern of the city and take a nap during the heat of the day?'

'They do not.' Hierocles was emphatic. 'We'll work until sunset. When I return from work this evening, I shall be ravenous again.'

'That I know.' Antoninus pushed him back in the chair as he started to rise. 'But Dorca told me they had only a light supper – bread and milk and a honeycomb, with perhaps some plums or pears. But, Carissimus, you said you were sleepy and we are not real farmers. The shutters in the bedroom are drawn against the sun and it is cool in there. The big bed brought from Rome has a mattress of hare's fur and dried rose leaves. The sheets are of fine silk.'

'Tempter!' Hierocles pushed his hands away and stood up. 'See how the flies swarm around your dirty plates. Would you be a slattern? Get you to your work. There is the cow to be milked . . .'

'An old man arrives from the tavern to do that. I know not how to do it and neither do you.'

'That I'll grant you. But there is the courtyard to be swept, fruit to be gathered for our supper, dishes to be washed and towels laid out for our evening bathe. No, beloved, we shall not stop in the middle of the day to dally in the cool shade of the bedroom.'

'Wise Hierocles,' Antoninus said and began gathering up the soiled plates.

The days passed – a perfect necklace of golden beads strung together on the silver cord of their happiness. They were up soon after dawn when the dew still lay heavy on the fields, to a breakfast of bread and warm milk with fruit, frosted from its night in the spring. Hierocles then went off to the fields and Antoninus, in the house, baked, swept and garnished the rooms with sweet-smelling herbs and fresh pine boughs. But after their midday meal, they no longer worked apart; the hours were speeding by too swiftly. The work of the farm was forgotten and they would stroll away on long walks to gather armfuls of wild flowers, or idle out the long afternoons in the shade of the vine. When evening came, they ate the simple meal they had prepared together, swam in the cool waters, and without lighting a lamp, sought the big Roman bed and watched the moon as it made silver patches on the rough tiles of the floor.

It was a week of complete understanding, during which

they grew to know each other even better, to understand each other and to make allowances for the disparities in their characters and upbringing. Hierocles became more tender. The sharp edges and the quick tempers of his barracks-bred roughness were softened and refined by Antoninus's gentleness. Antoninus became less petulant, more mature. He lost some of his mincing walk and airy affectations, and was coarsened a bit by Hierocles's masculinity. His voice deepened and lost its high-pitched querulousness; his face, without the white lead and antimony, lost its Syrian softness and became handsomer. There was a blending between the two of them, each taking from the other the needed qualities he did not possess. It was a week of miracles in which the chariot driver became a little more polished and the Roman Caesar a little roughened.

On the last night of their stay, Hierocles awoke in the night, noticing that the pool of moonlight on the floor had disappeared and that there was utter blackness in the little room. He had been dreaming and his dream was so forceful, so much of a reality to him, that he awoke the sleeping Antoninus.

'You call me Antoninus, Carissimus. Is something the matter, something wrong?'

'No, beloved, nothing wrong, but I had a dream.'

'Did you dream of me?'

'Yes, of you, but not in the manner you think. Listen, Antoninus, sometimes the gods speak to men through their dreams. I believe some god just spoke through me.'

'Some god, Carissimus? There is only one god and that one Elah-ga-baal.'

'You are right! That is what I want to talk to you about. First, let me tell you my dream.'

Antoninus stared into the blackness, listening to Hierocles's words.

'I saw you, beloved, as I first saw you that time in Rome, walking backward along a long straight road. You passed me, but this time you did not falter and as you passed me, you did not look at me.'

'Then your dream was not true, Carissimus. I could never pass without looking at you.'

'Yes, it was true, for you had something more important to look at than this poor mortal. Following you, came all the gods of the world. First was Roman Jupiter with his crashing thunderbolts in his hand; then Juno, the great Mother of Rome; and Venus with the golden apple, and Mars behind her fully armed with drawn sword; Mercury, running over the tips of the grass with his winged sandals; Eros, his arrows unquivered, and Diana, fresh from hunting the stag. All the others were there – Bacchus with vine leaves and purple grapes in his hair; the drunken Silenus; even Priapus with his huge swollen member. And after them came strange gods – Isis of Egypt and the dog-faced, cat-faced gods of the Nile, with the creeping crocodile and other fantastic gods of Nubia and Africa. Astarte and the Moon Goddess of Sin; Mithras leading the mystic bull and all the myriad Baals. A great cloud passed that was the Jewish Hahveh, and after that a white-faced figure, bearing a cross that was this Jesus of the Christians. Plodding along behind them were a multitude of unknown gods, some wrapped in skins which belong to the Barbarians of the north; other gods with blue stained faces from Britain bearing golden boughs – all the gods that men have ever worshipped, in a long and endless procession behind you.

'Suddenly a blinding flash exploded, a light so bright that it burned everything before it, leaving only you and me. All the gods had disappeared and in their place there was only this bright and blinding light, which was so beautiful that neither of us could take our eyes from it, and yet for all its brightness we could look at it without burning our eyes. Then, out of that whirling brightness, there was formed a man – a man of light. Everything about him radiated light. His flesh glowed as a living coal and from his head darted rays of light. I marvelled at his beauty and then I recognized his face as that of your Zoticus, until it changed and I beheld myself as in mirror. Then my features too disappeared and only the form of the god was left. He was not a human such as was Jove or Isis but he was a god.'

'He was Elah-ga-baal.'

'Yes, he was the incarnate Sun. He was so holy that both you and I kneeled before him.'

'How were we kneeling, Hierocles?'

'Together, with our arms around each other.'

'I am glad. I feared we might be separated.'

'Never, beloved, not even a god could do that.'

'Carissimus.'

'And then the god spake and he spake to both of us.'

'What were his words?'

' "There is but one god and I am he. Upon your shoulders lies the task of bringing me to all the world. All the other gods men worship are as nothing beside me. You, Caesars both of you, govern Rome but Rome is such a little thing. Turn, Caesars, turn from Rome and bring the world to me." '

'And then, Carissimus?'

'And then I awoke.'

'It was indeed a wondrous dream, Carissimus, and I am glad that we were together. Tomorrow when we return to Rome we shall call in the augurs and let them interpret it for us.'

Hierocles sat up in bed. 'Augurs? What know they? Think you that the twists and turnings of a chicken's guts can interpret this dream? No, beloved, I had the dream and I can interpret it for you. Listen to me.'

'I listen, Carissimus.'

'You, my beloved, are the Emperor of Rome. Here in our bed we forget that momentous fact, and here in this little villa we have put it out of our minds for a week, but even though we try to forget it, we cannot ignore it. Listen! You can go down in history as one of the greatest of all Roman Emperors.'

'I?'

'Yes, you! What has made Rome great? Why is Rome the world?'

'Because Rome conquered the world.'

'And Rome united the world under one government.'

'That is right,' Antoninus agreed.

'And the great emperors of Rome were those who unified it – the Divine Julius, Augustus, Trajan, Titus and all the others who conquered and extended the borders of Empire. Thus Rome stands today as the world, but, beloved, Rome is still divided.'

'How? Rome is one, there is but one government, one Emperor, one Senate.'

'Agreed,' Hierocles nodded in the darkness, 'but, Rome worships many gods. Rome has no religion, for in one place it is Jove, in another it is Mithras, in another it is Urania, in yet another Isis or any of the multitude of strange gods which I saw following you in my dream.'

'How know you all these things, Carissimus?'

'Because I was not always a chariot driver. My mother and I were slaves of Marcus Salvius who was a noted scholar. Oft-times he would make me sit and listen to him while he talked. Thus I know. But hush, beloved, do not distract me. Tonight I speak not the words of Hierocles but of some divinity which is within me. Rome can be even greater. Now that Rome is unified in its government, another great Caesar can unify Rome in its religion, so that from the foggy coasts of Britain to the deserts of Libya, all men will worship one god. The emperor who can accomplish that will be as great, if not greater, than any other. And you, beloved, can be that Emperor.'

It was Antoninus's turn to sit up in bed. 'I? Yes, Carissimus, I could do that. I could lead all men to Elah-ga-baal.'

'And you would not fail, beloved, for Elah-ga-baal is a god, as I saw tonight in my dream. He is not a human, for although momentarily he had the face of Zoticus and then of myself, these faces vanished. No man can be a god. Those who have tried to make gods out of men have failed. They tried to make Julius, the first Caesar, a god. But who worships at his temples today? Hadrian tried to make his darling Antinuous a god, and built temples to him throughout the breadth of Empire, yet Antinuous never achieved godhood. The Jews have tried to make a god of this man Jesus but they have failed because he too was only a man. Elah-ga-baal is a god. I saw him tonight, compounded from the brightness of the sun, obliterating all the false gods. You are Caesar and Elah-ga-baal is your god. You are Pontifex Maximus of Rome, High Priest of all the Roman Gods, but before that you were High Priest of the Sun. You are the supreme religious leader of the world. This, then, is your path to greatness, beloved.'

Antoninus sank back beside Hierocles. 'You have said wondrous things to me tonight, Carissimus. Great things, unselfish things. Never before have I found in the mind of man such greatness. But, Carissimus, I am only a boy. How can I do all this?'

'You have me to help you, beloved.'

'Yes, perhaps together we can change the old gods of Rome and Greece and Egypt to one god, the supreme Elah-ga-baal. I think we can – I say we shall. It is a great work, Carissimus, and now I burn to return to Rome and start it. When we sought this bed last night, I was sorrowful that our week of joy was over. Now, Carissimus, we have work to do in Rome.'

17

ANTONINUS'S SATYRIC SEXUALITY and his mystical religion were deeply and inextricably linked together in his character. One was the offshoot of the other and it would be difficult to say which was the cause and which the effect. From his mother and his Syrian ancestors, he had inherited an overwhelming sensuality which had been nourished and encouraged in the phallic worship of his god Elah-ga-baal, whose symbol was the phallus. In the mind of the young Antonine, his physical desires and his spiritual obligations were one and the same. Elah-ga-baal, the Emesene prototype of that same Baal who was worshipped under so many different names in all parts of Asia Minor, was a god of natural potency and fertility and this particular Elah-ga-baal, exemplified by the sun, was strictly a masculine god as opposed to the femininity of the moon. Thus, the worship of Elah-ga-baal was one in which the eastern sensuality of the Syrians had always found a most satisfactory outlet.

From his earliest years, Antoninus had been encouraged in his sensuality by his family, slaves, tutors and priests, and to him the gratification of his senses was a supreme right for it demonstrated his religious fervour and served his god. The more he indulged his desires, the greater his service to deity. He had never made any distinction for his physical desires were also metaphysical. Therefore, the introduction of Elah-ga-baal to Rome by the god's High Priest, who was also Emperor of Rome, had seemed obligatory to him and for this reason he had brought the sacred stone to Rome. Now, supported by Hierocles's dream, which clearly outlined Antoninus's pressing duty, Antoninus was determined both as Caesar and Pontifex Maximus to combine all of Rome which meant the world into one god, and that god his own Elah-ga-baal. It was a worthy ambition.

The gods of Rome were dead! True, a certain amount of superstition still remained and a desultory worship was maintained at all the various temples in Rome but nobody actually believed in the State Religion – the worship of Jove, Juno, Venus, Mars and all the lesser lights of their adapted Grecian theology. In her conquests, Rome had absorbed many other gods to compete with those already on hand. Mithras was claiming many converts; Christianity was making its inroads; Isis was increasingly popular, but, in spite of Antoninus's insistence, Elah-ga-baal had made but little impression on the Roman mind.

Elah-ga-baal was not fashionable, despite his imperial sponsorship, and to be worshipped, a god must be the fashion. What little religiosity still existed in Rome was in the province of Rome's female population. It was they who worshipped at the Temple of Vesta; who flocked to the

Temple of Isis; and were fast accepting the meek theosophy of the Jewish Jesus. Elah-ga-baal had never encouraged female worshippers. Men, and men only, were important to his shrine and although women were grudgingly admitted to the old Temple of Minerva, which had been refurbished as a temporary home for the sacred black stone, they were not encouraged.

Nor did the prostitution of Elah-ga-baal's priests prove as popular among Roman males as it had in Emesa. Why go to the Temple of Elah-ga-baal at night for the services of a dark-haired, swarthy-skinned Syrian, when the baths of Caracalla teemed with hundreds of beautiful lads whose services were easily procurable at any hour of the day? And the baths were not the only source, for there were as many if not more, lupanars in the Suburra, whose winged phallus over the door indicated that their luscious catamites were available to all for a price.

Here then, was Antoninus's opportunity to make the worship of Elah-ga-baal fashionable and desirous. By so doing he would exalt his own position and establish Elah-ga-baal as the one god of Rome and Empire. It was indeed a worthy project and far more challenging to him than mere political chicanery. He was bored by judging intricate legal debates, ruling on the sanctuary of far-off temples, listening to the sterile speeches of long-winded senators and frittering away his time on dusty questions of protocol. Rome was at peace! No wars threatened her borders or security. Rome was prosperous! There was no famine in the land. Rome was rich! The spoils of the world belonged to her and her Caesar. The government of Rome was proceeding as usual – Julia Maesa saw to that. Then, why not devote all his time to this higher pursuit – this joyful, happy, worthwhile objective of making his own god the god of the world, which coincided so well with his natural desires? Why not? Indeed, why not?

Consequently, on the morning that Antoninus and Hierocles arrived back from their idyllic week at the villa, they both plunged into the work. Hierocles was a worthy partner to set the work in motion, for he felt that he had been divinely inspired, and that through it both he and his beloved would acquire world fame, not only for their own day but for centuries to come. Hierocles, too, had a deep mystic soul and had always believed that his association with Antoninus was something in the manner of a divine miracle, ordained perhaps by this god that Antoninus worshipped.

Within an hour of their arrival at the palace, messengers began running through the streets of Rome. Antoninus had delivered an ultimatum to the wily Maesa and for once she was forced to accept. She foresaw that with Antoninus's preoccupation in religion, she would have a clear field in politics. Moreover, the entire history of her family had been vitally influenced by the Sun God and she too felt some desire that what had heretofore been purely a local deity, served by generations of her own family, should now be universally adored throughout the world. As she shared in the revenues of the temple, it would also add to her riches and Maesa was, above all, avaricious. Furthermore, she hoped that her grandson's religious fervour might heighten his popularity in Rome, as it had in Emesa, for she sensed that his prestige was beginning to wane. The common soldiers, whose love and affection he had won in Syria, were now outside his sphere and the haughty Praetorians, who were the real force in Rome, were already critical of their Caesar. A peacetime army was always a hotbed of revolutionary ideas.

The messengers sped off. Heterodorus, the Greek architect, was summoned from his early morning love-making and commanded to appear at the palace immediately. A fitting temple to house Elah-ga-baal was the extreme necessity – the old Temple of Minerva was neither adequate nor grand enough. Antoninus had ideas about what he wanted and together with Hierocles and Heterodorus, he sketched roughly on paper that which he desired. It was to be a temple that would put all others in Rome and throughout the Empire to shame. Even the great Temple of Diana of the Ephesians would not be able to compete with it.

Antoninus wanted an imposing edifice, something which

would be so overwhelmingly pretentious that it would gener-
ate awe and admiration not only in Rome but the world. He
conceived of it as being entirely open to sun and air so that
the light of the sun would be its most important component,
until night, when light would disappear and darkness would
envelop it in an air of mystery. The building proper, which
was to house the sacred stone of Elah-ga-baal, was to rise
high on three sides, but be left open in the front. On each
side of the main building were to be two long wings, extending to form the back of an enormous courtyard. These wings
would house the sacred symbols of all other religions,
making them a part of but subservient to the central Sun.
The other two sides of the courtyard were to be open porticoes, solidly walled on the outside but with rows of pillars on
the inner, making a covered walk where hundreds of priests
could walk by night. The front was to be a pillared portico,
with a high gateway in the centre, the whole square enclosing an enormous court which would contain altars for
sacrificing, space for dancing processions and priestly rites.

Heterodorus was commanded to put his entire staff to
work at once on the plans. All other buildings in Rome must
be stopped immediately so that the masons and carpenters
could begin at once on the temple. The rarest of marbles
must be found, especially those in the shades of bright yellow and pure white of which most of the building was to be
faced. Everything must convey a sense of light – a vivid, in-
candescent light – such as Hierocles had seen in his dream,
for this light was the sun and this sun was God. No represen-
tational figure of Elah-ga-baal was to be made – he was not
to be visualized in human form, only symbolized by the
sacred phallus, that which gives life and breath and being to
all.

These days of planning were impatient and frustrating.
Nothing ever seemed to go right. It was one thing for Caesar to command a temple to be built, but it was another
thing to get it built. At length, after much consultation, the
plans were finally approved by Antoninus and Hierocles,
and Heterodorus set his staff to work, compiling specifica-

tions for the material that was to be used in the building and for the marble that was to face it. Work on the new Senate Chambers, on the new colonnades in the Forum and the Flavian Amphitheatre was stopped, and all the workmen transferred to the Temple of the Sun which was to be on the Palatine Hill, adjacent to the Golden House of Nero. Even parts of the sprawling Golden House were dismantled to provide more immediate materials for the temple. The gold plates that faced the dome of the imperial throne-room were removed to line the shrine of the sacred stone; sections of mosaic pavement were taken up, pillars of rare porphyry, alabaster and malachite were taken out and replaced by plain marble.

The work progressed slowly. The foundations of the temple were eventually laid and the brickwork started. Then came the agonizing period when, in spite of the thousands who were employed on the building, progress seemed to be at a standstill. Day after day, regardless of the many workers, the walls seemed to stay exactly where they were. Ox-drawn carts arrived from Ostia with rare marbles that had been shipped from foreign countries. Others arrived from the marble quarries in Italy. Both disgorged their loads, which were piled around the building, and it seemed as though they would never be used.

Catastrophe after catastrophe dogged the building. A scaffolding collapsed, killing twelve men. A block of marble, being raised by rope and tackle, fell and killed another four. Signs and portents appeared. A workman arriving early one morning saw the Goddess Isis, riding on a dog on the uppermost pinnacle of the building, her face turned away, hidden in shame. A slave woman crawled among the debris one night and gave birth to a monster – half man and half pig. Lightning, one bright sunny day, descended from heaven, struck the wooden scaffolding of the building and burned it – surely a sign of Jove's displeasure. It had reached the point where workmen were deserting and Antoninus, in a frenzy of frustration, threatened death to any workman who did not appear on the job.

One evening, after a particularly disappointing day, which he had spent with Hierocles and an advisory staff of builders, Antoninus sat alone with Hierocles, attended only by Cleander, in their apartments in the Golden House. His dinner, untasted, was still on the table, and he paced the floor of the big room, his little whip flicking nervously at objects in the room. Hierocles tried in vain to quiet him. 'You're making yourself sick over this, beloved,' he said.

Antoninus did not stop his pacing. 'Sick? Of course, I'm sick! A slave woman births a monster and what happens? A rumour flies around Rome that the gods are angry. A workman gets his foot crushed under a stone. Again a rumour! A man falls off the walls and splits his head open on the ground. Another rumour! Come, Hierocles. Let us forget these miserable things. Let us leave tonight, at this very hour, and seek our little villa in the hills, where we can find peace again!'

Hierocles shook his head. 'We cannot leave Rome, much as we both desire. It would start another rumour. The Antonine has fled Rome! He is hiding! He is afraid of the vengeance of the gods! No, beloved, that is a pleasure we must defer.'

'And I shall go out of my mind if I stay in these rooms another minute. Oh, Hierocles! Life becomes complicated.'

'Come, no more of that,' Hierocles said. 'Let us dress and go out.'

'And where shall we go?'

'Let us go to the temple. The moon is bright and we can walk around and inspect what has been accomplished today. Surely the walls must be a course higher. Come, beloved, dress. See, I already have my tunic on and am lacing my sandals.'

Reluctantly Antoninus agreed. He knew that Hierocles was going out, not through any desire of his own but merely to provide him with an outlet for his energies.

They departed through the side door, out across the moon-washed palace garden and down the slope of the hill to where the temple lay beneath them, silvered now in the moonlight and deserted. They climbed over the palace walls and cut through the deep grass and weeds of a field, under a clump of stone pines which cast inky shadows on the ground, and finally emerged at the main portal of the temple.

'See, beloved,' Hierocles waved his hand to direct Antoninus's attention to a stubby pillar, 'two drums of a pillar at the entrance have been set up.'

'Two drums! What are two drums when we consider that there are a hundred pillars on each side – four hundred pillars. And two drums have been set up! I shall be an old man before the temple is finished.'

They entered the half-finished portals and stood within the vast emptiness of the court. There was a small thatched wooden structure, merely a roof on posts, which the workmen used for eating their midday meal. Aimlessly they wandered towards it and sat on one of the rough plank benches. For a long time neither of them spoke but Hierocles welcomed the silence for he knew that Antoninus was relaxing.

'*Carissimus*,' Antoninus spoke.

'Yes, beloved.'

'No sacrifice to Elah-ga-baal has ever been made here.'

'Naturally, why should there be, before the temple is finished. The sacred stone is still in the old temple. Your priests are conducting sacrifices there.'

'But one should be made here. Perhaps if it were, the curse that has hovered over this temple would disappear.'

'Then here I am, beloved, ready, willing and more than able to make that sacrifice. I am the victim, you are the High Priest, here is the temple. What more could be necessary.'

'Nothing! You are right as always, Hierocles. Stay here, until I cross the courtyard to where the god will some day stand. Then, do you come across the yard. Thus you will seek me as the suppliants in Emesa do the priests there.' He was up and away, leaping over the stones. Hierocles watched him cross the moon-drenched yard, then disappear into the yawning black abyss of the shrine. He waited a few moments until he was sure that Antoninus was inside, then started himself.

He reached the portal and stepped inside. The soft arms which enfolded him in the darkness were those of the Antonine. The darkness enveloped them. Hierocles unclasped the cloak from around Antoninus's neck and spread it on the rough pavement. The sacrifice was under way. Suddenly Antoninus raised his head. He placed a finger on Hierocles's lips. Together they listened in the darkness. Somebody stumbled over a stone outside and cursed. A shadow darkened the portal. It was a man, clad in a long cape. Antoninus lay down on the floor beside Hierocles. They were both trembling, not from fear but from the unknown.

The man in the doorway turned to look out over the court. As he turned, the moon struck his face. Antoninus gasped and sat up, pulling Hierocles up with him.

'Did you see?'

'I did.'

'And you know?'

'Yes, it is Zoticus. What brings him here? Didn't you forbid him to enter Rome.'

'I forbade him and I know not what brings him here, *Carissimus*. I only know this. On my first night as High Priest in the Temple of Emesa, Zoticus appeared. To me he was the incarnation of the sun. And, so he was afterwards proclaimed by Zenotabalus. Thus I have always thought of him. I know not what brings him here tonight but this only do I know. It is a sign – a portent. It was divinely ordained.'

Hierocles drew Antoninus close to him. 'I am a jealous man, beloved. Even to think of you in the arms of another drives me into a rage.'

'As I well know. I have borne many bruises that prove it.'

'But tonight there is something so strange about Zoticus's appearing here that I cannot be jealous. Surely, as you say, he was sent. Do you go, beloved, and intercept him before he leaves. He, not I, is the proper sacrifice. It is Zoticus who will dedicate your temple for you.'

'No, Hierocles! Almost you are right but not wholly so.

Zoticus has come at the direction of the God. But, do not forget that you are here too. I am the priest. Two sacrifices are better than one. Come, *Carrisimus.*'

They walked out of the shadows into the moonlight. Zoticus heard them and turned quickly. His hand reached under his cape and withdrew his sword. He advanced, sword in hand.

'Put down your sword, Zoticus,' Antoninus called out. 'Tis a formidable weapon but I happen to know you have another which is even more formidable.'

'You, little Lupus.' Zoticus sheathed his sword. 'How come you here?'

'Hierocles and I stole away from the palace to see what progress had been made on the temple today.' The two came farther into the light. 'And now the same question to you, Zoticus. How came you here, when I had forbidden you to enter the gates of Rome?'

'Ask me not, little Lupus, for I cannot tell you. This afternoon, after my midday meal, I began to think about you and the temple which you were building for Elah-ga-baal here in Rome. Call it curiosity, but whatever it was, the urge to see the temple was so strong that I had my chariot harnessed and drove in to see it. I waited outside the gates until it was dark as I did not want to be seen and recognized. Then I walked from the gates here.' His hand swept in a wide gesture that took in the courtyard. 'When it is finished it will be a wonderful temple.'

'If it is ever finished! But, Zoticus, here is Hierocles. You have met but once and that briefly. It is well that you become friends.'

Zoticus advanced with hand outstretched. His teeth flashed in the moonlight in a broad smile.

'Should I be jealous of you, Hierocles, that you took the Antonine away from me?'

The ready friendliness of his predecessor quite unarmed Hierocles.

'Should I be jealous of you, Zoticus, in that my beloved can never forget you?'

'Is that true, little Lupus?'

'He speaks the truth, Zoticus. You know I could never forget you. But, Zoticus, is it not strange that we three should be here tonight. Surely it is not an accident. I remember that night in Emesa when I saw you walk across another moon-drenched courtyard and you ascended the steps of the temple. I was there waiting for you. I believed you to be Elah-ga-baal come to earth. Dedicate this temple for me, Zoticus. Together you and Hierocles can lift the curse that has settled upon it. Will you, Zoticus?'

'I will. 'Tis but a little thing to ask of me. But you, Hierocles, what think you? I do not want a dagger in my back from a jealous husband.'

Hierocles found the ability to smile. 'Yes, I am jealous, Zoticus, consumed with jealousy this very moment, but what my beloved says is right. Tonight we share him, but we do not share Antoninus, we share the High Priest of Elah-ga-baal.'

'Then come,' Antoninus stepped between them and took them both by the hands. 'Here, when the temple is finished will stand the sacred stone of Elah-ga-baal. I shall kneel here as Hierocles says, not as Lupus or Antoninus, but as the priest. Do you two face me and prepare.'

An hour later, the three of them appeared from the darkness of the shrine into the moonlight. They crossed the silvered courtyard and once again were swallowed up in the shadows of the half-built portal. Here they stopped and stood, the three of them, in a close embrace. One, the tallest and heaviest, separated from the other two and took the path that led down the hill. The others, arm in arm, started up the hill to where the lights of the Imperial Palace showed.

18

THE UNOFFICIAL DEDICATION of the temple by Antoninus, Hierocles and Zoticus evidently met with favour in the eyes of Elah-ga-baal, for the very next morning the full complement of workers appeared at the temple. A light shower, during which the sun continued to shine, was considered the best possible omen for it proved that the Sun God was supreme.

A thousand men were on hand – masons, carpenters, sculptors, mosaic layers, painters, artisans of all ranks.

It was evident first to Hierocles, and later more reluctantly to Antoninus, that the worship of Elah-ga-baal must be changed from a purely masculine one to include both sexes. What little religion still existed in Rome was in the hands of the women and the problem now became how to attract them. It would be necessary to offer some inducement and, although Antoninus was loath to let them participate in the worship of his god, he nevertheless came to recognize the logic of Hierocles's arguments and was finally won over. But, merely including women in the religion would not necessarily draw them to the temple – there must be some inducement. Again it was Hierocles who pointed out the way.

The pleasure legion of godlings that Eubulus had handpicked from the far stretches of Empire had lately languished in Rome. True, Antoninus had personally inspected many of the conscripts which Eubulus had sent – mostly without Hierocles's knowledge – but his old dream of an army of men for his gratification had vanished. Eubulus was again in Rome and now Praefect of the City as a reward for his having combed the Empire. The legion of stalwarts was still on hand, some five hundred strong. Why not, Hierocles suggested, sanctify these men as priests of Elah-ga-baal and put them on duty in the temple at night, along with the

Syrian priests. Surely a choice of stallions that ranged from blond Allemani to coal black Nubians would attract *both* men and women to the temple. Rome had nothing in her baths or *lupanars* to compare with this handpicked assembly.

Antoninus agreed. They were indeed an attraction – they even tempted him. Then, as Hierocles pointed out, instead of five hundred idle men eating their heads off at the expense of the state, and doing nothing all day but keeping their bodies in condition, they might as well be earning money for the temple. Allow each man a minimum of only twenty *sestercii* a night – that would be 10,000 *sestercii* a day – no little sum for the support of the temple and the money bags of the High Priest.

Antoninus agreed. In one night the five hundred were herded into the temple, where a mass circumcision took place that completely covered the black stone with bleeding foreskins. This, too, was auspicious, for on the opening of the temple some weeks later, all Rome pushed its way up the Palatine hill – a milling crowd of men and women, who elbowed each other in frantic haste to enter the moonlit courtyard. Instead of the modest estimate of 10,000 *sestercii* which Hierocles had made, the first night netted the temple coffers almost five times that amount. And, in addition, the members of the pleasure legion seemed most satisfied with their lot.

But in spite of the popularity of Elah-ga-baal among both sexes, there was still an important element in Rome which did not hasten to worship the Sun God despite the new attractions. This was that small but powerful and influential segment of Roman matrons, who, in defiance of Rome's careless morals, had retained some of the dignity and austerity of old Rome. These were powerful women of the patrician and knightly gens – too elderly to be overwhelmed by the appeal of the pleasure legion; too conservative to adopt a new religion; and too moral to identify themselves with the obscenity of this Syrian upstart of a god. It would take more than a German giant or a satin-skinned Nubian to entice them.

They continued to worship at the sacred shrine of Vesta, the ancient Roman goddess of the Hearthfire. It was here that the Palladium was kept – that ancient wooden statue of Pallas Athena which tradition claimed Aeneas had brought to Italy from Troy, before Rome was even founded. It was by far the most sacred object in all the world. Its shrine was the inner room of the beehive-like Temple of Vesta – the *penus Vestae*, so holy that even the Pontifex Maximus of Rome could never enter. Only the six Vestal Virgins and the Virgin Maxima could gaze upon it.

No foreign god could hope to compete with Vesta. Her worship was important in Rome and even the most decadent Roman, either through fear or superstition, still retained a feeling of awe for the goddess whose eternal fire was a symbol of Roman strength and Rome's ability to endure.

But to Antoninus, who was not a Roman and for whom the goddess Vesta had little if any significance, her worship presented the only really dangerous competition to his own Elah-ga-baal. Vesta must either be destroyed or amalgamated as all other religions had been. The Palladium must join the other sacred symbols which were now enshrined in the wings of the temple. Here it would take its place alongside the Bull of Mithra, the entwined Lotus of Isis and the Cross of the Nazarenes. Yes, the worship of Vesta must merge with the worship of Elah-ga-baal and, when looked at logically, this seemed to provoke no basis for a theological argument. Elah-ga-baal was the God of the Sun – Vesta was the Goddess of Fire. Sun and fire! The greater and the lesser. Elah-ga-baal was not represented by any statue in human form and neither was Vesta. The symbol of one was the sun; of the other fire. Why not combine the two? Why not – and by so doing destroy the last vestige of competition?

But Hierocles objected. Although he was of Carian ancestry, he had been born in Rome and the worship of Vesta was as curiously and as deeply ingrained into his consciousness as it was in all other Romans. To despoil her temple of the sacred Palladium would be an act of sacrilege so momentously terrible that he, along with all Rome, would shudder. Even Caesar, as Pontifex Maximus, the supreme arbiter of all the religious in Rome, could not dare do such a thing. No! Hierocles was adamant.

But Antoninus was equally adamant. Vesta and Elah-ga-baal must combine. He would brook no interference with his conception of all-deity and either Elah-ga-baal must be all, or he must divide his worship with an antique and out-moded goddess such as Vesta. It was unthinkable. There should be more than one way to gain his point and his cunning brain would find a solution.

Hierocles had never seen Antoninus quite so determined before. He was beginning to learn that the softness of the Syrian boy was only a deceptive covering for the iron will that lay beneath. Usually Antoninus could be cajoled, begged, entreated or bribed out of any idea.

'I'll make Vesta a part of Elah-ga-baal, even if I have to marry the Virgin Maxima myself!' Antoninus said. 'I'll swear old Aquilia Severa has been dying for a man all these years. Every time she gets near me, she manages to rub her thin shoulders up against mine while she smirks and ogles me.'

'You? Marry Aquilia Severa!' Hierocles howled with laughter. 'What could you do for her?'

'Nothing!' Antoninus shuddered. 'But methinks the dry and dusty wood of those locked gates would crumble fast enough under a forceful battering-ram.'

'Yours?' Hierocles's guffaws were even louder.

'Well, I was married once before and they carried poor Julia Paula out the next morning, torn and bleeding.' Antoninus winked at Hierocles.

'Thanks to Zoticus! Do you intend to recall him?'

Antoninus shook his head.

Hierocles pointed an accusing finger at Antoninus. 'If you have any idea in that mind of yours that I . . .'

'That I would relinquish you even for one night to thread Aquilia's rusty needle? Never! Although you were good enough to share me with Zoticus that night at the temple, I am not as generous as you. I will never share you with anyone. But wait! We have five hundred priests at the temple, or rather four hundred and sixty-two, allowing for the thirty-eight who died from their circumcisions, and if the sacred mother of Rome can't find one of them to satisfy her, she's harder to please than I am.'

'But there is some merit in your idea,' Hierocles said. 'Why not a spiritual marriage between the Sun-God and the Fire Goddess – between Elah-ga-baal and Vesta, exemplified by a similar marriage between you as High Priest of the Sun and Aquilia Severa as Virgin Maxima of the Sacred Fire?'

Antoninus leaped up and threw his arms around Hierocles.

'What would I ever do without you, wise Hierocles? That is the solution! Come, let us go at once to the Temple of Vesta. We'll propose to Mother Aquilia and offer her two bridegrooms. Elah-ga-baal for Vesta, and myself for her! And if it is to be a spiritual marriage, the old turkey won't expect me to bed her. But, on the other hand, if there is nothing that will satisfy her itch but a man, I'll tell her she may have her choice of any of the priests of Elah-ga-baal.'

Antoninus clapped his hands to summon Cleander. When the slave appeared, Antoninus instructed him to lay out his most elaborate priestly robes, order the state litter and proceed immediately to dress him. Hierocles dressed himself in armour – a virile foil for Antoninus's long flowing feminine robes. When they were ready, they descended the marble stairs to the front of the palace where the gold and gemmed imperial litter was waiting, carried by sixteen bearers instead of the four employed for ordinary litters. They were quickly borne to the Forum, where the circular Temple of Vesta, which housed the sacred fire, occupied a small island of sanctity in the busy centre of Rome.

Having been notified only a few moments before by a lictor who had run all the way from the palace to the temple, Aquilia Severa, the Virgin Maxima, was still in a flutter of adjustment of her white veils, as she stood on the top of the steps to greet Antoninus, not as the Roman Caesar but as Pontifex Maximus. She was a woman of middle-age but age

194

had not mellowed her. Instead it had sharpened her features with frustration, hollowed her cheeks with unsatisfied desires and whitened her hair with wakeful nights which she preferred instead of the erotic dreams which peopled her sleep.

Everyone in Rome respected Aquilia Severa but none loved her. Her tongue, sharpened by repressions and her quick temper inflamed by her frustrations, was merciless. Even now, standing to welcome the only person in the world whom she considered her superior, she was resentful and ill-tempered. Why had he not given her sufficient notice of his arrival? What was he coming for? Why didn't he stop meddling with things he knew nothing about? Why didn't he leave that handsome chariot driver behind? One glimpse of him, especially the muscled thighs which showed between the hem of his tunic and his thigh-bound sandals was enough to disrupt any virgin's thoughts.

She advanced to the edge of the top step and kneeled to the only person in the world to whom she owed obeisance.

'Vesta welcomes you to the home of the Sacred Fire.'

Antoninus allowed her to kiss his hand and then lifted her up. He would have implanted a kiss on the sere cheek, but the thin, dry, dusty smell of her virginity repelled him.

'Praise and honour to Elah-ga-baal, the omnipotent Sun,' he answered, 'the one and only God to whom all Rome pays homage, and to his hand-maiden, the Goddess Vestal.'

Aquilia glared at him. 'A strange greeting, especially from you, my lord, who rule the flame of Vesta. The goddess stands in second place to no other divinity in Rome. Were those words spoken by other than the Pontifex Maximus, I would have the speaker's tongue torn out!'

Antoninus gently propelled her inside the temple, aware of the stares of the crowd who had congregated around the steps. They continued on through the temple, through the garden behind, then into the *Atrium Vestae* the home of the Vestals. Not until they were all three seated in the shady *peristylium* did Antoninus speak.

'I meant no disrespect to the great goddess, Sacred Mother,

195

when I greeted you. My only desire is to gain greater distinction for both her and yourself. I have come to ask your consent to the removal of the Palladium from your temple to the new Temple of Elah-ga-baal.'

The look of horror on her face was genuine.

'Never!' Her thin lips froze in a straight line only to open reluctantly. 'Even as Pontifex Maximus of Rome, you are not even privileged to look on the sacred image, let alone touch it or have it removed. As long as Rome stands, the Palladium will guard the sacred fire and the sacred fire will remain there.' She rose in a floating aura of white veils and pointed her finger dramatically to the nearby temple.

Antoninus motioned her to sit down.

'Either the Palladium is moved to the Temple of Elah-ga-baal or the sacred fire is quenched.'

'You would not dare.'

'I am Pontifex Maximus of Rome. And . . . I am Caesar. I dare anything, Aquilia Severa.'

'But to quench the Sacred Fire. The Senate! The army! The people of Rome! I am not helpless.'

'They will only know one thing: that the Sacred Mother of Rome has been entertaining a man in the *Atrium Vestae*! That when she was taken ill a month ago and was confined to her bed for two weeks, she had, in fact, given birth to a child, old as she is! That the so-called Virgins of Vesta are no better than the grey-clad whores who accommodate their customers in the alleyways of the Suburra, except that they get paid, whereas the Vestal Virgins pay big money for their studs.'

Aquilia twisted the white veils between her white fingers.

'A lie! Nobody would believe such a monstrous lie!'

'Yes, a lie, as I well know, but I could buy the testimony of a hundred men who would swear that they had all been here. With a little coaching they would describe in detail how the Sacred Mother entertained them. I could have the body of a newly-born infant exhumed from your garden. I could have you and your virgins sealed up in separate tombs with a loaf of bread and a jug of water to die slowly and miserably. And,' he continued to smile, 'I shall do just that.'

'But why?' Aquilia realized that she was beaten. The penalty for a Vestal's loss of virginity was to buried alive.

'Because from now on there can be but one god in all Rome. My God – Elah-ga-baal!'

Aquilia regarded him with frightened eyes.

'As the sun is superior to all else, so is Elah-ga-baal superior to all gods. But, Sacred Mother, although I threatened you a moment ago, I do not intend to carry out my threat. Not if you co-operate. I only wanted you to know to what extremes I would go if necessary. I have no desire to dishonour you or Vesta. Instead, as I said before, I wish more honour and greater reverence for both of you.'

The priestess slumped forward in her chair.

'Attend her, Hierocles. I believe she is going to faint.' Antoninus did not move from his chair as Hierocles ran to the priestess. He put out his hand to steady her but hesitated.

'I dare not profane the Virgin Maxima by touching her.'

'It is all right, Hierocles. I command you. She will not resent it.'

Hierocles lifted Aquilia and eased her back into the chair, supporting her head on his arm. She opened her eyes and saw the near maleness of him, smelt the musk and sweat of his body, felt the strength of his arm. Her thin hand reached up and clasped his but she did not sit up. Instead she pillowed her head more comfortably on his arm.

'I am sorry, my lord. A touch of faintness.'

'Are you quite recovered?' Antoninus was all gentle solicitation. 'Do let Hierocles support you. He is strong.'

'Indeed he is!' Aquilia seemed quite recovered.

'Far stronger than any of the maids who attend you, is he not?' Antoninus closed his eyes slowly and sighed, 'Were Praxiteles alive today, how he would have glorified this Hierocles. Such rounded muscles on his chest, such rippling muscles on his belly, such strong, sleek muscles on his thighs. Truly, Sacred Mother, when he steps from the bath, he is another Apollo – a veritable god.' He opened his eyes slowly to see the effect of his words. A faint tinge of pink dyed the white cheeks of the priestess. 'Forgive me, Sacred Mother. For a moment I forgot where I was. Are you quite recovered?'

'Quite.' She withdrew her hand reluctantly from that of Hierocles and sat up straight. 'I am quite recovered.'

Hierocles resumed his seat.

'You were speaking, my lord, about new honours for both Vesta and myself.'

'Yes. Although I intend that Elah-ga-baal shall be the only god in all Rome, I do not discount the sacred power of Vesta. That these two may survive, it is necessary that they become one. I propose a sacred marriage between the two godheads – a marriage between the Sun and the Flame – a mystic marriage which will unite the two great faiths in Rome. Each will strengthen the other, and Vesta will survive, not as the cold virgin she has always been but as the warm, pulsating bride of the Sun.'

The smell of man still lingered in Aquilia's nostrils. It was the first time a man had ever touched her – a cold, immaculate virgin in spite of her lascivious dreams. Oh, why not a warm pulsating bride? Her hands gripped the ivory arms of her chair until the knuckles showed whiter than the ivory.

'I begin to understand, my lord. Perhaps your plan has some merit.'

Antoninus rose slowly and walked the few steps that separated them. He reached out a hand and lifted hers which looked strangely white and slender in the moist olive of his palm. He lifted the hand to his mouth and brushed it with his lips. He cringed from the dry, dead-leaf feeling of her skin but he did not allow his distaste to show.

'And Sacred Mother, as the Goddess of Vesta joins with the great god Elah-ga-baal, I propose that you, as Virgin Maxima and I, as head priest of Elah-ga-baal, enter into another spiritual marriage which will be but a human exemplification of the divine union.'

'A purely *spiritual* marriage, my lord?' Aquilia turned quickly, withdrawing her hand. A look of annoyance drew down the corners of her mouth as she regarded the white-robed Vestal who had just entered.

The intruding virgin stopped in her steps, at a loss for words in the presence of men.

'Well, what is it? Why do you interrupt us?' Aquilia had suddenly been brought back to reality.

'A priest from the Temple of Elah-ga-baal,' the woman stuttered. 'At the command of great Caesar. He waits in the anteroom of the temple.'

Antoninus answered. 'Conduct him into the garden. Remain near. When I clap my hands, bring him in here.' He nodded in assurance. 'It is quite all right. He is a priest and quite as holy as you.'

They waited for the woman to depart. Aquilia slipped back into her dream. 'As I was saying – a spiritual marriage, my lord?'

'Between a priest and a priestess it could not be otherwise, could it?'

'But, if Elah-ga-baal is to warm the virgin coldness of Vesta, should not the Priestess of Vesta experience the same,' she smiled hopefully. 'With Vesta no longer a virgin, can a virgin priestess serve her?'

'How right you are, Sacred Mother, and how logically you reason.' Antoninus noticed her eyes straying from him to the bulk of Hierocles. 'Naturally, the Priestess of Vesta must emulate the goddess in all things. While the goddess was a virgin, it was unthinkable that aught but a virgin should serve her. Now that the goddess is to be married, you should be also, in fact as well as name.'

'I think I am going to faint again.' Aquilia leaned back in her chair. 'Then you mean that you, as the priest of the Sun would . . . ?'

Antoninus shook his head. 'I am but a boy, Sacred Mother. I have just passed my seventeenth birthday. Surely in my young body there is not the power and vigour of the sun.' He clapped his hands sharply, 'No, I do not feel worthy to consummate this great and holy union. We must find one truly representative of the God.'

Aquilia's hands fluttered among her veils.

'It shall be as you wish, my lord. The Palladium shall be moved to the Temple of the Sun. The Sacred Fire shall gild the holy stone of Elah-ga-baal. Your god will marry my goddess, and I shall marry you.'

'With this handsome Aegenax as my proxy.' Antoninus pointed to the youth who strode across the *peristylium,* his thin silk robe moulded to his body as he walked. He was indeed all that Antoninus had painted – sloe-eyes, sinuous as a leopard, virilely handsome, exuding maleness.

Aquilia took one look at him and fell back in her chair.

Antoninus looked down at the crumpled figure.

'This time she has really fainted. Aegenax was too much for her. Summon her women and let us get away from here before she comes to and changes her mind. Come, Hierocles!'

19

THE MARRIAGE BETWEEN Elah-ga-baal and Vesta, manifested by the marriage between Antoninus and the Virgin Maxima, was celebrated between an expectant bride with the exciting image of Aegenax for inspiration and a bored bridegroom. After the ceremony the Palladium was moved from the *Penus Vestae* to be displayed in the wings of the Sun God's temple, along with the Sacred Fire which was placed directly in front of the stone phallus. During the elaborate rites, with the large donative which Antoninus made to everyone in Rome, the people were willing to be amused and interested.

He provided spectacles such as they loved – elaborate processions, clouds of precious incense, the sacrifice of hecatombs of oxen, with all the general licentiousness that accompanied the holiday mood of celebration. Antoninus caused thousands of wild beasts to be killed in the arena, fountains of wine to flow in the streets, and suspended all charges for the services of the priests of Elah-ga-baal, to whom had now been added an equal number of hastily gathered prostitutes who were initiated into the service of Vesta and attended the temple as priestesses.

But, like most drunken orgies, there was a sad morning-after and then the whole weight of adverse public opinion fell upon Antoninus. The most sacred shrine in all Rome had been despoiled. Those who had most enjoyed the orgy were the first to raise their hands in outraged horror. The revered Palladium was now hung as a trophy along with other sacred relics on the walls of the Sun God's temple. The great Virgin Maxima of Rome was no longer a virgin. The very backbone of Rome's awe and veneration had been broken, and Antoninus was blamed.

The August Fathers of the Senate, who had hitherto been subservient to Antoninus and granted his every request, now that the tide of public opinion was beginning to go against him, had the temerity to demand his presence in the Senate Chamber. The Senate thundered, Rome seethed, the Praetorians were surly, and Antoninus raged at the failure of his carefully laid plans, but for once he had to admit defeat. He, Emperor of all Rome, Caesar and Pontifex Maximus, was to be summoned before the Senate. He, the divine Caesar was commanded – yes commanded, to appear before the Senate.

He rebelled at their audacity but he went – his face stormy with anger and his apparel the most effeminate he could find. He knew it would anger the venerable Romans and he was right. The high golden network of his tiara sparkled with gems; the flowing embroidered robes were full and diaphanous; the dainty high-heeled linen shoes were mincingly feminine, and the jewels which hung from his neck, dripped from his ears and encrusted his fingers, caused just the amount of disgust he planned that they would. He entered the Senate Chamber, languidly supported by Hierocles, listened to the speeches with an air of utter boredom, replied in his highest falsetto, then gathered his draperies and flounced out again.

But . . . the Palladium was returned, the Sacred Fire re-lit in the Temple of Vesta, and poor Aegenax, who by this time was thoroughly limp, was permitted a well deserved rest from the consuming embraces of Aquilia, pure again and restored to her virgin status, at least in name.

Now that the Senate had dared to summon Caesar before them and tell him what to do, the thinly veiled opprobium of the Praetorians became more apparent. No longer was it an honour to guard the Emperor's door by night. Instead the unlucky recipient of that post of duty was reviled and name-called by all his companions on the following morning. The Praetorians had made emperors in the past and they had broken them. They considered it their right and privilege. Now they were embarking on another campaign of evil propaganda.

Antoninus could not understand why. He had always treated his Praetorians well – every favour they asked had been granted. He began to understand when he heard of the frequent complimentary references made by the Praetorians about his cousin, Alexianus. When the Praetorians erected a gilded marble statue of Alexianus in the middle of their camp, at their own expense, Antoninus understood even better. There was only one answer – Mamaea.

But she had covered her tracks well. Antoninus's spies could find nothing against her. They were certain that she was distributing gold to the Praetorians but apart from a sudden acquisition of many new pieces of gold armour among the guards there was nothing to point to Mamaea. Not until Gordius, who had been raised from Praefect of Sports to Praefect of the Night Watch, appeared at Antoninus's apartment in the palace one night with the newest Praetorian recruit with him. The frightened guard was hardly more than a boy, with a haze of beard which had never been shaven and the callow look of a rustic knight.

Gordius pushed him into the Presence and the young lout, frightened out of his few remaining wits by Gordius's severity and now finding himself in the presence of Caesar, became silent and tongue-tied.

'There's something afoot here, Great Caesar.' Gordius gave the young Praetorian another push nearer to where Antoninus and Hierocles were seated. 'This young bastard, who less than three weeks ago was spreading manure on his father's farm near Capua, got into the Praetorians because his father happened to be a Roman *Eques*. Now suddenly the boy blossoms forth in a gold breastplate that must have cost him a thousand *sestercii*.'

'The one he's wearing?' Hierocles asked.

'The very same! It's made by Marius, the goldsmith, and you know what his charges are.'

'He could have a friend – some rich Roman,' Antoninus suggested.

Gordius looked at the fellow and spat. 'With those pimpled cheeks, those puny arms, that hollow chest? And that?' He stepped up to the trembling guard and lifted his tunic. 'Who'd pay for that? You couldn't find it on a dark night. No! There's no rich Roman buying presents for Dung-Toes here.'

Antoninus advanced to the guard, whose livid face and trembling lips evinced his fear.

'Who are you?' Antoninus demanded.

'Quintus Pamphilus,' the soldier stuttered.

'Then, Quintus, do you want to live?'

'Oh yes, Great Caesar.'

'Then tell me, where did you get the breastplate you are wearing?'

The soldier hesitated. 'My father sent me the money to get it. I wrote him and told him all the other guards had gold breastplates.'

Antoninus looked at Gordius. 'The man lies, does he not?'

'He does, Great Caesar.'

'Then Hierocles, strip off his precious armour. And you, Cleander, run below to the freedman who disciplines the palace slaves. Bring his heaviest lash, and you, Gordius, hold the lout still while Hierocles strips him and when Cleander returns, ply the whip.'

Antoninus watched them as they unbuckled the armour

and stripped the tunic from the struggling guard. When he tried to resist, Gordius felled him, then grasped him by the scruff of the neck and pulled him up again. Stripped of his clothes, he bore out Gordius's prediction. The fellow was impossible with his scrawny legs and his flat chest. His skin had the colour of whey and he was covered with fine black hairs. Antoninus hated him for his very ugliness. He enjoyed watching Gordius mistreat the fellow.

Cleander returned with the whip and handed it to Gordius.

'And now,' Antoninus came close to the man – so close he could smell the sour perspiration of fear, 'do you still insist your father gave you the armour?'

'He did.' There was an attempt at bravado in the answer. 'Is there anything so unusual in that?'

'Do you question Caesar?' Antoninus struck him across the face. 'Gordius!'

The whip rose and came down on the pimply back. Quintus started to run, but Hierocles tripped him and he fell to the floor. The whip whistled again and as it descended, Quintus raised his head, receiving the lash full across the face. His hands went up to his torn cheeks and he began to blubber.

Cleander, standing near, delivered a vicious kick to the fellow's groin and the clutching hands, which were on his cheeks, reached down in a vain effort to assuage the pain.

'You'll kill me,' he cried. 'Oh, you'll kill me if I don't tell you and if I do, the guards will kill me when I return.'

A third lash caught him around the throat, cutting off his words. He gasped and crawled to Antoninus's feet.

'I'll tell you! I'll tell you all I know, Great Caesar, but don't let him hit me again.' His lips sought the toe of Antoninus's sandals and he slavered over them. 'No more lashes, Great Caesar, no more! I'll talk.'

'Then talk.' Antoninus restrained himself from kicking the slobbering fool in the teeth. 'Talk and be quick.'

Quintus raised his head. 'The day before yesterday Hostilanus Herodius, my Centurion, called me to his tent. He asked me if I had noticed the armour the other fellows were wearing and if I liked it. All the others in the cohort have gold armour and I did like it and I told him I did. Then he said it would be easy for me to get a breastplate like theirs and if I followed his instructions, I could get myself gilded greaves and a crested helmet too.'

'And what were those instructions?'

'That I hate you, Great Caesar, but I was to love your cousin, Alexianus. Whenever you appeared in public I was to revile you, but cheer for Alexianus. Also, that when the Augusta Soaemias appeared, I was to say bad things about her, but when the mother of Alexianus appeared, I was to hail her as Augusta and then tomorrow afternoon, I was to go with a number of the guards and kill you.'

'Where?'

'At the Circus Maximus, when you and yon Hierocles are practising with the chariots.'

'And do you know why your Centurion wants to kill me?' Antoninus threw a napkin down to the man to wipe the blood and slaver from his face.

'I do, Great Caesar, but I cannot tell you.'

'The lash again, Gordius.'

'Spare me that, Great Caesar, but if I were to tell you why the guards want to kill you, you will lash me anyway. It would make you angry.'

'I am angry now but I shall not hold you responsible for repeating your Centurion's words.'

'Then,' the fellow looked at Antoninus as if trying to gauge what his reaction might be, 'Herodius said – and do not blame me for repeating it, Great Caesar – that Rome did not want a silly catamite for emperor; a prancing he-whore; a dirty priest of a filthy Syrian god. Rome needed a man, like Alexianus, with a noble woman such as his mother behind him, instead of the slut that mothered you. And he said that the noble mother of Alexianus was willing to pay us all well if we would kill you tomorrow at the chariot practice.'

205

Hierocles reached for Gordius's sword. 'Shall I kill him, Antoninus?'

Caesar's uplifted hand arrested the sword thrust. He walked slowly up and down the room, the eyes of all four upon him. His face betrayed no emotion. Finally he returned to Quintus, who had raised himself to a sitting position on the floor. He spoke to Quintus but his eyes looked beyond the man on the floor.

'You live, Quintus. You live because you are stupid but perhaps that's reason enough. All Rome lives and all Rome is stupid. I've given Rome the most peaceful and the most prosperous reign she has ever had. Not one barbarian has crossed our boundaries. Throughout the breadth of Empire there is no war. The harbour of Ostia is filled with ships bringing the produce of the world to Rome. The citizens of Rome grow fat with idleness and satiated with continuous games. The December Saturnalia extends throughout the whole year. For this, they want to kill me and put Alexianus on the throne and, believe me, Quintus, he is even more stupid than you.

'Is it any worse that I bed myself with legionaries than that he does with tavern wenches. Would that make him more of an emperor? Does it make me less of one? No, do not answer me,' Antoninus silenced the protesting Quintus. 'Don't answer me, for I already know the answer. The Praetorians desire Alexianus for only one reason. Mamaea's gold is the answer. That is all. Little they care who is Emperor of Rome as long as their pockets are filled with *sestercii* and as long as they are able to sport golden armour. I brought peace and prosperity to Rome after wars and conflicts and famines. I tried to introduce one supreme god to Rome who would replace all her impotent divinities. But Mamaea has undone all this with a few gold pieces.'

Antoninus looked down at Quintus as though seeing him for the first time.

'Stand up, Quintus. Tell me more about this plot to murder me.'

Quintus carefully outlined all that he knew of the Praetorians' plans. He was not acquainted with the details but he said that the next day, when Hierocles and Antoninus repaired to the Circus to practise with the chariots, as was their custom, a group of Praetorians would take them by surprise. They were aware that no soldiers guarded them at that time. As they dismounted from their chariots at the end of a practice race, the guards would set upon them and slay them both.

Antoninus listened carefully and when Quintus had finished, Antoninus summoned Gordius to him.

'This Quintus has done me a favour tonight – perhaps he has saved my life. If he returns to the Camp, the guards may discover that he has betrayed them. I have promised him his life. See that he does not return to the barracks. Have him held under protective arrest but treat him with every consideration. Transfer him to the garrison at Antioch and give him the rank of Centurion. See that no harm comes to him.'

Antoninus rummaged through a jewel chest and brought a heavy bracelet of gold set with rubies which he handed to Quintus.

Quintus started to deliver a speech of gratitude but Antoninus silenced him, bade Gordius take him away and then return. The two left. Antoninus dismissed Cleander and was alone with Hierocles.

'They seek to kill us Hierocles.'

'Yes, little Antonine, perhaps they are jealous of us. And now I shall prove my love to you. I shall leave you. Rather that you be alone without me than dead. I fear not for my own life, but I fear for yours.'

'Did I not know you better, Hierocles, I would say that you were thinking first of your own safety, but I know that is not true. No, Hierocles, you shall not leave me. I need one friend – one person in the world whom I can trust. Rome has turned against me and my family also, for I doubt not but Maesa is privy to Mamaea's schemes. You are all I have but if you wish to go, you are free to leave, although I beg you to stay.'

'Then stay I shall, even if it brings added hatred to you.'

'That is unimportant. It is Mamaea's gold that we must fight against. She is ambitious for her brat. When Gordius returns, we shall make plans to outwit the murderers tomorrow and then I shall settle with Mamaea.'

'Then you intend to kill Mamaea and Alexianus.'

'I will not kill, Hierocles. I would not have their blood on my hands, even though they wish mine. No, we shall compromise. We shall give Mamaea enough to keep her quiet. I think, Hierocles, I am growing up. I am now eighteen. Perhaps it is time for me to be a man – a Roman instead of a Syrian. These robes, these jewels, these cosmetics, I tire of them. And my excursions to the baths and the countless ways I have tried to deceive you, Hierocles – I tire of them too.'

20

IT WAS WELL that Antoninus and Hierocles had been forewarned, for the plot to assassinate them had been cleverly conceived and would no doubt have been carried out successfully, had they been taken by surprise. As it was, they repaired to the Circus Maximus as usual, soon after their midday meal. At this time the huge Circus was usually deserted except for the hostlers and stablemen and the few charioteers who acted as instructors to the imperial pair. But this day, Gordius, disguised with a leather helmet that covered his face was among the instructors and all the hostlers in their patched and ragged tunics were members of Antoninus's own household guard.

While Gordius and Antoninus in one chariot, and Hierocles and a guard, disguised as a charioteer, were rounding the *spina* at the far end of the Circus, a cohort of Praetorians arrived. They forced the gates of the Circus without opposition and as the chariots thundered down the last stretch, the Praetorians formed a tight little group where they would stop. But, instead of stopping, the twelve frenzied horses tore through the group of soldiers, scattering them, trampling them and killing some six outright. Those who escaped the fury of the horses were rounded up by the ragged hostlers, now miraculously fully armed soldiers, and quickly dispatched. All except Hostilanus, the commander, who had survived the onslaught of the horses and was being held by the hostlers while Gordius and Hierocles managed to calm the horses sufficiently to turn them and drive them back to the scene of carnage.

Hostilanus, even though protected from torture by his status as an Equestrian Knight and a Centurion in the Praetorians, was immediately hustled to a room under the Circus and there put to the torture until he confessed Mamaea's part in the attempted assassination.

Antoninus watched the entire proceedings impassively, which was unusual for him as any form of physical suffering was repugnant to him. Hostilanus had been a hard man to break and had uttered no word on the rack or with his feet encased in the boot. However, when the guards stretched him for the second time on the rack and proceeded to break his bones one by one with iron rods, he broke down and confessed. Antoninus gave Hierocles the welcome task of dispatching the traitor with his sword and, with twenty dead Praetorians left behind in the Circus, Antoninus and Hierocles, accompanied by a strong guard under the command of Gordius, returned to the palace.

Antoninus summoned Mamaea and Maesa to appear before him. With Gordius and Hierocles behind him, he sat on the ivory curule throne, still dressed in the sweaty tunic of a charioteer. The walls of the presence chamber were lined, man by man, with the Palace Guards, each with sword in hand. Julia Maesa and Mamaea entered under heavy guard and were forced to walk the entire distance of the vast room, unaccompanied and alone. When they approached the throne, Antoninus demanded in a loud voice that they abase themselves before him. Old Julia Maesa's bones creaked as she sought her knees and Mamaea's face was dark and vindictive, but kneel they did and they remained on their knees throughout the entire audience.

'I have a deposition here,' Antoninus motioned to Hierocles to hand him the wax tablets, 'taken down by scribes from one Hostilanus Herodius, before his death by torture an hour ago, a Centurion of the Praetorian Guards. Would you, my dear aunt and you, my venerated grandmother, desire me to read it to you aloud?'

Julia Maesa started to rise but Antoninus's finger pointed scornfully at her caused her to sink to her knees again.

'I know no Hostilanus Herodius, Antoninus . . .'

'You will address me as Caesar, and not only as Caesar but Great Caesar for that is what I am.'

'I know no Hostilanus Herodius, Great Caesar,' Julia Maesa repeated. 'Why should this deposition interest me?'

'And you, dear aunt, do you find the name of this Centurion familiar?' Antoninus was having difficulty in curbing his anger. His voice trembled in spite of himself.

'I do not.' Mamaea's answer was quietly decisive but Antoninus's warning finger caused her to add, 'Great Caesar.'

'Then I shall refresh your memory.' Antoninus now had full control of his voice. 'On the Kalends of last month, you, Mamaea, summoned this Hostilanus Herodius to your apartments. He had previously been detailed with a cohort of men to guard you on a recent trip you made to Capua. I know that you wanted to murder me. I know that you connived with Hostilanus to do it. I know that in addition to giving him your body, you paid out vast sums of money to subvert certain of the Praetorians. Why did you want to do it? Do you hate me so?'

Mamaea lifted her head and glared at him. 'Rome needs a man to rule her.'

'But it is you and not your stupid son who wants to rule Rome and you are a woman. But come, dear aunt, I have a forgiving heart. The one god teaches mercy to all men and even though you desire my death, I can find it possible to forgive you. I could have you killed at this moment. One word from he and fifty guards would fall upon you with fifty swords and then they would slit your precious Alexianus's throat. But let us compromise, dear aunt, and let us both live. I shall bear you no ill will. Bear me none. I have always had every intention of making my cousin my heir. His blood is probably as imperial as mine.'

'Do you mean that, Antoninus . . . I mean Great Caesar?'

'I do. I shall adopt him as my son and heir. I shall legitimize him through a decree of the Senate so that upon my death, he will become Caesar. But, in order that you may not hasten my death to put the laurel leaves on Alexianus's greasy hair, I shall go even farther than that.'

Julia Maesa spoke for the first time.

'What do you mean by "farther", Great Caesar?'

'I mean that I shall make Alexianus Consul of Rome for the coming year along with myself. Next to being Emperor that is the highest position Rome can offer. As Consul of Rome he may learn something, in fact, he may even learn to speak Latin. He shall be my son and, as my son, I shall be responsible for his upbringing. He will be separated from both of you and will see you only when I permit it. Do you agree to that? Alexianus to be legal heir and Consul of Rome, and entirely under my supervision?'

'You intend to hold him hostage?'

'He will not be a prisoner, except that he will be forbidden to visit either his mother or his grandmother. I shall supervise his education and training. One more attempt against my life and your precious son will either die or wish himself dead.' Antoninus reached down and touched Hierocles and bade him stand up. Together they walked out, leaving Mamaea and Julia Maesa still on their knees. That same day Alexianus was moved from his own apartments adjoining those of Mamaea to rooms in the same wing as Antoninus. A detachment of the Palace Guard replaced the Praetorians who had hitherto guarded him.

21

WITHIN A FEW days, true to his promise, Antoninus set the cumbersome machinery of Senate politics in motion which would make Alexianus his legal son and heir and raise him to the high post of Consul of Rome. For once the August Fathers were more than anxious to comply with his wishes and the two decrees were issued forthwith. Alexianus's name was changed to Alexander and he was confirmed as Consul of Rome for the coming year.

Julia Maesa discreetly kept herself in the background, smugly satisfied with the way things were progressing. It had become increasingly unimportant to her which of her grandsons ruled Rome as long as she retained the power in her own hands.

Mamaea caused a scene at Alexander's appearance in the Senate to receive the consulship because she found that she had been placed next to the Lady Dulcilla, Hierocles's mother, and that Dulcilla's jewels were far more elaborate than her own. But, although she made her dislike for the Lady Dulcilla apparent, she was forced to walk beside her in the procession. However, she consoled herself that it was a small sacrifice to make, even though Dulcilla outranked her as mother of the Caesar Honoralibus as compared to mother of the Heir Apparent.

Soaemias managed to separate herself from the arms of her latest lover, the young patrician Ahenobarbus, long enough to come to Antoninus's apartment and congratulate him on his wily move, and cast longing eyes on Hierocles.

Hierocles felt it his duty to keep an eye on Alexander and frequently checked to make sure that the boy was safely in custody. The day after the official ceremony, Hierocles entered the new Consul's room. Alexander was lolling on a couch. The boy looked up at Hierocles and spat at him. 'Know you, slave, what my first act as Caesar will be?'

'Something stupid, I imagine.' Hierocles itched to slap him.

'Not so stupid, slave. I'll order you crucified, and naked too, so that all Rome can gaze upon my dear papa's plaything.'

'But you are not Caesar yet.' Hierocles left and returned to Antoninus.

'This Alexander is impossible. May all the Gods protect Rome if he ever becomes Emperor! Would it not have been better to slit the lout's throat, banish your aunt to the Pandatarian Rock and send your grandmother to Syria? You will never be safe as long as you have those three plotting against you.'

Antoninus looked up, overturning the bottle of oil with which Cleander was massaging him. A wave of his hand dismissed Cleander.

'Since the day I became Caesar, nay, even before that, I have never been safe, nor has any Caesar before me. Even the divine Julius was murdered in the Senate.'

'Shall you continue with this,' Hierocles swept the room with its bronze, gold and marble with his hand, 'and never know when you go to bed at night whether you will awaken in the morning? Or shall you eliminate your enemies before they eliminate you?'

Antoninus shrugged his shoulders.

'As for me, I desire only one thing. To die!'

There was a long silence. Hierocles did not move. Finally he forced himself to speak one word and that haltingly.

'Why?'

'Because except for you, Hierocles, I have nothing else to live for. What new joy can life hold for me? Lust? I have already experienced everything that could possibly be invented. Power? I have been Caesar for nearly four years. Wealth? I tire of gold and jewels, of silk robes and soft beds, of fawning slaves and fawning senators. My ears have been surfeited with music. My nostrils are deadened by cloying perfumes so that even the smell of honest sweat becomes more satisfying than the odour of lilies. My palate has tasted all the delights of every country from India to Britain. I no longer crave the caress of silk on my body, the deft fingers of slaves, the weight of diadems. There is only one thing left that could make life worth living for me.'

'Name it, beloved, and I will get it for you,' Hierocles pleaded.

'You and I together, apart from the world, seeking sanctuary on our little farm, working for our daily bread, sleeping the tired sleep of exhaustion and then waking in the morning to the sound of birds singing. Thus let me live, Carissimus, and I shall no longer desire to die. Let us flee this palace today.'

Hierocles's hand covered Antoninus's mouth.

'Hush!'

'Order the chariot, Hierocles, we leave now!'

'And guards?'

'Half of my Palace Guards to surround the farmhouse at a distance of a quarter of a *millia*. None to approach closer unless we alert them.'

'And messengers to ride from Rome in case they are needed?' Hierocles asked.

'Alas, Hierocles, whom can we trust in Rome to send a messenger if one was needed?'

'Only one.'

'My mother?'

'No, she rarely leaves the arms of young Ahenobarbus.'

'Then who?'

'Gordius! Since you spared his life and made him Praefect of the Palace Guards, he is faithful to you.'

'And methinks he still loves you, Hierocles.'

'This is no time to waste words in senseless jealousy.'

'And he can send Aegenax. I trust him.' He shouted for Gordius.

'Yes, Great Caesar.' Gordius stepped inside.

'Close the door. Hierocles will have instructions for you, but now attend me well. Once you told me you knew everyone in Rome.'

Gordius nodded.

'I have heard of a certain Hardranes, a quondam priest at the Temple of Isis.'

'Hardranes the poisoner?'

'The same.'

'While we are gone, you will seek him out, Gordius. You will find out from him if he knows of a very subtle kind of poison – one which does not kill at once but which produces the symptoms of a lingering illness that defies all physicians. Ask him if he knows of such a poison and how it can be administered.'

'The sword is quicker and it is deadly sure. Let me go to Alexander's rooms. In five minutes I shall return here and the job will be done. In truth, I shall enjoy doing it.'

'And make Alexander a martyr for all Rome to mourn? Ah no, Gordius. It would be quicker and surer but it would mean my end as well as his. No, seek out Hardranes. And now, heed Hierocles, and have your men ready to leave in an hour's time. Mount them on horses so they will arrive even before us.'

'Where do you go, Great Caesar, and who goes with you?'

'As immortal Jove took the young Ganymede in his eagle's talons and carried him to Mount Olympus, so do I go to seek a taste of heaven in the arms of an immortal god. Death is near me, Gordius. Ask me not how I know, but I know. You nor all your guards cannot save men from it so I would have one taste of heaven before I seek the shades.' Antoninus was sobbing.

Hierocles walked slowly to the weeping boy and took him in his arms. Gordius stood by the door, his fingers on the bronze latch. Suddenly he turned, walked to the two and spread his huge arms around both of them.

'We shall protect you, little Antonine.'

'That you cannot do, even with your great strength, Gordius. But . . . promise me one thing.'

'Anything, my lord and master, my Caesar, my friend.'

'Promise me that when they kill me, you will not allow them to desecrate my body or mutilate it. Carry me to the little farm and bury me secretly in the glade by the pool.

Secretly, Gordius, so that no man may know my grave except you and Hierocles. Then, Gordius, plant hyacinths around it – purple ones for Imperial Caesar; red ones for the moments of passion I have known; and white ones for the purity of my love for Hierocles.'

22

THE SOFT BLACKNESS of the night with its welcome cloak of anonymity enfolded them as their speeding chariot thundered over the paved road from Rome. It was a night unrelieved by either moon or stars, with a chill breeze that turned even colder as they sped along, cutting through their thin tunics and numbing their flesh. As they turned off the road into the dirt lane that wound over the hills to the farmhouse, the blackness of the night was studded with a comforting ring of far-off camp fires, and the questioning hail of a posted sentry was reassuring evidence that the Palace Guards had bivouacked for the night.

The *quadriga* came to a grinding stop before the dim outline of the little farmhouse and Antoninus leaped out, shivering in the night air, while Hierocles drove the horses around to the stable in the rear. While he was unharnessing them and bedding them down, Antoninus fitted the clumsy key in the lock and entered. The chill inside was even worse than that outside and there was a close smell of stale air in the house. He knelt on the cold stones of the floor.

'Oh, almighty Elah-ga-baal, even though your power is now gone, swallowed up in the night, when you arise once more in the morning, grant to me your son, wisdom and strength, and above all courage to protect him whom I love.'

He stood up. 'And myself,' he added.

A spark leaped in his hand and caught the tinder. In its feeble light, he saw a small oil lamp on the table, exactly where they had left it when they had departed in such high hopes only a few months earlier. The flame caught and the steadier light from the lamp enabled Antoninus to locate other lamps and light them.

He threw open the closed shutters to allow the night wind to sweep the stale dampness from the house, then knelt on the crude hearth to scrape together sticks and half-burned pieces of wood from their last fire. The wood was damp and would not catch but by pouring some of the oil from one of the lamps over it, he finally managed to ignite it and in a few moments, a feeble fire was blazing on the hearth.

He carried two of the lamps into the bedroom, threw down the covers of the bed and closed the shutters that he had previously opened, coming back into the common room and closing those also. By the time Hierocles had finished his work in the stables, there was light and a semblance of warmth in the house. Antoninus heard his footsteps outside and opened the heavy front door. They entered the house and closed the door behind them, slipping the heavy wooden beam into place that double locked the door.

The hamper yielded a stock of provisions and an *amphora* of wine which Cleander had packed hastily, together with a change of tunics for both of them. Soon Antoninus had water heating on the fire and when it boiled, he mixed wine with it. The fire was slowly robbing the stone walls and floor of their accumulated dampness; the lamps were flickering cheerfully; their senses were pleasantly dulled by the wine and they gradually relaxed.

Hierocles pulled a heavy black bearskin rug over the floor to the hearth and they lay down on it, so near the fire that by stretching their arms out, they could add more fuel to it. The ruddy flames played over their faces, propped on their hands, and they looked into the glowing embers as though to discover some sign or portent in them.

'Are we or are we not the most fortunate beings in the world?' Hierocles asked.

'If you mean at this moment,' Antoninus agreed, 'we are. I know, without asking, that your happiness equals mine. But, if you mean we are the most fortunate beings in the world because I am Caesar and you are Caesar's friend, I cannot answer you so well. I suppose if any man, high or low, within the whole stretch of Empire, were given the opportunity to change places with me, he would leap at the chance. To be Caesar! Augustus of Rome! The world at his feet! And yet, I would pity the man who might accept, even though he be a slave in the mines of Egypt.'

'Ah but, beloved, you do not know what it is to be a slave. I do.'

'To be a slave? Who knows better than I. You had one man for your master. I have a million. Were you more of a slave when you were on the block than you are here beside Caesar? Then you feared only the lash of your master but today you fear the sword of the assassin . . .'

'I fear it not for myself. I fear it for you.'

Hierocles, contrary to his usual custom, had not refused the hot wine. They continued drinking until the *amphora* was empty. The wine and the heat of the fire began to take effect.

Hierocles's eyes were glazed and his speech came thickly.

'So you intend to poison Alexander?'

Antoninus pondered the question with drunken deliberation.

'Within the week. Gordius will arrange it for me. Cleander will administer it in food or wine. It will not have an immediate effect but within the month Alexander will be dead. Then I shall have Hardranes killed, and perhaps Cleander, and nobody will ever know how Alexander died. Am I becoming another Caligula in that I dispense death so freely?'

'No, you are acting wisely, beloved.'

'I would have preferred to make Alexander my son and heir. I thought perhaps I could make him intelligent, clean and honest. But I have seen that it would be impossible. He will always be the boor Mamaea has made him. As an heir to Rome he is useless, and a threat to me. So he must die, but I regret his death and that of the luckless Hardranes – as I would a hare which was trapped, or a stag which was killed, or even the worm I crush beneath my foot.'

'And your Aunt Mamaea?'

'The rock of Pandataria was a fitting place for Nero to exile his wife Octavia. She was murdered there. Mamaea can end her days there but I shall not order her killed.'

'And your grandmother?'

'With Alexander dead and Mamaea out of the way, she will cause no problem. All she desires is to sit behind the throne and manipulate Caesar. I could not do without her.'

'There you are wrong. Dispense with her and together we shall rule Rome and rule it far more wisely.'

'Can we do it, Carissimus?'

'Together we can do anything.'

'Then my grandmother goes too. Back to the palace at Emesa.'

Hierocles shook his head. 'From the Palace of Emesa she once climbed to the throne. She might again.'

'Then where?'

'Another island as barren as Pandataria.'

Antoninus thought for several moments then nodded his head in agreement. 'And my mother?'

'Allow her to remain in Rome. She is harmless. Just now she thinks of nothing else but Ahenobarbus. Next month it will be someone else, and the month after still another.' He smiled at Antoninus who was once more stretched out on the rug beside him and his hand rumpled Antoninus's hair roughly but tenderly. 'How could I blame you for being what you are when I remember that you are the son of your mother.' Again his arm drew Antoninus closer. 'Like mother, like son, but I am grateful to the gods that you inherited your mother's passions. Come, little Caesar, the stone floor under this rug is not as yielding as our soft mattress, and the stiff bristles of this old bear are not as soothing as our silken sheets.'

A clamorous pounding on the heavy door of oaken planks roused them both.

They stirred and listened, trying to orient themselves to the strange room, to the fact that there were no slaves to answer the door and the continued threat of the pounding.

Hierocles was the first to assemble his scattered wits. He wrapped a sheet around himself, toga-wise, and went out into the common room, took down the heavy wooden bar that bolted the inside of the door and opened it.

'Aegenax!' He focused his eyes on the man standing in the bright sunshine. 'What brings you here, Aegenax? Why aren't you in Rome, guarding Alexander?'

'Would that I were, but you can thank whatever god you and Caesar worship that I am here. Chaos has broken out in Rome. I had just been relieved by the morning watch when the rioting started. The Praetorians marched on the city, slew the Palace Guards, freed Alexander and have taken him with his mother and grandmother to the camp. They intend to proclaim him Emperor. I witnessed it all, hidden behind the statue of Augustus which stands in the corridor. Gordius sent me here. He had already been informed and had heard that another contingent of Praetorians is marching here. Word got out where you were and they are already half-way here from Rome. Get Caesar and flee, Hierocles, or you will return to Rome battered corpses, dragged by the Praetorians' chariots.'

Hierocles pulled Aegenax into the house, closed and bolted the door. He looked around the room in dazed bewilderment, unable to decide what to do, his wits still dazed. Aegenax, unmindful of the law which made it a crime to touch Caesar's person, rushed into the bedroom and shook Antoninus.

'Dress, Caesar, every moment is precious and while you and Hierocles dress, I will harness the *quadriga*. When I am finished you must be ready. Fortunately the Praetorians march by foot, else they would have been here before me. As it is, we have an hour's start on them.'

'But where to, good Aegenax? Where do we go and why are we going and what is the terrible hurry? Hierocles and I have but arrived.'

Hierocles was in full possession of his senses now and he quickly explained to Antoninus the *coup d'état* that Mamaea had managed.

'And where shall we flee?' Antoninus repeated the question.

Hierocles hesitated, looking from Aegenax to Antoninus.

'Why not Caprae? Tiberius lived the last years of his life there in security.'

'Banish myself to that little island and live every day in fear? No, Hierocles. I am either Emperor of Rome or I am not. This is a test of my greatness. I thought I would be content to spend my days as a peasant farmer – and perhaps I would have been, with you beside me. But it was only a dream. I am Caesar and nothing can change that, not even my own desires, for I have a duty to Rome. I cannot let Alexander sit on the throne. I may have been a poor Emperor but, by Elah-ga-baal, he would be worse than I! I have desired many men but I have sought the death of none. He's a bloodthirsty brute who has delighted in killing since he was a child. And first he would dispense with me, Hierocles, and then you, and then you, Aegenax, and then, in senseless vengeance, he would murder everyone on whom I have looked with favour. Were I to flee to Caprae, all of my friends would be dead by nightfall, and within a week the triremes of Rome would have landed on Caprae and Hierocles and I would die. No, we will not flee. I have a duty to Rome and a duty to my friends. Instead of running like frightened rabbits, we go to the camp of the Praetorians. We may go to our death but we go. Today it is Alexander against me. One of us, and only one of us will be Caesar tonight.'

'It is certain death, Great Caesar!' Aegenax again forgot himself and laid a restraining hand on Antoninus's arm. 'They say that even the Roman Legions have deserted you.'

''Tis madness, beloved, sheer madness! The Praetorians will tear you to shreds.'

'I do not fear for my own life, only for yours, Hierocles.' Antoninus had never been more imperial as he stood there naked and shivering. 'I go but I go alone. I command you to seek sanctuary somewhere. Take a cohort of the Palace

Guards and go yourself to Caprae. If I know you are safe I shall be stronger.'

'And leave you to face the Praetorians alone? Never! I am the only man in Rome who can disobey Caesar. I go with you.'

'And I,' Aegenax added, 'but come, unless we start now and go by a different route than that which brings the Praetorians, we shall never reach there.' He ran from the house to harness the horses to the chariot.

Antoninus and Hierocles dressed hurriedly, chewed a few morsels of dry bread and were ready when Aegenax drove up. They stopped the chariot only long enough to call the sentry posted at the point where the dirt road joined the paved road.

'Who commands the cohorts who are on guard here?' Antoninus asked the startled man.

'The Tribune Eubulus.'

'Then go at once. Tell the Tribune Eubulus that I go to the Camp of the Praetorians. There is a detachment of the Praetorians marching here now from Rome. Tell the Tribune to withdraw his men into the hills. He is not to enter into battle against the guards. When they arrive they will find a deserted camp. Hurry!'

The chariot thundered on. Aegenax avoided the paved roads and kept to cart tracks that wound over the hills. Once, high on a rutted road, they glanced down into the valley below and saw the sun glinting on the gold armour of the marching Praetorians. Antoninus stood erect, bracing himself with his hands on the guard rail of the chariot. Hierocles was behind him, his arms outstretched to the same rail, enclosing Antoninus.

'Farewell, little Caesar,' he whispered. 'This is not the way I would bid you good-bye for ever, but something tells me we shall not live to see your god set tonight. Every moment I have spent with you has been a taste of heaven. My only prayer is that they kill me before you because I could not bear to see you die.'

'Neither of us will die today, Carissimus. Suddenly I feel

stronger than I have ever felt before. I know not what it is that makes me strong but this I know. As my god is strong in the heavens, so have I strength. I shall outwit them all. Aegenax, whip the horses. Faster! Today Rome will see that their Emperor Antoninus can be a man.'

23

THE CAMP OF the Praetorian Guards, located just outside the City Walls of Rome, was a permanent camp – a small city within itself complete with paved streets and stone build-ings. The Praetorians were the only soldiers who were al-lowed to be permanently stationed in Rome – in fact it was forbidden for any of the Legions to enter the city, so the Praetorians combined both military and police duties in the *urbs*. Being Roman residents and rarely sent away from the imperial city, they were always deeply involved in politics. Even as private soldiers they were drawn from the *Eques*, and the officers represented both knightly and patrician ranks so they were all from families with some political in-fluence.

Under many reigns they had set themselves up as critics of the emperor, and every Caesar rose or fell according to his popularity and influence with this pampered élite. The Prae-torians welcomed change. They knew that their own position was always secure. No Caesar had ever dared to interfere with them. Changes brought added donatives, promotions and a currying of favour from the new emperor which was always acceptable to these money-hungry younger sons of Rome's greatest families. They had tired of Antoninus. Mamaea's gold had influenced them towards Alexander, and with Alexander once on the throne there would be a new period of favouritism, patronage and power.

Antoninus had not encountered the marching Praetorians who were on their way to the farm to arrest him and his sudden appearance at the gates of the camp was a surprise.

The chariot wheels ground to a stop before the gate and a sentry, resplendent in gold armour and scarlet cape, stepped up to challenge the three drivers in soiled tunics.

'Entrance is denied to all civilians by order of the Praefect Eutychianus Comazon.' He repeated the words mechanically, hardly glancing up at the three in the chariot. 'If you have commercial transactions with the stewards, drive to the west gate. Their representatives are outside.'

'Commercial transactions!' Antoninus howled. 'Commercial transactions, you insolent puppy!' He grabbed the whip from Aegenax's hands. 'Down on your knees, guard, your Emperor speaks to you.'

The guard looked up with a silly smirk on his vapid face. 'What emperor?'

'Since when has Rome had two emperors? Look well, guard, and mistake me not. I need no jewelled litter or purple toga to proclaim that I am Caesar. Unlock the gates and make way.'

The guard came closer. He scrutinized Antoninus carefully, then Hierocles. Suddenly he was frightened. 'I must report this to the Centurion.'

'The Centurion! Since when does Caesar wait on the word of a lowly Centurion?' Antoninus let fly with the lash and opened a gash in the guard's cheek. 'Open the gates or in another five minutes, you'll be screaming on a cross.'

The commotion before the gates had caught the attention of the officer in charge. He came running from the guard house, some six guards following him. He recognized Antoninus, but he hesitated. Alexander and Mamaea were within the camp, but Antoninus was still Caesar. It was difficult to know which course was best to follow. He knew that if he refused Antoninus admission to the camp, he would be guilty of *lèse majesté*, punishable by death if Antoninus should win. On the other hand, were Alexander to triumph, he would be equally guilty if he were to admit Antoninus now. But . . . Antoninus was still Caesar. He still lived and while he lived he *was* Caesar. That could not be denied.

He saluted sharply, wheeled and marched in a straight

line to the gates. A ponderous key creaked in the locks and a crisply barked order sent the six guards flying inside to let down the bars which further locked the gates. In another moment the ponderous plank leaves started moving slowly inward. Antoninus took over the reins from Aegenax and drove the chariot through. Once inside, he reined the horses and beckoned to the Centurion to come closer.

'Your name, Centurion?'

'Gaius Lepidus Claudius.'

'A Claudian!' Antoninus could afford to smile now. 'You must have imperial blood, Gaius Lepidus. This day you have chosen well. Report to the Praefect Eutychianus Comazon and tell him that your Caesar has promoted you to the rank of Tribune.'

'My gratitude, Great Caesar.'

'And these men?' Antoninus indicated the six who were now standing at rigid attention.

'Private soldiers, Great Caesar. Do you wish to know their names?'

'Later, Tribune. For the present inscribe their names along with your own for promotion. Each one of them is to be a Centurion.'

'*Ave* Caesar!' The hail came from six throats at once, echoed by the new Tribune's shout, 'Great is Caesar! Great is the Emperor Elagabalus!'

Antoninus smiled again. 'You confuse me with my god, Tribune. And yet perhaps it is a good omen to be identified with my god. I like the title. Continue to use it.' He touched the whip to the horses and they galloped up the broad paved avenue to the centre of the camp. Here, where the four principal streets, which led from the four gates of the square walled camp, converged, was the building of white stuccoed stone which housed the Praefect. Opposite it, gleaming in the light of the sun, was the gilded statue of Alexander which had been erected by the Praetorians themselves. Antoninus regarded it carefully.

'I had no idea Alexander was so handsome. I only hope the sculptor gave him clean fingernails.' He pulled up at the broad steps which led to the entrance of the Praefect's quarters. Again he looked at the statue. He turned to Aegenax. 'Wait here until the Tribune Claudius arrives.' He pointed down the avenue to where the former Centurion and his six men were marching up in military formation. 'When he arrives, tell him that the effigy of my son and heir displeases me. I order it torn down before nightfall and one of myself placed there. The new statue of me made for the Flavian amphitheatre can be transferred here.'

Aegenax realized that the time for informality was over. Suddenly Antoninus was no longer a youth in a soiled tunic. He was Caesar. 'May I have leave to speak, Great Caesar?'

'Leave is granted.'

'The statue is the property of the Praetorians, paid for by popular subscription. Might they not resent it if it were torn down?'

'There is nothing in Rome that does not belong to Caesar. Convey my order, Aegenax. When I come out of this building later, I want to see my own face there.'

Together he and Hierocles walked past the dumbfounded guards at the door who regarded them silently, their mouths agape. This was indeed Caesar. They could not deny him admittance.

Antoninus hesitated in the marble paved atrium. On each side were leather curtained doorways. His eyes looked a question at Hierocles and Hierocles pointed to a doorway at the right from whence issued the hum of voices.

'Probably the office of Comazon,' he whispered.

Antoninus strode across the marble tiles and lifted the curtain. There was an audible gasp from those inside. He saw his grandmother, his aunt and his cousin, all of whom sat with their backs to him. Comazon, who faced the doorway, was the first to see him. With a look of frightened amazement, he rose from his chair. The others turned their heads. Mamaea turned deathly pale. Julia, faced with the necessity of making an immediate decision and not knowing whether or not Antoninus had the entire Alban Legion behind him, rose unsteadily from her chair and sank to her quaking knees.

'Great Caesar,' she mumbled.

The assembled officers, taking their cue from her, saluted, giving Comazon time to walk to the doorway. His feet seemed unsteady as he made his way through the press but he arrived at the doorway and dropped to one knee.

'Great Caesar,' he said as he scanned Antoninus's face, trying to read his expression. All he saw was an imperial determination which he had never thought possible on the Antonine's pretty features.

In a loud voice so that all might hear, Antoninus acknowledged the greeting.

'I received your message to attend this conference, Praefect. It is not Caesar's habit to be summoned, but your messenger urged extreme haste and I did not have time to change clothes before coming. I trust you will pardon me for my informal attire. The Caesar Honoralibus and I were seeking relaxation at our farm. Had I been in Rome, I would have been better prepared.'

Antoninus's words threw the assemblage into confusion. Comazon did not dare give him the lie and deny that he had sent a messenger. Mamaea and Julia turned suspicious looks in his direction and the assembled officers darted quick glances of distrust at their Praefect.

'I was waiting for you to arrive, Great Caesar,' Comazon accepted the lie. 'We have some momentous affairs to discuss and it is well that you are here. My messenger must have had difficulty in finding you.'

The lie had been confirmed.

Aegenax had not accompanied Antoninus and Hierocles into the room but had remained outside in the chariot. Now, however, Antoninus felt a slight pressure on his shoulder. He turned his head to see Aegenax. He whispered low so that only Antoninus and Hierocles could hear.

'A Praetorian Guard has arrived on horseback. I heard him speak to an officer. Ten cohorts of the Alban Legion, led by their Tribune *and* by Eubulus and the Palace Guards, are marching double time and should arrive here in an hour. Eubulus must have sensed your need and alerted them.'

As if to corroborate his statement, a guard entered, saluted Antoninus and Eutychianus and handed the Praefect a brass-bound tablet. Eutychianus rose from his knees, asked permission from Antoninus to read it, opened it and read the words that it contained. His frown was covered by a quick smile and when he addressed Antoninus, his words had a deeper ring of respect.

'Your Praetorians welcome you, Great Caesar. We would have you address us, assembled on the parade ground. There are a few minor matters the body of Guards would like made clear.'

'The *Guards* would like made clear! There are some things that *Caesar* would like made clear,' Antoninus confronted Eutychianus fearlessly. 'The Praetorians are not Rome, Praefect. It is time they realized that. Caesar is Rome! The Army is Rome! The citizens are Rome! Even the poor feeble Senate is Rome. If there are any things to be made clear all Rome must be represented. Send messengers to the city! Tell the August Fathers that Caesar commands that they assemble here within the hour. The Alban Legion, which is on its way here, will represent the Army, and with all the city rabble heading in this direction there will be plenty of Roman citizens in the audience.'

'But that will take time, Great Caesar.' Eutychianus realized that with the coming of the Alban Legion, his power was slipping fast.

'Rome can well spend an hour in waiting while Caesar dines,' Antoninus dismissed the matter. 'The urgency of your messenger this morning gave me no time for breakfast. I am hungry and I desire to eat. I shall dine here, Praefect. My Praetorians shall be my host. I shall eat whatever has been prepared for them. You shall join us, Praefect.' He pointed to his grandmother. 'And you, Augusta, and my beloved aunt and my son Alexander. Where is my mother, the Augusta Soaemias? Send for her! We shall make this a family gather-

228

ing, which will of course include you, Eutychianus, as I once considered you one of my family.'

Antoninus touched Eutychianus's arm. 'The *latrinae*, good Eutychianus. You will show us where it is and you will accompany us.'

Eutychianus followed them through the leather-curtained door. When they had passed the sentry who stood before the door and were half-way down the narrow hall, Eutychianus, who had asked permission to precede Caesar and show the way, stopped.

'Your comment on my messenger took me by surprise, Antoninus.'

'The title is *Caesar*, Praefect, and *Great Caesar* at that. Once you called me Varius and I can remember casting jealous eyes on you when you were my mother's lover. But ... it seems that even the friendship we had for each other then does not influence you now. You were about to betray me and place the crown on Alexander's head. It was stupid of you, Eutychianus. You underrate my intelligence.'

'Not only your intelligence but your bravery, Great Caesar. Only a brave man would have dared to come here today. That is why I accepted your lie about the messenger and cast my lot in with yours. I shall never underrate either your intelligence or your bravery again.' He looked up at Antoninus, searchingly, 'That is, if I live beyond today.'

'You shall live, Praefect. If you remain loyal to me, you are more valuable alive than dead. But make not a second mistake. I am still Caesar, and in the eyes of your men and all Rome you are now my ally. The fact that no messenger but a cohort of Praetorians were dispatched to arrest me is our business.'

Eutychianus commenced to walk again. He turned his head and his eyes disclosed his fear.

Antoninus reassured him. 'I have no sword, Praefect, and had I one I would not stab you in the back. Once again you can consider yourself in Caesar's favour. I owe you something for the quick wit you showed about the messenger. It is time you became a general, Eutychianus.' This time Antoninus used the name instead of the title.

'A general!' He clutched Antoninus's hand and kissed it. 'But a general does not command the Praetorians, and it would be well for your safety if I remained in command.'

'Would it?' Antoninus smiled. He did not remove his hand from Eutychianus's lips.

'It shall be. My solemn promise.'

'How easily men are bought, Eutychianus. Today since I arrived at your camp, I have purchased a Centurion, six private soldiers and now the Praefect himself. Yes, I think you will be loyal to me until Mamaea offers you more, so we shall create the post of General of the Praetorians.'

'You will not regret it, Great Caesar.'

'Now that I have bought you, Eutychianus, you can again call me Antoninus. And stop slobbering over my hand and get up off your knees. Show me where your cursed *latrinae* are, otherwise I shall spatter your clean walls!'

When they returned to the officers' muster room, they saw that a table had already been set up with a collection of chairs, benches and stools for the diners, rather than the usual formal couches. Someone had found a folding bronze camp chair, furbished it with cushions and had placed it in the centre of the table for Antoninus. Hierocles sat on his right, the young Alexander on his left. Aegenax, unused to such lofty company, was placed on Alexander's other side, balanced by Comazon beside Hierocles. Directly across the narrow board from Antoninus, an empty place was reserved for Soaemias, flanked on one side by her mother and on the other by her sister, neither of whom had been successfully able to hide their chagrin over the unexpected turn of events.

A few moments after they sat down to eat, Soaemias arrived, perturbed and worried – the expression on her face showing all too plainly that she did not know whether she had been summoned to the Praetorians' camp to be murdered or honoured. She had gained some assurance from the cohorts of the Alban Legion drawn up in front of the gates, and still more when she entered and saw Antoninus, already seated at the head of the table.

He rose to welcome her and sent Aegenax to escort her to her seat. The sight of this new, handsome and strikingly masculine face set Soaemias entirely at ease, despite the fact that her mother and sister were fidgeting in their seats. One by one the white-togaed senators arrived from Rome, and when there were no longer places for them at the table they stood around the walls of the room, discussing their strange summons in whispers, and trying vainly to arrive at some conclusion as to why they had been so summarily summoned.

Antoninus did full justice to the rough meal of boiled pulses, stringy beef and turnips, washed down, however, with a superior wine, which evinced that the Guards, although not particular about their stomachs, did favour their palates. Despite Antoninus's attempts to give the meal some semblance of ordinary conversation, it was a strained and difficult occasion. He paid particular attention to Alexander, trying to draw him out by leading questions, but all he received in reply was a monosyllabic *yes* or *no* or, failing that, a nod or a grunt. Alexander did not quite comprehend why he was there, or what had happened but he sensed by the dark looks on his grandmother's and mother's faces that once again Antoninus had managed to triumph. Never before had Antoninus so openly shown as much favour to his cousin, keeping his wine glass filled, cutting off the tenderest portions of meat and transferring them to Alexander's plate and all the while, touching him affectionately, calling him 'beloved son' and giving him his full title of Consul of Rome.

This display of affection only served further to confound the two women who, separated by Soaemias, were unable to communicate with each other except by their startled glances. Soaemias was quite oblivious of their unease. She had eyes only for the handsome Aegenax, to whom she directed all her conversation, accompanied by languishing glances and a provocative dropping of her eyelids which promised much to the youth whenever the present festivities would be over.

He, nothing loath to court the favour of the Augusta herself, rose to her coquetry. Antoninus, anxious to please everyone, requested that his grandmother change places with Aegenax, which placed the old lady beside Hierocles and even farther away from Mamaea.

As each senator entered, Antoninus greeted him effusively, inquired about his health and that of his family, supplied places at table as long as they lasted, and then regretted most lamentably that there was no more room.

At length the meal was finished and Comazon, who had adopted the role of host, followed Antoninus, with Hierocles and Alexander a step behind him, from the room. Once out in the hall, with permission from Antoninus, he led the way out. Antoninus paused for a moment, noting with interest that a crew of men were already engaged in moving the gilded statue of Alexander, and glanced back at his relatives to see if they had also noticed. Apparently they had, for Mamaea looked blacker than ever, although Julia Maesa only appeared more puzzled. Both women were conscious that their carefully-laid plans had gone astray. Where or how they did not know, but somewhere along the line vital information had leaked out and they didn't know who were their friends or their enemies. Antoninus's sudden arrival at camp, ostensibly at the invitation of Comazon, pointed to the latter as the traitor. At least he would serve as a convenient scapegoat.

The entire procession of senators, Praetorian Officers and officers of the Palace Guards, with some prominent Roman citizens, followed the imperial party. They descended the steps of the building and took their places on the already crowded parade ground. Here the officers' reviewing stand had been hastily draped with scarlet military cloaks, and chairs had been placed upon it. Comazon bowed low for Antoninus to ascend the platform. He was followed by the family which included Hierocles and Aegenax, from whom Soaemias refused to be separated. Below them the entire parade ground was filled – the Senators in the front ranks, behind them the serried ranks of the Praetorians, the Legionaries and the Palace Guards, with the civilians of Rome in the rear.

Comazon rose, and with another deep bow to Antoninus walked to the rostrum. Although he received no ovation he held up his hand for silence which served to quiet the host before him. Movement and conversation ceased.

He turned to the imperial party.

'Great Caesar, Caesar Honoralibus, Consul Alexander, The Augusta, Augusta Mother and the Lady Mamaea.' He then faced the assemblage. 'Senators, Praetorians, Soldiers and Citizens of Rome, I bid you welcome to our camp as Praefect of the Praetorian Guard.'

No sooner had he spoken than Antoninus arose, walked to the stand beside him at the rostrum, and with one arm around Comazon's shoulders, took Comazon's place.

'You are far too modest, General Comazon. Or, perhaps in your modesty you have forgotten that you are no longer merely a Praefect of the Praetorians, but a *General* of the Praetorians. Today, my faithful Guards have been raised to the rank of a Roman Legion with you, General Comazon, as their commander.'

There was a brief silence.

Antoninus dismissed Comazon, who went back to his chair. For a long minute or two, Antoninus looked at the sea of faces before him. He realized that the danger was not entirely over. Three enemies were behind him – his aunt, his grandmother and his cousin, and there were many more in front of him. The Praetorians were not, and never had been, his friends, but if he could not befriend them, at least he could make them fear him. Caesar did not rule through love. It was not time for half measures. Either he was Caesar or he was not. Perhaps it would be necessary to give a little in order to gain his ends. He had not entirely made up his mind to that point but he was convinced of one thing: from this day on he would be Caesar! The Divine Julius had staked his all when he crossed the Rubicon to lead his armies to Rome. The Senate had forbidden it. Well, curses on the Senate, he would dispense with it *before* he crossed his

233

Rubicon. There might be death on the other shore but he would leave the Praetorians' camp this night either as Caesar of all Rome or a bleeding corpse.

He had an audience, not the largest but perhaps the most critical he had ever faced, and all he wore was a sweat-stained linen tunic that reached half-way to his knees and a pair of leather sandals. But his confidence in himself was certain. He would win as many as he could through his charm and generosity. Those whom he could not win he would command through fear.

He raised both hands from the rostrum and lifted them, palms up, to the crowd below.

'My Romans,' he began. He inclined his head to the front line of white-togaed corpulence which represented the Senate.

'August Fathers!'

He looked over their heads to the gold armour and the scarlet capes of the Praetorians behind them.

'My Praetorians!'

There were a few cries of '*Ave* Caesar,' and a few scurrilous epithets but these he ignored.

'Brave soldiers of my Alban Legion!'

Now the air was full of shouts for Caesar.

'And my beloved Palace Guards who have come from the ends of Empire to serve me and the great god Elah-ga-baal, both as priests and soldiers.'

Again the *Aves* rang out.

'Illustrious Citizens of Rome!'

There was only a smattering of shouts.

'General Eutychianus Comazon of the Praetorians and I have summoned you here today that we may meet together and discuss a few matters of great importance to our Empire. First, I would like to inform you, without taking undue credit to myself about the state of our Empire today.

'My illustrious father, Antoninus Caesar, established the boundaries of Empire from the island of Britain to the outposts of Syria and the great desert that lies beyond. From Mauretania to Egypt, we control Africa and we have penetrated far into the interior of that vast continent, establishing other outposts of Empire so that from north to south and from east to west, our boundaries are secure and greater in extent than Rome has ever known before.

'During my reign Rome has fought no wars, lost no legions, paid no money for costly campaigns . . .'

'And won no victories . . .' an anonymous voice from the audience interrupted.

'Or taken no plunder,' another voice called out.

'No, we have won no victories and taken no plunder because we have had no need for either. We have conquered all the world and I can only sigh, as did Alexander, that there are no worlds left for us to conquer. Today Rome is the world and the world is Rome. That is sufficient. I intend my reign to be one of peace – a strong peace, upheld by my legions throughout the breadth of Empire, and I do not desire that one of my brave soldiers loses his life in battle or is buried on an alien shore.'

'*Ave* Caesar!' The men of the Alban Legion raised their voices in a mighty shout.

'And for the man who just complained that there was no plunder, I shall satisfy even him. A donative of a thousand *sestercii* will be paid from the treasury of the Temple of Elah-ga-baal to every legionary.'

'*Ave* Caesar!' This time there was a tumultuous roar from the throats of the legionaries but the Praetorians kept silent.

Antoninus had bought the legion and all the soldiers of Rome.

'And now for my Praetorians!'

He lowered his gaze to take in the ranks of gold and scarlet. 'Today your status has changed. No longer are you merely the Praetorian Guards, because I have placed a general over you. Now you will rank with the Legions of Rome, as soldiers of Rome.'

'We've always ranked above them,' a voice from the ranks cried out.

Antoninus happened to see the man who spoke and now he answered him directly, pointing his finger at him. 'As a

Praetorian, you are ignorant of the history of your organization. The Praetorians were formed merely as a police force for Rome. They have never legally been soldiers. You have never had precedence over any Roman legion. Do you wish to remain merely as policemen, or do you desire status as military men? You there, state your name and rank and then answer me!'

The guard who had been so vociferous now found difficulty in speaking.

'My name is Antoninus Marcus Torus, private in the 8th Maniple of the 1st Cohort.'

'You bear the same name as I do.' Antoninus had decided to be gracious. 'Surely if Antoninus is Caesar, his namesake should not be a mere private. Caesar raises you to command of a maniple, and trusts that you will show sufficient ability to become a Centurion. And now, Antoninus, again my question: do you wish to be merely a policeman or a soldier?'

'A soldier, Great Caesar!'

Antoninus had bought another man.

'Then soldiers you shall all be, and you shall continue with your police and guard duties. As soldiers you will receive the same donative as the legions but,' he paused and smiled at the men below him, 'for the extra duty which you will incur in policing Rome, I add another 500 *sestercii* for each Praetorian, to be paid from the treasury of the Temple of Diana at Ephesus.'

This time it was the guards who led the shout, '*Ave* Caesar!'

But it was neither as loud nor as strong as the applause from the Legion. Antoninus had purchased some of the guards but many were not for sale. He felt, however, that he had made a substantial inroad.

The row of white-togaed elders before him made him aware of the deficiency of his costume. And yet by the very deficiency of his costume he had aligned himself with the soldiers and the common citizens of Rome rather than with the patrician nonentities who sat before him.

The Senate had lost all power in Rome. To be sure they met daily for long-winded arguments, but since the time of Tiberius they had merely voiced the opinions of the Emperor.

Antoninus regarded them with distaste. They had outlived their usefulness and the government of Rome was none of their concern. He was Caesar! The *camaraderie* which had been apparent in his words to the Praetorians was now lacking in his voice. His words were coldly formal.

'August Fathers,' the flashing smile had gone from his face, 'I regret having called you from your homes, and from your deliberations in the Senate today, for I realize that you are not young men. And truly this troubles me, for many of you are approaching senility and it does not seem fitting that the burden of government should rest on your shoulders. Old age is a time for ease, for contemplation and for writing memoirs. I have kept you at your tasks too long. Rome has demanded too much of you.'

He had caught their attention. They were already apprehensive. What was coming next? Surely the Senate was necessary to Rome. Since the early days of the Republic it had met, deliberated and supposedly solved Rome's problems. Could Antoninus dare? Antoninus dared.

'Therefore I relieve you of your duties. I order the Senate disbanded. You will return to your homes today and tomorrow you will quit Rome.'

One of the senators rose and harrumphed, preparatory to one of his usual long-winded orations, but Antoninus impatiently gestured to him to be seated.

'Any senator remaining in Rome after tomorrow will be arrested.' He had spoken, and as he had expected there was a rumble of opposition in the white-togaed ranks but he looked over their heads to the soldiers behind them.

'Legionaries of Rome, and now I can include my Praetorians in that name, we are a nation of young men. Old age has no place in our Empire. You are young and so am I. Shall we rule Rome or shall we allow these old ones to do it in our place? I say let us do it ourselves. What say you?'

There was little love lost between the army and the Senate. For years the greedy senators had been cutting the pay of the army, supplying them with mouldy meal and rotten meat, issuing shoddy uniforms and inferior armour. The smouldering hatred of centuries burst forth.

'Away with them, let them quit Rome. *Ave* Caesar!'

Antoninus spread his hands in a helpless gesture.

'Caesar has spoken, August Fathers, and so has the army. Yet I do not want you to feel that you are leaving Rome in disgrace or under any condemnation. You will retire to your country estates, but each one of you will have the choice of one hundred prime slaves or the value thereof. Also you shall have my gratitude, and from time to time I shall call on you individually to come to Rome and confer with me. Each man that is so called will receive a stipend of honour commensurate with his rank and ability.'

He could afford to smile at them.

'And you shall have my deep gratitude for all you have done for Rome. To show you further honour, I order a maniple of Praetorians to attend each of you at your home tomorrow, exactly at noon. They will escort you to the city gates, and there a maniple of soldiers from the Alban Legion will escort you to your homes in the country.'

Although they realized that the guard was primarily to arrest them rather than do them honour, they were somewhat mollified by the substantial offer of the hundred slaves, and even more by the fact that their heads were still on their shoulders. They slumped back in their seats, confident that their canny minds, long schooled in the devious ways of politics would soon dispense with this callow upstart who called himself Caesar and had the temerity to dismiss the Senate itself.

The voice of a Praetorian called out from the ranks.

'And now, we would have Caesar answer some of our questions.'

Antoninus picked out the man who had spoken – a Tribune with a sullen look on his handsome face.

'Step forward, Tribune, and state your name.'

The guard showed no hesitancy in proclaiming himself.

'Africanus Germanicus Agrippa.'

'A combination of names which would seem honourable as well as geographical. You say you would have Caesar answer some questions? Know you not that Caesar is not in the habit of answering questions? Caesar asks them. And Caesar asks you now if you value your life.'

Mehercule! Antoninus thought, I could not order his death, even if he had a sword uplifted to strike me. He is too handsome!

'Fear not, Agrippa, Caesar will not harm you.'

'But surely Caesar would like to know what complaints some of his Praetorians might have.'

'Surely Caesar would wonder why his Praetorians might have any complaints. Do they?'

'Yes, Great Caesar, serious ones – so serious that they have started to sow the seeds of revolution in the camp in favour of your son and heir, Alexander.'

There were a few scattered shouts of *'Ave* Caesar,' and Mamaea anxiously pushed Alexander to his feet that he might acknowledge them but before he could stumble to the front of the platform, Antoninus barred his way.

'Back to your seat, whelp,' he muttered, 'defy me not to-day, or you will never return to Rome tonight.'

Alexander retreated and slunk down in his chair.

'Revolution is not a pleasant word to use before Caesar, Tribune Agrippa,' Antoninus again addressed the Praetorian. 'But as you have brought the word out into the open, let us discuss it. Today is a day of frankness. Speak, Tribune, and for the first time in the history of Rome, Caesar gives a man permission to speak whatever words he desires. You will not be punished for any statements you make here today. I shall appreciate your honesty. Come nearer, man, that we need not shout at each other like hawkers in the Forum. The August Fathers, who are already contemplating the delights of retirement, will make way for you.'

The crowd parted and even the disgruntled senators in the first row grudgingly inched their chairs so that the Tribune might pass through. He stood directly beneath Antoninus, his stance fearless, his feet wide apart, his crested helmet crooked under one arm so that the full light of the sun fell on his face.

He was indeed handsome with the stern beauty of a male animal – a transcending masculinity that reminded Antoninus of the rare black panthers he had seen in the arena. Not since the day that Hierocles had reached out to steady him in his procession into Rome, or since he had seen the moon-dappled Zoticus walk across the temple courtyard, had Antoninus been so completely bewitched. Suddenly he desired him and with his desire he was no longer Caesar.

'Begin, Tribune Arippa.' Antoninus leaned forward a little and smiled, as if to create a sense of intimacy between them and bring them closer together. 'I would like to hear your opinion of me, Tribune, and if you will be frank, I shall promise you immunity.' He hesitated, looking down into the man's eyes, 'Perhaps even more.'

'I desire nothing from Caesar except that he listen to my words, but despite his pledge of immunity I scarcely dare speak, although I have been chosen spokesman for hundreds of my companions.'

'You have permission to speak. Through you I would learn how to rule Rome better. Proceed, Tribune.'

'Then I would begin first by condemning your religion, secondly by criticizing your morals, and thirdly by censuring your companions.'

'Which would leave me very little of life,' Antoninus was smiling still, 'because I believe in my religion, I have no desire to change my morals, and I am devoted to my friends. But, go on, Tribune, let Caesar hear why you disapprove of him, his life, his god and his companions.'

Agrippa walked a half step nearer – so near that by reaching up his hand, he could have touched the tips of Antoninus's sandals. 'I am a follower of Mithras, as are many of the soldiers . . .'

'A dour faith, if what I have heard is true. Quite different from the joyous worship of Elah-ga-baal.'

'The followers of Mithras believe in chastity. We practise it ourselves and we would that our Emperor practised it.'

'Chastity? It is a word with which I am little acquainted. My religion does not enforce it nor approve it.'

'Then we would have you give up your religion and become a follower of ours. But no man comes to Mithras unless he comes in his own heart and it is difficult to compel a man to change his religion. So we would have you relinquish the office of High Priest of Elah-ga-baal, and if you insist on practising your religion do it in private and not in public. It is hardly fitting for Rome's Caesar to dance round the altars of any god.'

Antoninus stared at the man beneath him. He was well aware of the rapid growth of the austere cult of Mithras, particularly among the soldiers. Mithras, like Elah-ga-baal, was a man's god but Mithras, unlike the Syrian Sun God, demanded absolute chastity from his worshippers. Antoninus could not relinquish his faith in his god – had not Elah-ga-baal triumphed in him today? – but he could accede to relinquishing the priesthood. He had already lost interest in its pageantry and mummery. If he must choose between the two he preferred to be Caesar than High Priest.

'Then you desire that I retire as High Priest?' He looked over the Tribune's head, 'And how many others feel that I should devote more of my time to government and less to religion?'

There was a mighty shout. Elah-ga-baal had never been popular in Rome.

'I grant your request, Tribune. I shall no longer serve as High Priest, but I shall not close the Temple of Elah-ga-baal. However, that you may know I shall devote no more time to religion, I appoint the Consul Alexander as Pontifex Maximus.' He disposed of the exalted office and his cousin with a backward wave of his hand. 'Are you satisfied, Tribune?'

'My gratitude, Great Caesar, to which is added that of many others.'

Antoninus felt he was winning the man, slowly perhaps,

but he had made a beginning. Already the eyes of the Tribune had softened.

'I am not difficult to deal with, Tribune. We have amicably settled one of your grievances and now to the second, which I am sure is far more serious – my morals.'

Agrippa hesitated. He was on dangerous ground. He had a violent disgust, which had grown into a deep hatred, for the youth he was addressing and yet that youth was Caesar – for the moment all powerful. He must choose his words carefully.

'As a man cannot always change his faith in god, so he cannot change his nature. We do not condemn you for what you are, Great Caesar,' Agrippa was trying hard to hide the fact that he was lying blatantly, 'but we wish . . .'

'That I might be more discreet.' Antoninus was still smiling. 'In that I agree with you. Perhaps if I had had you as my mentor I could more easily mend my ways. But, believe me, Tribune, another has already pointed it out to me,' he glanced briefly at Hierocles, 'and from now on, I promise you, I shall be Caesar. Is that what you desire?'

Again a shout arose from the soldiers, but few of the Palace Guard joined with the Praetorians and only a smatterring of the legionaries.

'We seem to have reached an agreement on two points without too much difficulty,' Antoninus nodded gravely. 'And now the third – my friends and associates. Shall we discuss them?'

Agrippa felt that the worst was over. Now he was on safer ground.

'The Palace Guard must go. They have usurped the place of the Praetorians. It is our ancient duty to guard Caesar.'

'Then guard him!' For the first time Antoninus let an edge of anger sharpen his words. 'The Palace Guards are Priests of Elah-ga-baal, recruited for duty at the palace because I could not rely on you. If you were faithful to me, I would send the Palace Guards back to the temple. Can I be sure?'

'We will guard you with our lives, Great Caesar.' The Praetorians shouted their answer to him.

'And dismiss Gordius from Praefect of the Night Watch,' Agrippa was enumerating on his fingers, 'and Eubulus as Praefect, Quadratus from the post of Sustenances, Maxentius as Collector of Customs and Hellenus as Praefect of the Palace. These men, Great Caesar, have abused their positions. They are ex-slaves, ill-fitted to preside over your affairs and those of Rome.'

'Gordius has not abused his position,' Antoninus said, 'but I will remove him as Praefect. As to the others, I shall accede to your wishes. They will all be replaced, but their retirements shall be honourable and designated by a statue to each in the Forum.'

Another shout hailed his decision.

Agrippa was emboldened by his success. 'There yet remains one other,' he began.

'Go no farther.' Antoninus had guessed this last demand and suddenly with the thought of losing Hierocles, his desire for the man below him vanished. 'In one thing and in one thing only I shall not comply. Hierocles remains with me and retains the title of Caesar.' He walked backwards a few steps and grasped Hierocles by the shoulder, pulling him up and bringing him to the front of the platform. 'Behold a man who loves Rome and Rome's Caesar. Hadrian was not criticized for his love for Antinuous and Antinuous sacrificed his life for Hadrian. So would this man gladly sacrifice his life for me. For the little that is good in Caesar today, you can thank him. It is he who has guided me and led me away from my former ways. Do not voice the words that would demand I dispense with him for I will not answer that demand. In all else I shall either comply or compromise but not in this. So . . . ask it not and I shall not need to refuse you. The Caesar Hierocles remains at my right hand.'

'And in your right hand,' a Praetorian sniggered, but Antoninus had seen the speaker.

'Tribune Agrippa!' Antoninus had again become Caesar. 'Arrest that man!'

'Gladly, Great Caesar.' The Tribune's sense of fairness overcame his dislike of Antoninus.

'Give him thirty lashes and read him out of the Guards.'

'I shall personally give him the thirty lashes and after that it will not be necessary to read him out. He will be dead. Today we have met on common ground, Great Caesar. You have complied with our demands and we will comply with yours. We are satisfied.'

Antoninus spread his arms wide and waited. For a long minute he stood there and the response did not come, then it started, led by the legionaries, augmented by the common citizens, swelled by the Palace Guard and finally bellowed out by the Praetorians.

'*Ave* Caesar!'

Antoninus dropped his arms and one encircled Hierocles's shoulders. Agrippa retreated into the anonymity of the cheering mob to where the luckless Praetorian stood, securely held by two guards.

'*Ave* Caesar!' Again it rang out.

Hierocles dropped to his knees. So did Soaemias and then Julia Maesa.

'*Ave* Caesar!'

Mamaea pushed the stubborn Alexander down and managed to find her own place on the floor beside him.

'*Ave* Caesar!'

Antoninus turned and looked down at Hierocles. Slowly and almost imperceptibly one eye closed and he whispered.

'And what do you think now of your little Antonine?'

'*Ave* Caesar!' Hierocles shouted as if to drown the rest.

24

THE RETURN TO Rome was something in the manner of a triumph, heralded by cornets and trumpets and with Mamaea and Alexander being figuratively dragged by the conqueror's chariot, even though they rode in litters. Julia Maesa, always on the winning side, had abandoned them immediately and now cast her lot in with the victor, Antoninus. Where only the day before she had courted Mamaea and Alexander, she was now all affection for Antoninus and Soaemias. But Soaemias saw nothing else but the glabrous limbs of Aegenax who rode with her in her litter with the curtains closed. He had suddenly become a personage in Rome, both from his elevation to the highest hierarchy of the Emperor's religion and from his status-designate as the Augusta's new lover, for it was apparent to all from the languishing looks and the straying hands of the Augusta that young Ahenobarbus had already been displaced and forgotten.

Antoninus and Hierocles, still in their soiled tunics, reclined on the silken cushions of the imperial litter, speaking but little on their return to Rome from the camp. Hierocles had been pleased and more than astonished at the Antonine's wily diplomacy in seizing the situation by the horns, implicating Comazon irrevocably on his side, winning the confidence of the soldiers, meeting the demands of the Praetorians half way and – his greatest stroke of all – dismissing the Senate. The painted Syrian priestling had suddenly grown in stature and had become Caesar. Hierocles was proud of him.

Gordius, still in his military uniform, his handsome face grimly set, rode beside the litter. Antoninus's quick dismissal of him as Praefect of the Night Watch had hurt and puzzled him but it had not changed his loyalties to the two inside the litter. He was somewhat reassured when Antoninus parted the litter curtains and beckoned him to ride closer.

'I have not abandoned you dear and good Gordius.' Antoninus put his fingers to his lips secretively. 'There are greater things than being a mere Praefect. Attend us when we arrive in Rome. I have business – important business – for you to attend to.'

It was dusk when they entered the city and the lamps were lighted in their apartments when they arrived. Cleander, who seemed to have heard the news already, was in attendance and when Antoninus entered with Hierocles and Gordius, the slave, who had always treated his master with an easy familiarity and faint respect, now fell on his knees.

'*Ave* Caesar!'

'Up, bitch.' Antoninus pushed him over backwards into a sprawling tangle of arms and legs. 'I've had that shouted in my ears so often today that I tire of it.'

'And yet how you love it,' Hierocles added, looking at Antoninus with pride.

'Not as much as I love you,' Antoninus was quick to add. 'That Agrippa was ready to demand that I abandon you. That Agrippa . . .' Antoninus's words trailed off as he recalled the almost feral beauty of the Tribune.

'Handsome, wasn't he?' Hierocles knew Antoninus so well he could follow the capricious wanderings of his thoughts. He had detected that certain unctious tone in Antoninus's voice when he had been speaking with the man – a tone Antoninus unconsciously adopted when he was on the make, but he had rejected the idea and rejoiced in the change in Antoninus when Agrippa had demanded his banishment.

'Jealous, as usual?' Antoninus's finger touched Hierocles's cheek as he turned to Cleander. 'If you've stopped hailing Caesar, get yourself down to the kitchen and hail the cooks. Tell them that there are three starving men up here – yes, bitch, I said *men* – and we want something to eat. I still have the taste of the Praetorians' meat in my mouth.'

Cleander's running steps had no sooner died away than Antoninus stripped off his soiled tunic and motioned to Hierocles to do the same. He beckoned to Gordius to follow them into the bath and as the three soaked in the warm water, relaxing after the strenuous day, he outlined to Gordius the plans he had in mind for him.

The little farm, with Hierocles's name carved in stone over the lintel, was to go to Gordius. In fact, it was not really small now, as Antoninus had bought up all the adjoining farms. There Gordius was to retire for the present, and a most fitting place of retirement it would be, for the name of

Hierocles over the doorway would always remind him of his loyalty to the two Caesars. Antoninus would stock the farm with swine – the special breed of Frankish swine which had proved so delicious in Rome. In addition, Antoninus would further stock the farm with slaves, a hundred or more and, even more important, Gordius would be given the exclusive right of supplying the Praetorian Camp and the imperial household with hams, bacon and sausages which would quickly set him on the road to becoming a very rich man.

But that was not all! Gordius was to engage an overseer to attend to the duties of farm work and allow him to sleep there during the day but his nights would be spent in the palace, in a small room adjoining the imperial apartments where he would be a special guard, watching over both Antoninus and Alexander.

Hierocles marvelled at all these well-thought-out plans which Antoninus had made even without consulting him. The boy was thinking for himself these days!

As an additional reward to Gordius, Eubulus, now dispossessed of his duties in Rome, was to start out again on another search of Empire but this time, instead of taking the golden replica of Zoticus's fame for a yardstick of selection, he was to take a painting of Hierocles with him to find, if possible, that replica of Hierocles which must exist for, as Antoninus pointed out, there were two persons made in every mould, so somewhere there must be another who twinned with Hierocles. Not that he might have Hierocles's disposition or character, but the physical replica would do much to assuage Gordius's loneliness. These things, together with the statue of Gordius which was to be erected in the Forum would amply compensate the ex-chariot driver for the loss of the Praefecture. Did Gordius agree? He did.

Well, then, to the more pressing business at hand. Alexander! He must go! Had Gordius located Hardranes? In a deserted tomb along the Via Appia? Then tonight, after the palace had quietened down they would go there, cloaked, masked and disguised. There was no time to be lost.

Cleander reappeared with his tray of ointments and oils,

but Antoninus waved them aside. He had neither time nor desire to perfume his body this night. He disdained the silk robes that Cleander had laid out for him. Once again, he donned a simple linen tunic and slipped his feet into leather sandals instead of the high heeled linen shoes he had always favoured. Cleander alone served their meal.

Hierocles was well aware what Antoninus was thinking. He thought it best to bring these secret thoughts out into the open.

'This Tribune Agrippa . . .' he began.

Antoninus was startled from his reverie. He had been thinking about the man, comparing the Tribune's apparent dislike for him at first with his willingness to punish the Praetorian for the scurrilous remark he had made. Had he won the man? He could not get him out of his mind. He was as handsome as Mars.

'Yes, what about the Tribune Agrippa?'

'I fear him.'

Antoninus laughed indulgently.

'Truly, he's the most jealous person that ever lived, Gordius. I cannot even talk with a man who stands six paces away from me in the presence of all Rome; a man who comes into my life demanding that I change my belief in God, my way of living and my friends; a man who obviously hates me, without Hierocles being possessed with jealousy.'

'But he is handsome,' Hierocles persisted.

'And so are you,' Antoninus replied. 'He is as handsome as one of the wolves that fight in the Flavian. His beauty is cruel. But if you think him so handsome, and his face remains with you so strongly in your thoughts, banishing mine, perhaps I am the one to be jealous rather than you. Yes, perhaps I should be, Carissimus, for it may be that he favours you more than me because he made no objections to my keeping you with me. But I warn you, keep away from him. His devotion to Mithras girdles him with an iron belt of chastity more effective than those we put on male slaves to keep them from breeding. You do not have the key,

248

Hierocles, and neither do I. Methinks if I were to touch him he would strangle me.'

'I do not think of him because I am jealous of him, and you know me better than that, beloved. His stern face would never appeal to me. I think of him because I fear him. Suddenly he appeared from the crowd today, daring to approach you, daring to make demands on you. He is not a man to be dismissed lightly. Like all worshippers of Mithras he is a fanatic and I fear fanatics.'

'The trouble with the Mithras devotees,' said Gordius, 'is that they have no outlet for their pent-up emotions. They sleep alone and sleeping alone does strange things to men's minds.' Gordius had rarely slept alone but he felt himself an authority on the subject. 'The best thing that could happen to them would be a two-*sestercii* Suburra whore. Bah! The Mithras men bore me.'

'But they are dangerous,' Hierocles persisted. 'All dedicated men are dangerous. And the men of Mithras are willing to die for their god. That is why the religion has been fostered by the generals – it teaches men to lose their fear of death. And that is why I fear this man Agrippa.'

'Carissimus, today I twisted him around my little finger.' Antoninus had a lingering regret that he had not been able to do so. 'We came to terms.'

'To his advantage,' Hierocles agreed.

'Not entirely, Carissimus. You sit here beside me tonight with no fear of banishment. But come, let us abandon the grim-visaged Agrippa to his lonely bed. Cleander! Long cloaks for the three of us and go to the armoury and fetch three gladiators' helmets with visors that close. Tonight we must not be recognized. We shall go on foot to the Circus and there take a racing chariot which will not mark us as from the palace. Gordius, leave your armour here and put on one of Hierocles's tunics. Hierocles, bid the guards at the door admit no one. Tell them that Caesar is sleeping after a tiring day. I would that Aegenax were here to guard the brat Alexander, but if I know my mother she is already tasting the delights of this Egyptian-Persian hybrid. But Alexander is safe tonight. He has probably slipped out to meet his Flacca. Well, let him, it may be his last night of pleasure for some time.'

Shortly after, three cloaked and helmeted figures crept out of the private door of the imperial apartments and sought the shadowed side of the narrow streets leading to the Circus Maximus. When they arrived there, Antoninus and Hierocles waited outside while Gordius entered. He was well accustomed to the place and without waking the grooms, he harnessed a *quadriga* to a chariot and drove out to where the two cloaked figures awaited him. As they neared the city gates, Gordius unfastened the grating of his helmet, gave the guard a brief glimpse of his face and the guard, recognizing the former Praefect of the Night Watch and evidently not knowing that he had been removed from duty, allowed them to pass through.

A dim moon shone wanly through scudding clouds as they passed the white marble tombs along the way. Antoninus shuddered. He disliked the aura of death and desolation, the black cypresses, the spectral tombs, the darkened sky. He disliked even more his decision to murder his cousin but he was now convinced of its necessity. Bereft of Alexander there would be no further plotting, at least in his own family, and if Alexander died what appeared to be a natural death, he would not be blamed nor would Alexander be worshipped as a martyr. His father, Caracalla, had killed his uncle Geta.

Antoninus had always regretted that, for the few busts that remained of Geta showed him to have been a handsome fellow. And now he regretted Alexander. He would have preferred his cousin as a brother. Their lives had been lived in common, they should have shared much but there had never been the slightest bond of sympathy between them. Well, the decision was made! Alexander must go! To that end Antoninus had dismissed the Senate. There would be none to question why Alexander did not appear in his role of Consul or his newly acquired role of Pontifex Maximus.

As they drove farther and farther away from the city, the

tombs became less pretentious, with here and there one fallen into disrepair and ruins. By a thick clump of black cypresses, Gordius turned off the paved road and halted the horses in the shadow of the trees. He whispered to Antoninus to dismount and they made their way over fragments of marble and broken columns to where a tomb, ghostly white in the fitful moonlight, reared two marble walls. There were two other walls of wattle and daub and a thatched roof replaced the tiles that had fallen in. The yawning blackness of the doorway showed them the only entrance.

Gordius entered first. Antoninus followed with Hierocles and they encountered complete blackness except for the circle of watery moonlight at the doorway.

'Hardranes,' Gordius spoke softly. 'Get up, you have visitors.'

There was a rustle of movement in the far corner – a rustle which turned to soft footsteps on the dirt floor. Antoninus was aware of a presence in the room and as the footsteps neared the faint circle of light, he saw the outline of a foot and above it an ankle and hairy calf.

'Who calls for Hardranes?' Antoninus had expected the voice of an old man but this one was vigorous, almost youthful.

'Three citizens of Rome, who will pay you well for your services.'

'And what would those three citizens of Rome consider by paying me well?'

'This bag of gold.' Antoninus proffered a weighty leather pouch in the direction of the voice.

'It is indeed ample,' Hardranes replied, 'if I can be assured that it contains gold, not lead.'

'Open it and see.'

Two hands appeared in the light. One pulled the drawstring of the pouch and emptied the contents into the other. The gold glinted palely in the moonlight.

'It is not lead. How can I serve you?'

'You are skilled in poisons,' Gordius answered, 'so much

so you were banished from Rome. You are supposed to be somewhere in the deserts of Egypt.'

'Your information is correct, my lords and masters. I am skilled in poisons and I was banished from Rome, but I am here.'

'It happens that there is another citizen of Rome who has already lived too long,' Antoninus whispered although he did not know why he lowered his voice. 'He must die but he must seem to die naturally – of some disease. It must not appear that he has been poisoned. Do you know of such a poison? Have you such a potion?'

'I do and I have. But before I give it to you, I should draw up the horoscope of the one to whom it is to be given. Sometimes even the strongest poison will have no effect if the stars will otherwise. Know you the birthday of this person?'

Alexander's natal day had never been over celebrated except by his mother, but fortunately Antoninus remembered the date. 'He was born three days after the Ides of July. He is now in his fifteenth year.'

'Three days after the Ides of July and in his fifteenth year? Then I shall not need to draw up his horoscope for it coincides exactly with that of a very well known personage – the Consul of Rome, Alexander, the adopted son of the Emperor Antoninus. I have already drawn up his horoscope. It is interesting to see how the stars rule the lives of important people.'

'If you have dared to make the horoscope of the Consul Alexander, have you also dared draw up the horoscope of Caesar himself?'

'No, that would be against the law. It is forbidden to look into Caesar's future.'

'Liar!' Antoninus reached out into the darkness and grabbed the man's hand. 'You know! You know how Caesar will die. Tell us!'

'I know not! I know not!' Hardranes was frightened. He had already guessed the identity of his visitors. 'I cannot tell you.'

Antoninus released him. Suddenly he did not want to know his own future.

'Then give us the posion. You have been paid. Are you sure that it will cause death only slowly, and it will not be apparent that the victim has died of poison?'

'Yes, certain. Here.' There was a sound of rummaging in the back of the hut. A vial was placed in Antoninus's hand. 'This vial contains a coarse powder. Only one grain a day. When dissolved in wine or water it is tasteless. After three days the victim will weaken. He will be overcome by a severe lassitude. The learned doctors of the court . . .'

'Why do you say *court*?' Antoninus was quick to catch the word.

'It was merely an expression, my lord and master, merely an expression. As I was saying the learned doctors will diagnose it as a flux of the bowels. They will administer their nostrums which will do no good. The poison is accumulative and at the end of a week, the victim will be confined to his bed. During the second week, he will become weaker and weaker. The third week will find him wasting away and the fourth week should see him dead. I say *should*, but I am not sure.'

'You are not sure? Are you not certain that the poison will kill?'

'It cannot work against the stars. The planets say that the Consul Alexander will die by the sword, so poison will have no effect on him, unless . . .'

'Unless what?' Antoninus questioned.

'Unless something happens to change the very stars themselves.'

'Nothing could do that.'

Hardranes's feet appeared in the circle of light. An arm went up and he pointed through the doorway.

'That could.'

Antoninus followed the direction of the pointing finger. Low on the horizon, scarcely discernible through the fast moving clouds, a wan star appeared. From it there was a path of light, a trail of star dust that seemed to be drawn through the heavens behind it.

'The comet.' Hardranes dropped his hand. 'My calculations were right. It has appeared. It plunges the heavens into confusion. Yes, my lords, the poison may work now.'

'But doesn't a comet signify the end of one reign and the beginning of another?' Antoninus drew in his breath sharply.

'So it is said, Great Caesar. So it is said.' Hardranes disappeared into the blackness of the sagging hut.

Silently, without speaking to each other, they left. The clouds had now hidden both the comet and the moon and they found the path difficult. The clouds parted and before them they could see the black outlines of the cypresses and hear the animal noises of the horses.

'Do you have your sword, Gordius?' Antoninus was whispering again.

'Of course. I would not go out at night without it.'

'This man Hardranes! He recognized us and he knows the poison is for Alexander.'

'Wait for me in the chariot. I shall be back in a moment.' Gordius turned and started back to the ruined tomb.

Antoninus and Hierocles waited by the chariot. In a few minutes, Gordius returned.

'He died, but before he died he spoke.'

'And what did he say?' Antoninus dreaded the answer.

'He said that as he died by steel, so would Caesar.' Gordius handed the pouch of gold to Antoninus.

'There is no need to waste this.'

Antoninus took it, but when he felt the warm stickiness of the blood on it he dropped it on the floor of the chariot.

Hierocles reached a protecting arm around Antoninus.

'Believe him not, beloved. He was half demented as all these magicians are. But I would wish that this night you had dispatched the Tribune Agrippa rather than this half-witted Hardranes.'

25

THE VIAL, FILLED with a coarse-grained white powder
that resembled salt, remained locked in a secret closet in Antoninus's apartment for over a week after it was obtained.
Great as was his desire to use it, he hesitated. The taking of
any life was abhorrent to him yet he knew that the boy must
die. He must destroy Alexander or eventually Alexander
would destroy him.

The week, however, was not misspent. Cleander, the
pockets in his tunic well lined with gold, established an
elaborate system of espionage throughout the palace that
successfully reported every breath drawn by Mamaea, Julia
Maesa or Alexander. That there was little or nothing to report was sufficient evidence that for the present, they were
lying low.

Julia Maesa was the instigator and the brains that directed
all operations and she now appeared to be quite content to
bask in Antoninus's sudden new popularity, and his hitherto
unrevealed ability to be Caesar. Until he crossed her, she
would favour him. Although apparently free in all their
movements, the three were under constant surveillance. Antoninus was taking no chances.

But he faced possible danger in administering the poison.
Who could do it? Those whom he could trust were so few –
Hierocles, Soaemias, Cleander, Gordius and Aegenax – and
each one of them too closely identified with himself. It must
be someone who had been close to Alexander – someone in
whom Alexander had confidence. But outside his mother
and grandmother, there was nobody. Yes, he had once mentioned a friend. Antoninus struggled to recall the situation.
A friend? Alexander had desired a certain girl by the name
of Flacca who had a sister. That much Antoninus recalled.
Alexander was enamoured of this Flacca – and his friend,
whoever he was, was interested in her sister. Oh yes, the

friend was a hostler, a slave working in the stables of the Circus. And the friend's name? Here Antoninus's memory went blank.

But a Caesar of Rome has means of gaining information even about a lowly stable slave. Gordius knew everyone in Rome and particularly everyone in the Circus. Gordius was ordered to bring a list of names of all the slaves who worked in the stables along with their approximate ages. Gordius did so and Antoninus went over the list with Hierocles. Undoubtedly the slave was young, otherwise he would not be friendly with Alexander. Antoninus was sure he would recognize the name.

Hierocles started to read.

'Galbus, age forty-five.'

Antoninus shook his head.

'Syromones, age thirty. Eutrax, age fifty. Polvero age nineteen.'

Antoninus held up his hand for Hierocles to stop. 'Polvero, nineteen?' The age might be right but the name caused no glimmer of recognition.

Hierocles continued.

'Ajax, age twenty. Byonto, age twenty-eight. Mercurio, age twelve. Helefontes, age sixty. Rufus, age seventeen.'

Antoninus stopped Hierocles again. 'Rufus? Age seventeen?' He was sure it was the right one. 'How many more are there, Carissimus?'

'Some four, no five, but all of them are over thirty.'

'Then Rufus it must be. Send Cleander to get Alexander. We shall all go to the Circus together, ostensibly for practice with the chariots. It will be well for us to be seen together. I'll let Alexander choose the horses he wants and that will take us to the stable. We shall see if there is any sign of recognition between him and any one of the slaves. If so, when we have gone out on the sands, stay behind and ascertain the slave's name. I'll wager it will be this Rufus.'

It worked out exactly as Antoninus had predicted. During the choosing of the horses, Alexander greeted a young slave, whose name Hierocles discovered to be Rufus. So this was

Alexander's friend and the lover of Flacca's sister. He was an ordinary type, big and beefy for his years, peasant-handed with a shock of almost white hair that, with his pale blue eyes, bespoke his Teutonic origin.

The lad seemed genuinely glad to see Alexander, and Antoninus noticed that for the first time Alexander seemed to react to another human being. His sullen look disappeared and he smiled during his conversation with Rufus. It was exactly as Antoninus might wish it to be . . . . exactly! With Alexander and Hierocles racing each other down the Circus together, Antoninus had an opportunity to confer with Gordius safely out of hearing.

'The lad Rufus – what could he do to deserve severe punishment?' Antoninus asked.

'Just lately he has been given charge of Sin, the black stallion that has won so many races for the Greens. He devotes all his time to this one horse. If the stall door should be left open and Sin should wander out and disappear, of course Rufus would be blamed.'

'And all Rome would clamour for him to be punished?'

'Crucifixion, no less,' Gordius nodded his head in agreement.

Antoninus smiled in return and Gordius understood. Antoninus had already condemned the innocent Rufus. 'But of course it could be whispered to Rufus that as he has such a good friend in the Consul Alexander, a word to him might mitigate the punishment.'

'The word will be whispered,' Gordius assured him.

The next morning all Rome was agog with the terrible news. The black stallion Sin of the Greens, who carried heavy odds on that afternoon's races, was missing. Some stupid slave had allowed the Blues to steal him. Anxious groups gathered in the Forum and in the wine shops of the Suburra. Millions of *sestercii*, wagered on the Greens, were already in danger. The tragedy was far greater than the appearance of the direful comet in the skies. A comet was a far-away thing but horse racing was very near to every Roman's heart.

257

Antoninus waited. Sooner or later he felt sure that Alexander would appear. He had not long to wait. An hour before noon, Alexander was announced in the Antonine's apartments while he and Hierocles were dressing for the afternoon races.

Alexander entered, respectful for once, with a look of genuine anxiety that erased the look of sullen stupidity which he usually wore. He dropped to one knee.

'Great Caesar,' he began humbly.

Antoninus, primed for the interview he knew would follow could afford to be magnanimous.

'Dear boy, how nice to see you and do get up from your knees. If you must kneel, always choose a rug – the marble tiles are hard and cold. I would not want you to catch an ague by kneeling on the cold stones. Do you want to see me?'

'I do, Antoninus, I do. You've no reason to grant me any favours. I've never granted you any but I've come to ask one of you.'

'And why not, my son? You are now my own beloved son, dearer to me than anyone in my Empire, except perhaps Hierocles who outranks you in that he is already Caesar, and you did not kneel to him.'

Alexander would have dropped to his knees again before Hierocles, but Antoninus stopped him.

'No more formality, dear boy. Now what is the favour to be? Let me guess! A new racing chariot, made of pear wood from Britain? A *quadriga* of black Arabian horses for yourself? Or,' he waved an admonitory finger, 'would you like the little Flacca to take up residence in your apartments? But whatever it is, be assured that I am prepared to grant it.'

'It's Rufus.'

Antoninus seemed to search his memory.

'Rufus? Do I know him?'

'My friend, the slave at the Circus.'

'Ah yes, the one who smells of horses.'

'They say that it is his fault that Sin has escaped. But I know better. Rufus loves that horse. He even sleeps in the stall with it.'

'No wonder the boy has a smell, sleeping with a horse,' Antoninus chuckled.

'They're torturing Rufus at the Mamertine Prison now, trying to make him confess that he was hired by the Blues to let Sin out. And when they finish torturing him, they are going to crucify him. Oh, Antoninus, don't let them. He's a good boy, and he's my friend, the only friend I have.'

Antoninus saw real consternation in his cousin's face.

'You could have had me for a friend. Perhaps it would have been better for you to have Caesar for a friend than a hostler slave. But the question is, how can you save Rufus, is that right?'

'A word from you will do it.'

'This really means a lot to you, Alexander?'

The boy nodded.

'Then I shall. Hierocles, hurry and finish dressing. We'll order our litter to stop at the Mamertine on our way to the Circus. And, Hierocles, be sure to cancel our bets on the Greens this afternoon.'

Alexander was impatient. 'If you don't get there soon, they will have broken his arms and legs. The gaoler that brought me the message from him said they were ready to stretch him on the rack. Hurry, Antoninus.'

Antoninus took him by the arm and led him to the door. When Alexander was gone, he turned to Hierocles with a smile of complete satisfaction.

'It's working out, Carissimus.'

Hierocles grinned. 'But if they do stretch him on the rack before you get there, he won't be of much use to you.'

'Then let us take Alexander's advice and hurry.'

Never before had Antoninus stepped inside the dark confines of the grim Mamertine Prison. The guards at the entrance and the whole staff were thrown into consternation, particularly when Antoninus demanded that he be taken at once to the torture chambers. A mere slave was being tortured – a worthless little son of a bitch who had sold out the hopes of the Greens so that the Blues would win. Now Caesar himself had come. What a day for the Mamertine!

Antoninus shuddered as a gaoler guide lighted them down the dark stairs, cut out of the living rock upon which Rome was built. The torch cast a flickering red stain on the greasy walls and their sandals slipped on the slimy stairs. Antoninus shrieked as a rat, startled by the light, reared up on his hind legs, bared its teeth, then scuttled to darkness and safety between Antoninus's feet. What he thought was an echo of his own shriek was prolonged into a series of agonized screams.

'Hurry, Hierocles, tell the gaoler to go faster. If they kill Rufus before we get there or even maim him, we shall be too late.'

The gaoler with the torch heard Antoninus and turned around.

'They've only given him one or two turns. 'Twon't hurt 'im none. There's them that have been on the rack for an hour and walked away. They's just a-stretching him but only a little because they be knowing he's a friend of the Consul's.'

When they reached a heavy door of oaken planks, the screams from within were even louder and more prolonged. The gaoler called through the iron grating set into the door, and a flat, Mongoloid face with curiously slanted eyes appeared. They heard the clatter of iron bars inside and the door swung inward. It opened to a cavernous room, lighted by torches, its raw rock walls roughly groined into a vaulted ceiling. At the far end a group of nude torsos were clustered around a machine. The torches high-lighted their sweaty bodies which surrounded the screamer. Antoninus quickened his steps, holding Hierocles's arm. Those around the machine did not look up until they heard him call.

'Stop.' His single word echoed between the vaults.

'Who says "stop"?' The same flat face with broken nose and slanting eyes peered out of the semi-darkness.

'Caesar.' Hierocles was abrupt.

'Caesar? Here?' The flat face laughed but as the gaoler guide with Antoninus lowered his torch, the better to light their faces, the laugh died in the brute's throat. He motioned to the other men – there were three of them – and they left the iron wheels to stand at attention.

Flat face came forward into the circle of light. He was a squat mountain of a man, with huge pads of muscles extending from his thick neck over his arms and chest, down to a flat belly which was lost in a wide belt and greasy leather rags of trousers. He put out a hand to help Antoninus and the strength of the hand guided Antoninus across the floor, avoiding strange looking contraptions of metal and straps. Once Antoninus's foot slipped and he saw a puddle of congealed blood, still wet on the floor. He signalled to the guide to hold his torch even higher so that when he approached the strange machine, he could look down at the body, spread-eagled between its four supports.

He recognized Rufus. Each foot was tied at the ankle and each hand at the wrist, with braided leather thongs which ran to the four wheels at each corner. The boy's body was stretched out between them, taut, stiff and unyielding. Only his head was relaxed and that fell back from his shoulders, the line of the neck stretched in an agonized curve, the long hair hanging down in lank, sweaty locks. The body, white where the tunic had shielded it from the sun gleamed red in the torchlight and the blond patch of hair at his groin was bronzed by the light. The lad was circumcised, which was rare for a German.

The sobbing subsided into a laboured breathing.

Antoninus came closer and the four men made way for him. He laid his hand on the hard, taut flesh. Strange thoughts flashed through his mind. He saw the Tribune Agrippa stretched out as this lad was.

'Rufus.' Antoninus reached one hand under the boy's head and lifted it so that he could look into the glazed eyes. 'Your friend, the Consul Alexander, has asked me to save you not only from the torture but from crucifixion. Do you recognize me?'

'Caesar.' The word emerged through a bubble of phlegm.

'Yes, Caesar.' Antoninus smoothed back the damp hair

tenderly. 'The Consul can beg for your life but only Caesar can save it.'

'Mercy, Great Caesar, they are killing me.'

'No, Rufus, merely making you confess that you accepted money from the Blues to let Sin out. After you have confessed, they will nail you to a cross – nail through your hands and feet. And you'll hang there until you're dead. Sometimes it takes three days to die on the cross, but that will be better because it will be a longer holiday for all Rome. They'll flock to see you dying and the adherents of the Greens will pelt you with fish-heads and rotten vegetables and vile offal. Yes, Rufus, it will be a holiday in Rome while you moan on the cross.'

'Save me, Great Caesar.' With an effort he lifted his head higher than Antoninus's hand supported. 'I swear by Elah-ga-baal that I never left the door of Sin's stall open. Somebody else did it.'

Now Antoninus understood the circumcision. This boy had become a convert to the Sun God. When he spoke again his tone was tender.

'Caesar will save you from the torture, Rufus, and Caesar will save you from death. But Caesar must be paid. Will you pay for your life?' He turned to the four men who were craning to hear every word. 'Retire to the other end of the room.' He waited for them to go. His left hand still supported Rufus's head, his right wandered over the straining chest, pinched the two nipples lightly then wandered down over the concave stomach. Again the thought of the Tribune Agrippa entered his mind.

'You will be released, Rufus, if you promise to do as I tell you.'

'Anything, Great Caesar, anything.'

'Then swear by the great God Elah-ga-baal whom we both worship.'

'I swear, Great Caesar.'

Antoninus released the ratchet on one of the wheels and it spun violently around. The braided thong fell slack and one of Rufus's legs dropped to the floor.

'Support him, Hierocles, otherwise he will fall.' He walked to the other wheel and released the ratchet. Again the wheel spun and the legs dropped limply. Hierocles caught the boy's body as Antoninus released the wheels which held the hands. At Antoninus's signal the four men came running back.

'Do you have a litter or something here?'

' 'Twon't go up the stairs. We'll have to carry him. He ain't hurt. We didn't put enough pressure on him. Ain't hurt a bit, that one ain't. Just scared. Course he may be stretched a little but he can walk.' It was the gaoler with the flat face speaking.

'Then a man can be put on that thing and stretched to a certain point without being injured? How do you know how far to go?'

Flat face grinned at Antoninus.

'Experience, Great Caesar. The rack has seldom a chance to get cold. When we take one off there's another waiting to be put on. Slaves mostly, because the law says that any confession a slave makes must be made under torture. But sometimes we get freedmen too and once in a while a Patrician but there's been few of them under your reign, Great Caesar. Nobody's wanted to put you off the throne. You're the best emperor Rome ever had.'

'You know, I believe you mean that.' Antoninus scanned the flat face which had a certain sensuous attraction despite the broken nose and the slanting eyes. His eyes traversed the thick neck and the broad shoulders. 'What's your name, man?'

'Glamus, slave here in the Mamertine since I was picked up half dead on the battlefield in Parthia four years ago.'

'Carry him, Glamus, and accompany us. Today you are a free man on Caesar's orders. I have need of men who think I am the best emperor Rome ever had. You shall attend me at the palace.'

With Glamus and Rufus following in a hired litter, they returned to the palace. Rufus was able to walk, but Glamus picked him up like a sack of meal and carried him through the halls to Caesar's apartments. Once there, Antoninus told Glamus to wait outside and he and Hierocles assisted Rufus. Antoninus took a quick survey of the room to see that nobody was there. The apartments were deserted – even Cleander was missing.

He poured undiluted wine into a silver cup and handed it to Rufus, bade him be seated and drink, which he did with some difficulty although he was now moving more freely and with less pain. Antoninus could see that he had not been harmed and apart from a stiffness of the muscles would soon recover.

Rufus gulped the wine and looked up at Antoninus who was standing over him.

'I didn't do it, Great Caesar. I didn't. The door of Sin's stall was secure when I went to sleep and I was sleeping in the stall with Sin.'

'I believe you. You are free now, thanks to Alexander's intercession and mine. You owe your lives to both of us. Therefore you will serve us here in the palace instead of remaining in the Circus as a hostler. Will you do that? Will you be the Consul's slave – to remain with him at all times and never leave him? Will you give him the devotion you owe him for saving your life – and me too? Agreed?'

'It will be a pleasure to serve you, Great Caesar, and to be the Consul Alexander's slave. He is my friend.'

'And I am your friend, Rufus. The life of the Consul Alexander is very precious to me. Not only is he my son and heir but he is my cousin and the only one to carry on the holy line of the Priest-Kings of Emesa. I want you to guard him well, Rufus. I want you to report to me everywhere he goes and everyone he sees.'

'I will, Great Caesar. I'll not leave him alone for a minute and I shall protect him with my life.'

'Good. Then remember, you must come to me every morning and tell me where he has been the day before and whom he has seen.'

'Yes, Great Caesar.'

'Then you may go. Report to my slave, Cleander. He will

see that you are bathed, given new clothes and taken to the Consul's apartments. You shall come to me every morning at the hour before noon when I am always in the palace, for it is the other Caesar's and my custom to bathe and change our clothes before we eat at midday. Come here to my rooms. The guards will have orders to admit you. Now go! Ask the Praetorian outside for my slave Cleander. You'll probably find him behind some pillar or in some dark corner with a soldier.'

Rufus got up from his chair slowly, reached for Antoninus's hand and kissed it. He hobbled slowly to the door. As he placed his hand on the latch, Antoninus spoke.

'My son Alexander is still a youth. He has not yet reached his full growth. I would that he be strong and healthy to fit him for the time when he becomes Caesar. Each day before he eats his midday meal, he must drink a glass of mulsum for 'tis very nourishing. It is the rarest of all wines and so scarce that I keep it here in my apartments. When you report to me I shall give you a cup of it to take to him and you must see that he drinks it before he eats. If you sample it yourself, I will have you flogged because it is worth its weight in gold.'

Rufus left and Antoninus looked at Hierocles. He nodded his head slowly and Hierocles nodded in reply. The little Antonine was arranging matters very subtly and very successfully. But one thing troubled Hierocles. He was not always able these days to follow the labyrinthine meanderings of Antoninus's thoughts.

'Well done, little Caesar. Alexander will never suspect Rufus of poisoning him, Rufus will never suspect you and Rome will never suspect. Not only well thought out but well carried out. Yet there is one thing I do not understand. This Glamus – who must even now be waiting outside your door.'

The tip of Antoninus's tongue appeared between his teeth. He pulled it in and clicked his teeth together.

'I have decided to have a little torture chamber of my own, Carissimus, here in the palace. Seeing Rufus stretched there fascinated me. Imagine what exquisite ecstasy the rack would provide, spicing pleasure with pain. It would be something entirely different, Carissimus, something I have never tried before.'

Hierocles shook his fist at Antoninus. 'If you intend to get me into that contraption . . .'

'Not you, Carissimus, not you. I do not need to rack you to obtain what I want. I had considered trying it myself. With the experienced Glamus to work the wheels, the whole process might be enjoyable and certainly would be different. And then, who knows, I might need a rack handy sometime. The dungeons of the Mamertine are such a dirty place. I would never want to go there again to hear a confession. My own torture chamber will be bright with sunshine and flowers. Even the thongs will be of violet plaited leather, entwined with purple anemones. I think I shall have the wheels gilded. It will be an honour to be racked by Caesar, an honour.'

'The day is going to come, little Caesar, when you will not need me any more. You seem to be able to think for yourself these days.'

'Only in little things, Carissimus. When it comes to big things, I shall always need you. Governing Rome is a big thing, bigger then violet leather thongs and gold plated wheels. While my evil mind plans its evil little things, you shall do the big things, Carissimus. That is why I shall always need you.'

26

A WEEK PASSED. During it, Antoninus arranged for the harbour at Ostia to be dredged of Tiber silt and new breakwaters to be constructed at Leptis Magna. He had a part of the Via Sacra repaved, the capitals of the columns of Capitoline Zeus regilded, the tax rate in Alexandria raised and the tax rate in Cisalpine Gaul lowered. He removed the Pro-Consul of Cyrenaica for misappropriation of funds, and organized a school for the blind sons of army veterans in

Rome. At least his name was signed to these decrees, but it was Hierocles who had decided on them. While Hierocles was busy with the weight of Empire Antoninus was not idle.

The rack was removed from the Mamertine and reappeared at the palace, washed, gilded and sprayed with perfume and with new thongs made of violet leather. It was installed secretly in the ground-floor room to which only Antoninus and Glamus had a key. Glamus was appropriately garbed in violet leather and made his home in the room of the rack, guarding its secret.

Each day, an hour before noon, Antoninus received Rufus and listened to the petty accounts of his cousin's doings. They were trifling and insignificant. Evidently Mamaea and Julia Maesa were lying low. The failure of the last palace revolution had taught them a lesson. Alexander was Caesar's son and heir, Consul of Rome, and apparently happy. He had his friend Rufus in constant attendance, and two new slaves by the name of Flacca and Arminia had appeared in his apartments where they were in nightly attendance. Each day when Rufus left, after his report to Caesar, he carried a cup of mulsum, that precious wine made of rose leaves, white grapes and spices, which the greedy Alexander always gulped without allowing Rufus to taste it.

There was only one small cause for concern. Alexander was complaining of slight nausea, and cramps in his stomach. Mamaea attributed it to his fondness for honey-glazed dormice, with which he stuffed himself. She forbade him to have any more but he persisted, even though he vomited them up ten minutes later. When his illness was reported to Antoninus, he called at Alexander's apartments; found the boy retching into a silver bowl, held by Rufus; showed the proper amount of sympathetic concern, even to holding Alexander's head himself while the boy puked; and summoned the imperial physicians who prescribed a vile-tasting syrup which Alexander refused to take.

Throughout the week, the boy did not seem to improve. He was still able to be up, attended the races with Antoninus and sat in the imperial box but he was beginning to lose weight and his face was drawn and pallid. The only thing he could keep on his stomach, so he said, was the cup of mulsum that Antoninus sent him daily. He begged for more but Antoninus confessed that his supply was running low and until he obtained more from Carthage, one cup a day must suffice. Antoninus was most patient with him.

He was patient about another thing too. Each day and night when the Praetorians changed guard, Antoninus inquired as to the officer of the day and seemingly showed no disappointment when it did not turn out to be the Tribune Agrippa. Here again, he could afford to wait. Sooner or later, the Tribune would commmand the palace detail. Antoninus did not want to appear anxious.

As Alexander's indisposition increased, Antoninus became even more attentive to his cousin. He visited him daily, and each time showed signs of his regard by increasingly elaborate presents. The racing chariot Alexander had always wanted was at the Circus, awaiting his recovery, along with a *quadriga* of perfectly matched blacks. Flacca was augmented by a tempting courtesan from Alexandria – another gift from Antoninus – who did her best to warm the boy when he was shivering with the cold after one of his violent seizures. The Lady Mamaea almost forgot her intense dislike of her nephew in view of his solicitude for her son.

Rufus remained in constant attendance and each day brought the vigour-building (but death-dealing) cup of mulsum to Alexander. Even Julia Maesa complimented Antoninus on sharing the precious wine with his cousin and agreed to its restorative qualities. So afraid was she that Antoninus's special private supply might be exhausted that she sent to Carthage herself in a vain endeavour to find a few extra bottles.

Never had the family been more united on the surface than by Alexander's illness. Soaemias, who had always disliked him now took pity on his suffering and left the smooth arms of Aegenax long enough to come and bathe his head in rose water. Some days he seemed to rally, enough to be up and about a few hours, then the cramps returned and he would be forced back to bed again where he would remain for a day or so.

The Greek physicians, after conferring with the priests of Asclepius, prescribed their most famous nostrums, one of which was a poultice of spider webs on the lad's stomach. Antoninus had all Rome searched for spider's webs, and offered a bounty. He obtained a great mass, far more than the physicians needed, but even this exotic remedy failed. Finally it was decided that the boy was too full blooded, so one of his veins was opened and he was drained of much blood which seemed only to weaken him instead of making him better. Only one medicine relieved him – the extract of white poppies from Persia which seemed to kill the pain, at least temporarily and give him a few hours of sleep. It was so efficacious that as time went on Alexander begged for more and more of it.

Aegenax led the priests of Elah-ga-baal in a full night of prayerful sacrifices for Alexander's health and Antoninus and Hierocles attended – Antoninus not as a priest but a suppliant. Indeed, Antoninus's conduct was so exemplary that all Rome marvelled at his regard for the boy and even Antoninus himself began to believe that he did not desire the boy's death. On such occasions, he would omit the fatal grain from the cup of mulsum, thus prolonging Alexander's life beyond the time allotted to him by Hardranes.

Alexander, as an invalid, did not endanger Antoninus's position and both Mamaea and Julia Maesa were so disturbed over the boy's health that they had no time for plotting. Antoninus was happy. Government under the able hands of Hierocles was progressing smoothly. Rome seemed to love its Emperor and the legions still worshipped him. Even the Praetorians held an added esteem for him, for he was leading an exemplary life, shunning the public baths and the bordellos, keeping his inquisitive hands from wandering under strange tunics, and having eyes and ears for nobody but Hierocles and Alexander.

When Antoninus acted any role he did it with consummate skill. Now he was playing at being Emperor of Rome, the father and protector of his son and heir Alexander; in fact he had quite convinced himself that he was the model youth who would never dally with another gladiator, seek another stallion from the legion or sacrifice as a priest of Elah-ga-baal.

And, with his histrionic concern for the welfare of his son and heir, there was birthed a real desire to have a son of his own. The line of the Priest-Kings of Emesa must be perpetuated and only he remained to do it. Could he? He had doubts but if he were to try, the first requisite was to have a wife.

Another wife! He dreaded the very thought of it as he remembered the pasty Julia and the dry-skinned Aquilia. But he longed for a son of his own – someone bound to him by ties of blood. How wonderful if he and Hierocles could have a son! But alas, the chirurgeons had told him it would be impossible. Therefore, he must marry.

When he approached Hierocles on the subject, he found him most willing that he should wed. Hierocles was aware that no woman could come between them, and that his relations with Antoninus were so firmly grounded that his hold would never be threatened. With Antoninus's apparently sincere attitude towards a new life and his willingness to abandon his role of bath-boy and prostitute, it was altogether fitting that he prove to Rome by a suitable marriage that he could accomplish the most important of male prerogatives – that of a father. And, even more to the point, with the anticipated death of Alexander, there would be no heir to the throne and Antoninus did not want to abandon Elah-ga-baal to oblivion. It would require a member of the Emesan dynasty to carry on the worship of the Sun God.

A wife for Caesar! A mother for Caesar's child! Once having decided, and having received Hierocles's sanction, it was now time to act. All the eligible matrons of Rome were alerted and fond mothers, regardless of the known reputation of Antoninus, were only too avid to place their daughters beside him as the new Augusta. The eligible ones ranged in age from twelve to twenty, although there were a few who were suspected of being over the twenty-year limit. They came from the best families in Rome – not only the old Patrician Gens but some of the newer and wealthier Eques order.

The better to study them, Antoninus decided to give a banquet and as the Greens had recently won ten consecutive victories in the Circus, he decided to combine the two occasions, certain that if the aspirants for his hand bored him, as he knew they would, he could assuage himself with the charioteers. In order to study the various virgins of Rome, Antoninus decided on a wholly different kind of banquet. It would start in the morning and last until early evening. Thus he would see the fair nymphs under different lights and different conditions. He would be able to view them with the freshness of their *toilettes* and the exuberance of a party's beginning, and later with their freshness gone and the lines of fatigue on their faces.

But a banquet lasting throughout all the hours of the day in the imperial banqueting hall would be boring and tiresome. Then – and he felt this to be a brilliant inspiration – let the banquet take place in different palaces in Rome. A course in each palace and, as they were celebrating the victory of the Greens, let every morsel of food served be green in colour. Not the same shade of green of course. And the guests would don silken tunics of the shade of the food be it the light yellow green of spring or the blue green of the sea.

For such an enormous crowd it would be necessary to requisition the largest palaces in Rome. The first course, naturally would be served in Caesar's Golden House. Then they would proceed to the vast pile of the Lentulli; on to the house of Gracchi; to the villa of the Cornelii outside the walls; back to Rome for a course in Caesar's own Pincian Gardens; then to the Palace of the widow Pompeianus. The widow Pompeianus had recently become a widow because her husband had plotted against the life of Caesar and had been forced to commit suicide. Because his wife had been a close friend of Julia Maesa and his aunt's, Antoninus had not confiscated the property so the widow should be willing to open her house to him.

The day arrived and the guests assembled at the Golden House for the first course which was oysters, dyed green by the juice of spinach, served on mountain snow in dishes of green murrhine glass. Every couch in the immense hall was filled by the eligible daughters of Rome's first families, along with their doting mothers, balanced by drivers and chief supporters of the Greens.

Antoninus looked them over carefully. Among the drivers there were many who appealed to him but among the carefully dressed and bejewelled damsels there was not a single one that interested him – not a one. They were either too large or too small, too fat or too thin, too blonde or too brunette and . . . they were all girls. He shuddered as he looked at them, trying to picture himself in bed with one of them. The very thought nauseated him so that he could not eat the verdant oysters on his plate.

Hierocles's place on Antoninus's right was balanced by that of Soaemias on his left, and as he glanced at his mother out of the corner of his eye he came to realize why none of the young chármers that had been marshalled for his choice could appeal to him. Soaemias's full-blown beauty was so magnificent in contrast to these pale young aristocrats that it completely overpowered them. Her voluptuous curves; the ivory globes of her breasts under her thin silk stola; her high colouring, vivacity and her easy companionship with Aegenax, who was sitting beside her, put all the others, airy affectations to shame.

Alas! If he could only marry his mother! Life with her would be interesting. Now, if he could only find someone like her. He scanned the expectant faces along the couches. Bah, there was none in Rome like her.

After the oysters were downed the party arose from their couches and progressed down the long corridors to the main entrance of the palace, where a procession of litters was waiting to convey them to the palace of the Lentulli. Here, before entering the *triclinium*, each guest was furnished with a silk tunic of a delicate shade of sea green and directed to dressing rooms. Eventually they assembled on the couches set up in the big dining room, ready for the second course which was a rare delicacy in Rome – camel's hooves, served with a pale green sauce of mint.

The entertainment that accompanied the meal was most unusual. Gaius Lentullus had sought hard to please his Emperor and he did, with a mime on the death of Attys, in which the young Greek actor would have eventually emasculated himself were it not that Antoninus, at the fateful moment, called a halt to the sweep of the knife and the fellow remained intact. Afterwards Antoninus rather regretted that he had not allowed the performance to continue. It was something he had never witnessed before, and it would have provided an interesting souvenir but it would certainly have been bloody and his stomach still felt queasy.

He had forgotten the girls in his interest in the pantomime but now he looked them over again. They were not quite as fresh-looking now as when they had first appeared at the palace. Some of their *maquillage* was streaked, coiffures disarranged and the anxious look of anticipation was beginning to wear thin. But Soaemias, now once removed on his left to make way for his host, was as bouyant as ever, her conversation as animated, and her hands on Aegenax's thigh as affectionate as before.

Off again, with thanks to Gaius Lentullus for an hour that must have used up a year's income, to the palace of the Gracchi, who were notorious throughout Rome for their penny-pinching traits. Here the tunics were of a rich emerald green and the couches were laid on the marble terrace at the back of the palace. Pasties of nightingales' brains, topped with pistache were served, and as the terrace overlooked a water pleasance they were entertained with the Ixion – a huge Persian water wheel with alternating boy and girl slaves bound to its rim. As it turned, plunging them into the water, they held their breath, rising on the other side with gracefully outstretched arms, the water dripping from their naked bodies. On one revolution, the complicated machinery became stuck for several minutes and the luckless boy who was immersed in the water was drowned when he surfaced. Otherwise the entertainment was most successful.

Now, out in the bright light of the sun, Antoninus discovered even less to interest him in the galaxy of Roman maidens. The white lead that covered their faces began to streak with sweat and he saw several adolescent blemishes coming to the surface under the paint. It was warm and the girls were sweating, staining their tunics under their arms. Soaemias still looked as cool as when she had started and her skin glowed smoothly with only the slightest touch of paint. Her vivacity had not diminished, her verve was unquenchable. She had expressed a desire for one of the male slaves who had been tied to the Ixion and when he was presented to her, dripping wet and still gasping for breath, she bade him crouch down beside her couch and with one hand twisted in his wet curls, she continued to fondle Aegenax with the other.

Antoninus had been amazed at the prodigality of the Gracchi until he discovered that one of the aspirants for his bed was a daughter of the house – a languid sixteen-year-old with lank blonde hair and the suspicion of a cast in one eye. As far as he was concerned, they had wasted their money – he wouldn't have the anaemic little bitch even though they served flamingo's brains, which were far scarcer and much more expensive than the nightingale variety. The whole affair was becoming boring. He looked first at Hierocles beside him and was grateful for his healthy maleness, then at Soaemias and marvelled at her seductive beauty and charm.

Into the litters again and on to the house of the widow of Pomponianus Bassus. Annia Faustina was a great friend of his grandmother. He had always liked her. Something about her reminded him of his mother. She had not wept many tears over the death of old Pomponianus and when they arrived at her house, she was at the portals to greet them, smiling a most lively welcome.

She knelt before Caesar, her gown of turquoise green matching the jewels in her coronet.

'Great Caesar,' she began, 'what a joy to welcome you to my humble home which is no longer humble now that Caesar honours it.'

Antoninus lifted her up. She smelled like his mother, faintly of sandalwood – a clean, spicy smell. Although she was older than Soaemias, her cheeks were full, round and pink; her skin white and fine; her bosom as artfully curved and her figure as amply voluptuous as that of his mother.

'I love your coronet, Annia Faustina.' Antoninus's eyes had been caught by the jewels.

'Then it is yours,' Annia Faustina laughed, unpinned it from her hair and set it jauntily on Antoninus's head. 'I've crowned Caesar. But come . . .'

She led them into the atrium where slaves were waiting with turquoise green tunics for the guests, but she personally handed Antoninus's to him and he could not help but notice that it was sewn all over with pale green pearls and Persian turquoises. Nor was the one proffered to Hierocles any less splendid. Annia Faustina had already made a most favourable impression.

'Dear Annia Faustina,' Antoninus could always be charming when he desired, 'decorum requires that we are separated while I change my dress . . . or does it?' He questioned.

She bowed her head. 'Great Caesar,' she fluttered her eyelids modestly.

He lifted her chin with one hand and pushed the coronet back on his head with the other. Strangely enough the touch of her skin did not repulse him.

'Such an honour, Great Caesar.'

He waggled a warning finger. 'Antoninus,' he said.

'Antoninus,' she laid her hand lightly against his cheek. 'Dear boy, of course decorum demands that I be not present while you change your dress. I must remember that I am a Roman matron and a grieving widow. Therefore I must be more careful than usual to avoid even the slightest breath of scandal but, alas, what is a poor lone woman to do should her beloved Emperor *command* her?'

'Then I do command you, Annia Faustina,' he lowered his

voice, 'But that strict decorum may be preserved, Hierocles and I shall retire behind a screen and thus we shall not be deprived of your company during the interval.'

They departed down the hall in a flutter of silk and while they were waiting for the screen to be set up, Antoninus felt the need to relieve himself. A whispered word to a slave and the man pointed to a door, through which Antoninus pulled Hierocles. Once inside the closet, he turned to Hierocles.

'I shall marry Annia Faustina,' he announced conclusively.

'Annia Faustina!' Hierocles stared at him. 'She's old enough to be your mother.'

'All the better! She probably knows how to arouse me whereas these other untouched virgins would have to be taught and you know, and I know, Hierocles that I am not one to teach them. For a boy who has never bedded a girl, and a girl who has never bedded a boy, to be on the nuptial couch together . . . ay, Hierocles, it's frightening.'

'A case of who does what and where and to whom!' Hierocles laughed. 'But don't ask me. I've had no experience along those lines. This is one time when you cannot come to me for advice. I've bedded no more virgins than you.'

'But Annia Faustina would know. She's been married.'

'I doubt if old Pomponianus taught her much, burdened as he was with that fat belly of his.'

'Who cares about old Pomponianus? Annia Faustina has always had the reputation for having the most gorgeous male slaves in Rome. Remember the one who brought us here!'

They went out. Annia Faustina was sitting in an armchair, facing a screen made of cedar wood. She smiled gaily and waved her hand to the screen. They disappeared behind it and the slave who was awaiting them, handed them the jewelled tunics. Antoninus took a second look – the fellow was indeed handsome.

'What's the name of your slave, Annia Faustina?' he asked from behind the screen.

'Electrus! His family have been slaves of ours since the time of my great grandfather, the divine Marcus Aurelius.

276

He's indispensable to me but if you care for him, he's yours, Antoninus,' she laughed with that same lilting laughter that Soaemias possessed. 'Anything in my house is yours. Anything that I have, dear Antoninus, is yours. I owe it to you for not having confiscated my wretched husband's estate when you had every right.'

'Did you say I might have anything in your house, Annia Faustina?'

'Anything. Is there something in particular which has struck your fancy?'

'Indeed there is.'

'And what might that be?' Annia Faustina looked up as the Antonine stepped from behind the screen. He was indeed beautiful – not virile or handsome as a man should be but beautiful as a girl with his clear skin, his large, luminous eyes. It was the face of Venus on the body of Apollo. The blue-green of the tunic was most becoming and now, with the excitement of his recent discovery, he had lost the customary air of bored lassitude. His feet danced across the marble floor and he stopped before her chair, dropped to his knees and flung his arms around her.

'You, dear Annia Faustina. I want you. I want to marry you.'

Annia looked down at the boy's head pillowed in her lap. He was handsome, yes, none in Rome was handsomer – unless it was his friend Hierocles. And he was charming, witty, agreeable, amusing and young – so young. But even more than all that, he was Caesar, Emperor, Augustus. All Rome revolved around him. His wife would be the Augusta – the real Augusta, taking precedence over old Julia Maesa who had always claimed the title, albeit wrongly; over Soaemias, over every woman in all Empire. Of course, she was well acquainted with Antoninus's peculiar desires but many women had husbands with the same proclivities. There was scarcely a Roman husband who did not have a *concubinus* as well as a wife. And perhaps with Antoninus bedded beside her he might forsake his precious Hierocles, and if not – well, it would not be difficult, in fact, not difficult at all to share this wonderful Hierocles with him. She looked up at Hierocles as he stepped from behind the screen. Her quick inventory of him decided her. She would be Augusta of Rome; this pretty boy would be her husband in name and this broad-shouldered giant with the curly yellow hair would be her husband in fact. Augusta of Rome! However, she must not appear too anxious.

'But, dear boy, there is a slight difference in our ages. I must be all of ten years older than you.'

'Twenty or even more,' Hierocles thought though he did not speak.

Antoninus brushed the matter away with a wave of his hand.

'What difference do a few years make? I have been married twice before and neither of my wives was capable of being an Augusta, but you, dear Annia Faustina, you would be truly imperial. How much better the purple would look on you than on any of those little empty-heads who even now await to ogle me and try to impress me with their charms? Oh, let me announce it, dear Annia, let me, and we'll see all those anxious Roman matrons fainting on all sides. Oh, what a delightfully wicked surprise! Every one of them is hoping to push her gangly, long-legged daughter into my bed and now, I can consign them all to the other side of the Styx with the announcement that I shall wed my own dearly beloved Annia Faustina. Dear Annia, do let me shock them!'

She looked up at Hierocles. Antoninus's choice had indeed pleased him for he realized that, faint though the chance might be, it might just happen that some pretty young thing, entwining her arms around the impressionable Antoninus might manage to snare him and his affections. The ageing Annia would never be anything but mother to him. Hierocles was quick to understand her appeal to Antoninus for he saw her resemblance to Soaemias.

'You will be good for my little Antonine, Annia Faustina,' he answered her look. 'And Rome will approve for you are of the old imperial family. Yes, Annia Faustina, allow Antoninus to make the announcement.'

She rose from her chair and embraced them, one in each arm. Again Antoninus smelled the spicy, clean scent of sandalwood. The pressure of her fat breasts through the thin silk of their tunics did not seem any more revolting than when his mother embraced him. He felt supremely comfortable with Annia Faustina; it was almost as though he were seeking security in her ample arms. She kissed him on the cheek, then turned and kissed Hierocles. Her lips lingered a fraction of a moment longer.

'I feel that I am marrying not one but two husbands – both of them Caesars.'

'And you will not mind that I continue to keep Hierocles with me?' Antoninus asked anxiously.

'With us, dear boy, with *us*!'

With Annia Faustina between them, they walked the dark corridor to the *triclinium* which was hung with green silk. The slaves who were to wait on them, were standing behind the couches, each with skin dyed the same shade as their tunics. Even the light, entering through the windows glazed with thin green cloth was the same watery shade.

Antoninus walked to the couch reserved for him. A green-skinned slave with green eyes and a wig of seaweed helped him to his couch. Antoninus drew Annia Faustina down beside him. Gently he implanted a kiss on her lips, then raised himself on one elbow and lifted his other hand.

There was complete silence in the watery green room, a silence as complete as though they were all under water, seated at the court of Neptune.

The silence endured for a long moment as Antoninus surveyed the expectant faces.

'Your new Augusta,' he announced. 'Caesar honours the Lady Annia Faustina by selecting her as his wife.'

27

HIS MARRIAGE WITH Annia Faustina was his own idea and as such it received all his attention. It must be the biggest, most splendid and spectacular event that Rome had ever witnessed, and he planned it in great detail even to the embroidered designs on his wife's stola. With so much activity and so many things to take up his mind, he became careless with the doses in the daily cup of mulsum and Alexander soon showed some signs of improvement. He was able to be up and even managed to keep some food on his stomach.

Mamaea and Julia Maesa were overjoyed, not only at Alexander's recovery but also over the fact that, as Annia Faustina was a very close friend, it would mean a third favourable influence over the Antonine. As for Annia Faustina, she was impressed with becoming Rome's Augusta; titivated over such a young and handsome husband; and anticipatory over the joys of sharing her husband's husband with him. If Antoninus would not give up Hierocles – and Annia Faustina hardly wanted that – there was no reason why three could not share the nuptial couch as well as two.

The wedding started off with a procession to the principal shrines of Rome – first, to satisfy Antoninus, to the Temple of Elah-ga-baal, then to the Temple of Capitoline Jove to satisfy the Romans, followed by the Temple of Vesta for the womenfolk, and lastly to the Temple of Isis for the many Romans who had turned to the Egyptian goddess. Antoninus would gladly have sacrificed at the temples of the Christians and that of Mithras, but as neither religion had a temple worthy of the name, that was impossible.

Followed then a banquet at the Golden House, and for once the entertainment was neither licentious nor salacious. A Roman poet read a long and detailed panygeric about Antoninus and Annia, in which he compared them to Zeus and Hera, Jupiter and Juno, Mars and Venus and practically the entire population of Olympus – with the exception of Priapus but he did manage to work the latter in during the stanzas on the blessing of the nuptial bed. By the time the brief ceremony was over and the various priests had invoked their various gods, the barley cakes had been broken and the solemn vows made, the lamps were lighted in the palace and another procession formed to escort Antoninus and Annia to the wedding chamber. Hymen was invoked and another sacrifice offered.

At length they were left alone with the red-draped bed, which had been the subject of so many bawdy jokes. Cleander came in to disrobe Antoninus and Annia Faustina's female slave removed her jewels and garments. Antoninus wanted to look but he did not dare. He dismissed the slaves, ordered them to extinguish all the lamps before they left and in the ensuing semi-darkness he sought the bed and the arms of Annia Faustina.

An hour passed. Nothing happened that would insure an Antonine heir. Annia Faustina had exerted all her charms, employed all her wiles and completed her entire repertory with most discouraging results. Antoninus remained as limp as a rag. She admitted defeat. It was useless to proceed any further. Antoninus was weeping, whether from disappointment, disgust or cnagrin, she did not know. Neither did he. Certainly no wedding night could have been more of a farce – a too willing bride, and a bridegroom who was both reluctant and impotent. Something must be done to redeem it.

Hierocles! Annia felt she knew the answer. Yes, Hierocles! The poor fellow was sleeping alone for the first time since he had come to the Golden House and doubtless he was wide awake too. She raised herself on one elbow and with her free hand smoothed the brow of the fretful Antoninus.

'Dear boy, do not make yourself ill. It is nothing unusual, I assure you. The excitement of the day and the wine has completely unnerved you, and I know what difficulties you are having. It is not easy to change one's life in an instant.

You are so accustomed to your darling Hierocles it is no wonder you miss him. Why don't you send a slave to fetch him? With him here with us, you would feel more comfortable.'

'Hierocles!' Antoninus stopped his sobbing, 'Hierocles sleeping alone!'

He suffered Annia Faustina's damp kiss on his mouth and then sat up in bed. He would send no slave to fetch Hierocles; he must see for himself if anyone was with him. He'd surprise him, for certainly Hierocles would not expect to see him this night. Yes, he'd surprise him and if there was anyone bedded with him it would be the luckless fellow's last night.

'I'll not send a slave to fetch him, I'll go myself.' He jumped from the bed, anxious for an excuse to quit it and in his bare feet ran across the chill marble floors. When he flung the doors open he saw that the guards were being changed – it was the middle of the night.

They were surprised to see Caesar in his long nightgown of white silk but he did not acknowledge them. One thought and one thought only impelled him to run the length of the corridor and demand immediate entrance from the guards at the door of his own apartments. He entered. The room was dark. He tiptoed carefully to his own bed, making no noise with his bare feet. When he reached it an exploratory hand fumbled among the covers, encountered only one figure among the crumpled sheets. He was content. Hierocles was faithful to him. He was indeed sleeping alone.

He climbed into the bed, putting his cold feet against the warm calves of the other. Hierocles half awoke, pulled Antoninus to him contentedly then, fully awakened, pushed him away.

'What are you doing here, beloved? This is no place for you.'

'This is the only place I want to be.'

'Granted, but you must not stay. You have abandoned two wives, now let Rome see that you have really married this one.'

'But Hierocles,' Antoninus began to sob again, 'I can't do

anything with her. Oh, Hierocles, what shall I do and how shall I do it?'

Hierocles gently pushed him further away. 'I cannot advise you, little Caesar. This time you are involved in something in which I cannot help you.'

'Then return with me. Annia Faustina herself suggested it. Come, hurry Hierocles.'

Hierocles swung his legs over the side of the bed and got up. He spoke to Antoninus as a man speaks to a child.

'Get up, Antoninus! I've never denied you anything you ever asked me but this one thing I do deny. Were I to return with you now, all Rome would know it tomorrow and all Rome would say that any child that might be born to Annia Faustina was fathered by me instead of you. Rome would never believe it was yours. Antoninus, go back at once, and the guards who saw you come will think you came only to answer the call of nature.'

'Oh, let me stay here,' Antoninus was wailing again. 'What do I care what Rome thinks or says? This is my life and you are my life and I can't go back to bed with Annia Faustina.'

Hierocles was adamant. Gently but firmly he pulled the Antonine from his bed, took him by the arm and led him to the door, opened it and gave him a little push out into the hall. The guards looked up. They were different ones from those who had been there when the Artonine had entered.

The midnight corridors outside the imperial apartments stretched endlessly vacant except for the two Praetorians which stood guard at the doors. Antoninus caught the smirk that passed between them as he closed the door behind him but he chose to ignore it. He felt strangely alone, faced with the awful possibility of passing the remainder of the night with the panting Annia Faustina.

Slowly and unwillingly, feeling sorry for himself, he dragged his feet along the corridor, hating each step that separated him from Hierocles, yet too proud to return and assert his right as Caesar to share his own bed. With each reluctant step, his displeasure rose, until he had managed to build up a towering case against Hierocles, blaming him for this luckless marriage, this forlorn wandering, this lonely vigil.

He wouldn't return to Annia Faustina! Of that he was sure. Let Rome talk if it would! He'd slip out of the palace and go to the Suburra! He'd get Cleander and spend the night in the baths. He'd coax one of the Praetorians into an empty room – yes, into the room where Glamus was – the room that harboured the gilded and perfumed rack. That is what he would do! He would! If Hierocles could turn him out so easily, then he would seek someone else. Let Hierocles be jealous. He wanted Hierocles to rage and stamp his feet and yell at him – call him all the vile names he had learned as a charioteer. Yes, he'd find someone else tonight. What about Glamus with his narrow slanting eyes that hinted at strange and unknown pleasures, and his wide shoulders that promised prodigious strength? He'd have Glamus put him on the rack. That would be something new.

Before he could turn to go back, he heard footsteps approaching and sought the deep shadows of a marble pillar. He waited until the footsteps drew nearer then looked out from behind the pillar.

The Fates had played into Antoninus's hands!

It was the Tribune Agrippa!

Antoninus gathered the long folds of his nightgown around him and sidled out from behind the pillar, directly into the path of the oncoming Tribune. The purposeful pounding of military boots stopped. Agrippa recognized Caesar and saluted him, grim-faced and unsmiling as usual.

Antoninus smiled and drew his robe even closer, hitching it up provocatively with one hand.

'You guard me well tonight, Tribune Agrippa. Do you guard me through love or duty?'

'It is my duty to guard you well, Great Caesar.'

Antoninus said, 'The Augusta is ill – perhaps too much wine at the wedding feast, and her women attend her. The other Caesar is sleeping soundly and I have not the heart to waken him. My mother shares her apartment with the High Priest Aegenax. Tonight it appears that Caesar has no place to sleep. I was about to seek a couch in an anteroom near my apartments. Perhaps you would accompany me there, Tribune Agrippa.'

'Greatly, Great Caesar. I shall go as far as the door with you and I will take up guard duty there myself.'

'Such devotion, Tribune! Yet could you not guard me better inside. I do not feel sleepy and I would talk with you. I would like to know you better – you and your religion of Mithras. Does it still keep you a virgin, Tribune?'

'Hardly a virgin, Great Caesar, for I was not that when I embraced Mithras, but since that time I have kept myself pure for him.'

Antoninus had turned and was retracing his steps along the corridor that led to his own apartments. The Tribune followed, a step behind.

'And do you enjoy this noble purity that you have enforced upon yourself?' Antoninus asked sweetly.

'It has come to be my life, Great Caesar, the most precious thing in the world to me, something which nobody can take from me.'

'You underestimate the power of our Roman girls, Tribune Agrippa. 'Tis said that some of them could excite a marble statue.'

'They present no problem to me.'

'Or the Greek boys. I have heard of one Apollonius who, 'tis said, gets one thousand *sestercii* an hour. If the girls can excite a marble statue, it is said that he can make a bronze one stand upright.'

'He would have less charm for me than even a girl, Great Caesar. My religion has come to be my life. It is all that matters to me.'

'Then perhaps I should try it. Are you certain that the reward is sufficient?' Antoninus stopped before a small door, almost hidden in the marble wall, opened it slowly and beckoned Agrippa to follow. 'Let me hear more of your faith, Tribune Agrippa. If you were this night to convert Caesar to Mithras you would be doing your god a service, and methinks Rome too.'

Agrippa hesitated on the threshold but followed Antoninus into the room. His eyes burned with the missionary zeal of the men of Mithras when they scented a convert. Inside the room, one small lamp burned on a low table beside a couch, throwing only a small circle of illumination on the floor. The rest of the room receded into darkness. The air was heavy with the cloying scent of dying flowers. Somewhere in the heavy smell of tuberoses and acacia, there was a movement. Antoninus heard it and called out.

'It is all right, Glamus. Do not leave. I may have need of you.' And to Agrippa he explained, 'My slave Glamus who sleeps here.'

Agrippa peered into the darkness but could see nothing except what looked like four golden wheels whose spokes dimly reflected the waving flame of the lamp. Antoninus indicated the narrow couch.

'There seems to be nothing else to sit on,' he deprecated the paucity of the room's furnishings. 'Will you sit here beside me, Tribune Agrippa, and talk to me? Perhaps you would start by telling me why you do not like me. Am I so evil that you hate me?'

Agrippa sat down on the edge of the couch. He watched the lamp flame for a moment as he formed the words of his answer. He turned to Antoninus who was beside him but in the shadows beyond the circle of lamplight.

'I do not hate you, Great Caesar. You are Rome and I cannot hate Rome.'

'But you do not love me, Tribune Agrippa?'

'I know not what you mean by *love*, Great Caesar.'

'There is only one meaning to the word,' Antoninus inched a little closer and Agrippa moved further away.

'I must be going, Great Caesar. It is not fitting that the Tribune in Command be away from his men. Should one have something to report to me, he could not find me.'

'Yet he could have nothing to report except Caesar's safety and Caesar is here with you, Tribune. Safe here beside you.' Antoninus squirmed on the bed until his hand reached the

286

bare flesh of Agrippa's thigh above the brazen greaves and below the leather kilt.

This time Agrippa did not move and encouraged by his silence, Antoninus's hand crept upwards. Agrippa brushed the hand roughly aside and stood up. His right hand reached for his sword and his left hand clutched at the thin stuff of Antoninus's gown.

'You . . .' In his anger he could not form the words. 'If you were not Caesar I would kill you, and perhaps Rome would be better off if I did. You want to know why I do not love you as a soldier should love his Emperor? Because you are what you are! Because of what you have just tried to do! I cannot love a man I cannot respect and how can I respect any man, even the Augustus of Rome, when he is nothing but a bath-boy. No, worse than a bath-boy for those boys sell themselves for money to live, and Caesar needs no money. By Mithras, I shall kill you, you . . .'

He never finished the sentence. Out of the darkness two gigantic arms clasped tightly around his neck, choking his words. The Tribune was a strong man but he had been taken off guard and he was no match for the strength of the arms which encircled him. Their vice-like grip caused him to drop his sword, their pressure forced him to his knees.

Antoninus jumped from the couch. 'Do not strangle him, Glamus. It is well that he lives, even though he threatened my life. Secure him, Glamus. He will be court martialled in the morning.'

'I'll hold him, Caesar, but reach under my apron. You will find a length of leather thong there.'

Antoninus found the thong and with one arm still around Agrippa's throat. Glamus forced the Tribune's arms slowly backward so that Antoninus could secure them. He wrapped the thong tightly around Agrippa's wrists. Glamus forced the Tribune to his feet and produced another thong which Antoninus bound around the man's feet.

'You heard him threaten me, Glamus?'

'That I did, Great Caesar.'

'It looks as if it were a plot to kill me, Glamus. Perhaps we should make him confess. Light the lamps.'

Glamus took the solitary lamp and went around the room, lighting a great tree of lamps which hung from a high bronze standard. Now, with the sudden illumination, the gilded wheels of the rack stood forth, proclaiming its purpose.

'There is no plot, Great Caesar,' Agrippa spoke dispassionately. 'It was only a personal difference between the two of us, not as between Caesar and a subject but between two . . .' he hesitated '. . . two persons.'

Antoninus grinned. 'You were about to say two men but then you thought me unworthy to be called a man. No, Tribune Agrippa, I am not a man, at least not such as you. To the rack with him, Glamus. Strip him of his armour and his clothes. Cut them from him. Surely Caesar has the right to know who desires his life.'

'It is forbidden by law to torture a Praetorian, Great Caesar. Kill me if you must. My sword is on the floor and your executioner is strong enough to do it in one swipe. Kill me you may, but you cannot torture me.'

'Cannot? You forget there is but one law in Rome and I am it. Glamus, get to work!'

A sharp knife severed the leather straps which secured the Tribune's breastplate, greaves and sandals. A quick slash with the knife to cut the waistband of the leather kilts. Another rent the linen tunic, and Glamus slashed a piece of the linen, forced Agrippa's mouth and stuffed the cloth in.

Agrippa did not struggle as Glamus wound the violet leather straps around his ankles and spun the wheels to take up the slack. With his feet elevated and his body on the floor, Glamus cut the straps at the wrists and fastened the others. Again the wheels spun and Agrippa's body rose in the air and tautened. Glamus ran his hand over biceps and thighs. He moved each wheel until he heard the ratchets click twice. His experienced hands told him that he had given the man all the stretch he could stand. He nodded at Antoninus.

Antoninus was poised expectantly, clapping his hands together in glee. 'I'll hear the confession in private, Glamus. Stand outside the door and permit nobody to enter. When I summon you, release the Tribune and give him his clothes to cover his nakedness and see that he returns to the camp.' He waited for the door to close. His fingers followed the same path as Glamus had charted along the tense hard muscles but where Glamus's had been professionally impersonal, Antoninus's were tender and caressing.

'Tribune Agrippa,' he whispered. 'Instead of converting me to the stern asceticism of Mithras, tonight I shall convert you to the wonderful pleasures of Elah-ga-baal.'

The Tribune's head shook violently in negation.

'Oh, yes.' Antoninus's voice was low. 'Tonight you sacrifice to Elah-ga-baal, and in spite of your wishes to the contrary, you will not be able to help yourself, Tribune Agrippa. You will not be able to resist. No one has ever successfully resisted me, Tribune. You are a man, and as a man you will succumb. The longer you resist me, the longer you shall remain on the rack. But have no fear, Tribune Agrippa, you will not lose your life, but only something you foolishly consider more precious than your life. Have you anything to say to me, Tribune Agrippa?' Antoninus took the linen wad from the Tribune's mouth.

'Only this, Great Caesar! Tonight you are making a grave mistake. You would be wise to kill me, Great Caesar, for I shall never forget nor forgive it.'

Antoninus stuffed the gag back. 'But, oh how you will enjoy it! I shall not kill you because Elah-ga-baal does not demand a blood sacrifice. He demands only joy from his sacrificants and when I have finished, you will have become converted to him. You will see how much more my god has to offer you.'

The Tribune raised his head with difficulty and glared at Antoninus. His eyes burned with a fierce hatred. When the strained muscles of his neck could hold his head erect no longer, it fell back. Antoninus knelt beside the rack.

The stones were cold to his knees but his hands were warm with the heat of Agrippa's flesh. The minutes sped by and one by one the lamps flickered out, leaving only the scent of dead flowers, and a silence that was broken by the straining gasps of air from the man on the rack. Antoninus stood up. His hand lingered on the panting chest of the Tribune.

'Tonight I have given you great joy, Tribune Agrippa, but in so doing I have made an enemy of you. Tonight you hate me as a vile creature who has robbed you of your purity and caused you to break a solemn vow to your god. But I do not hate you, Tribune Agrippa. Perhaps I should regret what I have done, and what I have caused you to do. But I do not. We are flesh, Tribune Agrippa, and no god can say that we cannot enjoy this flesh. Neither of us shall ever forget this night. I do not fear you, for one does not fear that which one desires and which one has enjoyed. Glamus will be here in a moment to unrack you.' He pulled the gag from Agrippa's mouth. 'Cannot you answer me one word?'

With a mighty effort the Tribune raised his head and stared at Antoninus. His breath came in fitful gasps. He closed his lips, worked his jaws and then opened his mouth and spat in Antoninus's face. His head sank back.

Antoninus rushed from the room, stumbling over Glamus who slept stretched before the door.

'Release him.' Antoninus kicked Glamus, jumped over him and ran to the door of his own room. Without waiting for the guards to open the door, he pushed it open and slammed it behind him. Once inside, he threw himself into Hierocles's arms and between hysterical sobs, he confessed. His uncontrolled hysteria mounted to a frenzied delirium in which Hierocles could only console but not punish. Not until daybreak was he able to quiet the raving lunacy of the boy beside him.

28

AFTER THE EPISODE with Agrippa, from somewhere down in the hidden depths of his personality, Antoninus managed to dredge up the remnants of a conscience, and with his usual ability to dramatize every emotion, he chastened himself for everything that he had done in his life, and particularly for what he had done to Agrippa! First he decided to allow Alexander to live. The prospects of his obtaining an heir of his own had vanished during the first night he spent with Annia Faustina and he now realized it would be a physical impossibility for him to produce a son. In order to acquaint himself with various techniques whereby others had achieved it, he had commanded special exhibitions staged that he might watch. Although he became familiar with the methods, he was never able to accomplish them himself.

His impotence with women had affected his former desires, for apart from Hierocles, he had eyes for nobody else. Annia Faustina also filled an important place in his life; she was the mother he had never had. Annia had been wise enough to know that she could never hold Antoninus as a husband but she realised that he needed a mother more than a wife. Soaemias had not been able to forget her own desires long enough to mother Antoninus. Annia Faustina did. He went to her apartments every morning, while Hierocles was busy with the government of Rome and her ample bosom cradled him as it would a little boy. Together they chose her clothes, her jewels and her perfumes. Together they discussed the latest gossip in Rome. He felt free with Annia.

But, more frequently than he desired, his thoughts returned to his wedding night and the picture of the Tribune Agrippa, stretched out on the rack, struggling against the unwelcome desires which Antoninus had stimulated and forced to the surface. Antoninus had revelled in the experience at the time, but from the moment Agrippa spat in his face, he had bitterly regretted it. For the first time, Antoninus's desire had been answered with hatred. There was almost something supernatural about the episode – as if the god Mithras were punishing Antoninus. It preyed on his mind and many times he was on the point of sending for Agrippa, even to apologize to him but when he recalled that forbidding visage and the almost maniacal hatred in the man's eyes, he shrank from ever seeing him again. He had forbidden Eutychianus Comazon to send him to the palace on guard duty.

At Hierocles's suggestion, Antoninus recalled the Senate and appeared among the August Fathers to welcome them back. On this occasion, he was accompanied by the Consul Alexander, still weak and plagued by the weak stomach which was to bother him the rest of his life. But he was alive, and although Antoninus still feared the Alexandrine faction, he was glad that Alexander lived. The boy had nothing more to recommend him than formerly but there was the family tie, deepened by the strong Syrian love of family.

Like most reformed rakes, Antoninus's new virtues sat heavily on his hands. There was nothing exciting to do – at least nothing new and unusual. There were the nights with Hierocles and they were wonderful nights. There were the mornings with Annia Faustina and they were pleasant interludes. There were the afternoons at the chariot races or the games and they were oftimes exciting. There were the evening banquets – and they sometimes promised new and different things to eat. But it was a deadly routine of pleasure without excitement.

He longed for the stimulus of the old days when he had first come to Rome and was able to taste and explore the multitudinous pleasures of the great city. There was the excitation of the baths, the wonderful uncertainty as to who might wander into his cubicle; the thrill of nights spent with Cleander, dressed in the silk robes of a courtesan, head bewigged, body padded, his smile enticing the grimy *sestercii* from the greasy purses of Roman scoundrels and Ostian sailors.

He often wondered about Zoticus. His secret police supplied him with constant reports about him – that he was passing a quiet existence at his villa, surrounded by all the luxury that Antoninus's ample payments guaranteed. Antoninus knew whenever Zoticus bought a new slave and whether his latest lover was male or female. He had wished to see him many times, but he did not trust himself. But surely a person had a right to see a friend – it was not the same as seeking a new companion? Old friends should see each other from time to time. Hierocles had no reason to object, but Hierocles would. Then why ask Hierocles? Surely Caesar could visit an old friend without asking permission.

It took a deal of elaborate arranging so that Hierocles would not know. Hierocles was dispatched to Ostia to welcome an ambassadorial delegation from Mauretania, and no sooner had his imperial litter quit the front courtyard of the palace than Antoninus in a racing chariot driven by Glamus, drove out through the rear. He did not even trust Gordius to drive him because Gordius might tell Hierocles.

Within an hour he was at the entrance to Zoticus's villa, and within minutes they were bedded together. The old thrill was still there but it lasted only a few moments, and Antoninus spent the return trip to Rome in bitter regrets and in anticipation of the scene with Hierocles which he intended to provoke. He confessed to Hierocles but Hierocles was hot and tired from the ceremony at Ostia and was not indulgent. He beat Antoninus without mercy, and left him lying semi-conscious on the floor.

When Antoninus recovered sufficiently to get up and rub the purple bruises Hierocles had left on his body, Hierocles was gone, leaving only a half-finished goblet of wine on the table. This in itself was peculiar because Hierocles never drank. Antoninus shouted through the apartments, and sent Cleander running through the palace but there was no sign of Hierocles. Antoninus stumbled through the halls, seeking some consolation from Annia Faustina.

When evening came and the lamps were lighted in the palace, there was still no Hierocles. Hours passed, the evening banquet was over without Hierocles in his usual place. Antoninus left the table early and rushed to their apartments, hoping to see the beloved face there but the apartments were silently vacant. There had been no word from him.

All the afternoon a detail of Praetorians had been seeking him in the city. For the first time in his life Antoninus was faced with an empty bed and he could not, would not go to sleep without Hierocles, even if it meant he would never sleep again.

Suppose Hierocles had been killed! Suppose Hierocles had been set upon and robbed and left to die in the streets! He sank down in a chair and wept. Why had he been so foolish? What did he care about Zoticus?

There were footsteps in the hall. With a bound he was up from the chair and at the door. It was true – a Praetorian in golden armour and red cape was coming down the hall and he stopped at Antoninus's door.

'Great Caesar!' he saluted.

'Yes, yes,' Antoninus waited breathlessly.

'The Caesar Honoralibus has been located. He is at a house in the Suburra.'

'In the Suburra?' Antoninus screamed his disbelief.

'Yes, Great Caesar.'

Antoninus looked long at the guard. Did he dare ask the next question. He dreaded the answer but he must ask. The words came slowly.

'Is he alone?'

'No, Great Caesar, he is not alone.'

'Then who is with him.'

'The Greek boy, the one they call Apollonius.'

'Not *the* Apollonius? Not that male whore who charges his clients a thousand *sestercii* an hour?'

'The same, Great Caesar.'

The guard had not finished speaking before Antoninus was out of the room. In his mad race down the hall, he called the guards who were stationed before the various apartments to follow him. There was more than a maniple behind him when he gained the main entrance of the palace. He leaped on a Praetorian's horse and whipped the startled animal to a gallop, the guards following him. Luckless citizens who were walking the narrow streets of Rome had barely time to duck into doorways as they galloped past.

When they arrived in the Suburra, one of the guards led Antoninus through the maze of dark streets and stopped before a wine shop, still brilliantly lighted and with the usual collection of Suburran bullies and whores at the tables. They dismounted and the guard led Antoninus through the shop to a door at the back before which was a tray with the remnants of food and two empty *amphorae* of wine.

'Here,' he indicated the door. The maniple of Praetorians filed into the shop, pushing the other occupants out.

Antoninus banged on the rough door with his fists until it was opened cautiously – only a crack – but Antoninus pushed it opened and stepped inside. A startled slave, gaudy with painted face and dyed hair was knocked over. Antoninus pulled him up, shook him and demanded to know where the other Caesar was.

The boy, not recognizing Antoninus in the dim light and certainly not in the dishevelled state he was in, refused to answer. Antoninus continued to shake him until his teeth chattered.

'Where is he?'

'He is not here.' The slave managed to say.

Antoninus turned to the guard who had brought the message.

'Who is lying, you or this slave? You say he is here, the slave says he is not. Whoever is lying shall die.'

The soldier stepped to the front, grabbed the boy from Antoninus's frantic hands, stood him against the wall and slapped his pretty painted face.

'Tell the truth, slave. This is Caesar himself who asks.'

The boy fell to his knees. 'Great Caesar, he is here, yes, but I was forbidden to tell anyone.'

'Then take me there quickly because each moment you delay means a hundred lashes for you tomorrow. Quick!'

The slave, with Antoninus and a dozen soldiers behind him, led them across the room to another closed door. Antoninus held up his hand, warning the guards to stay back. He tried the door but it was bolted from inside.

'He knows your voice,' Antoninus whispered to the slave. 'Say that you have come with more wine, warm towels or whatever it is that you might bring. Knock!'

The boy knocked four times, waited a second, knocked

twice again. Nothing happened immediately, then the door opened. 'What is it, Glycon?'

Antoninus was quick. The sole of his sandal entered the wedge of light and with the soldiers' help he pushed the door open.

The flashily handsome young man who faced them did not lose his air of superior sophistication. 'Who interrupts Apollonius?' he demanded.

'Are you Apollonius?' Antoninus scanned the fellow before him carefully. His long locks were dyed a brilliant shade of red, his eyelids were darkened with kohl and covered with gold dust, the better to set off the violet blue of his eyes. His body had that creamy perfection which betokens long hours of skilful massaging with costly oils.

'I am. And who are you?'

'Marcus Aurelius Antoninus, Caesar – Augustus of Rome.'

'Caesar?' Some of the fellow's arrogance vanished. 'But that is Caesar.' Apollonius pointed to the figure on the bed, one arm hanging over the edge, the hand resting inertly on the floor. It was Hierocles and Antoninus did not need a second look to see that he was dead drunk.

'Caesar, yes, but only Caesar, not Augustus.'

Apollonius fell to one knee. 'Great Caesar.'

Antoninus spoke to the Praetorians and pointed to the kneeling Apollonius. 'Arrest him and bring him to the palace with us.' He walked to the bed and shook Hierocles. 'Wake up, Hierocles! Wake up!'

The inert figure stirred into a more comfortable position, half opened his eyes and muttered incoherently. 'More wine, beloved.'

'Damn you, Hierocles. You call this bitch by my name. Wine? You want more wine? Then here!' He poured the almost full *amphora* over Hierocles. Hierocles struggled to sit up. The douche of wine had brought him partly to his senses. 'Bring them both to my apartments.' He turned and walked out of the room.

The slave who had admitted them was cowering in the anteroom, fearful of the lashes which Antoninus had promised him, but the Antonine, in a gesture of generosity, stripped off one of his heavy gold bracelets and handed it to the boy.

The palace had been alerted to Caesar's absence and it was ablaze with lights when they returned. The crowd of soldiers and palace slaves gathered at the door stared in stupefied amazement to see the Caesar Honoralibus, bound like a condemned slave, being led in. The nails on the soldiers boots clattered in the halls but the bare feet of Hierocles and the luckless Apollonius made no noise. Antoninus led them to his own apartments and when Cleander opened the door he nearly fainted. Hierocles had returned but he was a different Hierocles from the one who had left. Now, with bound hands, bleeding feet, his hair dishevelled, his body stained with dried wine, only his eyes were brave and defiant. All the aplomb of Apollonius had vanished. His brash good looks were still there but his face was livid with fear, the kohl on his eyes streaked on his cheeks, his whole body trembling with an ague of terror. Apollonius sank to his knees but Hierocles stood stiffly erect.

Antoninus did not deign to look at Hierocles but he studied the kneeling Apollonius carefully. He had heard about this fabulous fellow who had made his way to Rome from the brothels of Athens on the strength that he rivalled the world-famed Zoticus. Antoninus had always thought he would some day investigate him and now he was a little sorry he hadn't. The fellow was good-looking in a cheap, flashy way, with a straight Grecian nose, violet eyes and a slightly olive skin which gave the lie to the flaming red hair.

Antoninus gave up his study of the boy and addressed Hierocles.

'First, I shall strip you of all rank. Whatever you are I have made you, and from this moment you shall be as I found you.' He waited to see if his words had any effect on Hierocles. The beautiful face was impassive as ever. 'Carian slave, chariot driver, imposter, dung from the stables who do you think you are?'

Hierocles looked at Antoninus as though he saw him for

the first time. 'Carian slave, chariot driver, imposter, dung from the stables. I am what you say I am, Great Caesar, I have no desire to be anything else.'

'Then tell me why you did this. Why?'

'Have I committed a crime? Have I done more or worse than Caesar did himself this day?'

'Yes, a thousand times worse. I brought you to the palace. I made you Caesar. I raised you from nothing and this is the way you repay me – by bedding yourself with that.' He pointed to Apollonius who trembled even more.

Hierocles allowed his glance to depart from Antoninus for a second, during which he surveyed Apollonius. He shrugged his shoulders.

'I bought you!' Antoninus was stuttering in his rage, 'I bought you body and soul.'

'Oh no, Great Caesar. You bought neither my body nor my soul. Both were given to you.' He stopped suddenly. 'I refuse to discuss our private affairs before an audience.'

'But I command you to.' Antoninus was still shrieking.

'I refuse.'

'I shall have you tortured. Guards, conduct this man to the Mamertine and I shall follow. We shall see if the boot or the rack or molten lead or iron spikes will make him talk.'

'You know they will not, Great Caesar.' Hierocles lips closed in tight lines.

Antoninus knew him well enough to know that though he were tortured to his last breath, his lips would never open. It was useless to try it. He held up his hand.

'Take him not,' he said to the guards. 'If he will not talk, perhaps his pretty friend will.' He motioned to one of the soldiers to bring Apollonius closer. The soldier yanked him to his feet and led him to the chair where Antoninus was sitting.

'The Carian slave who shared your bed refused to talk. Perhaps you will. Not that it will do you much good, but if you tell the truth there is a possibility it might help you. Will you talk?'

'I will, Great Caesar, but first let me say that it is only through ignorance that I am here.'

'Through ignorance!' Antoninus laughed without humour. 'Surely you are well enough experienced in your profession not to claim ignorance.'

Apollonius shook his head so that the red curls waved. 'Great Caesar, I did not know that the man with me was Caesar.'

'Tell me the whole story.'

Apollonius seemed to lose some of his fear. He began haltingly but gained confidence as he spoke. His words had a ring of truth. 'I have rooms behind the tavern of the Doves of Venus in the Suburra.'

'I know the place.'

'Well, shortly after the hour of midday, before I got up, my slave came to my room, opened the curtains and told me that there was a young Roman, richly dressed and handsome as Apollo himself, sitting in the tavern with what seemed to be an inexhaustible supply of gold. He had been drinking steadily and paying for his drinks with gold pieces. My slave suggested that I dress and go out into the tavern and make his acquaintance before the gold was all gone. My slave was right. The man he pointed out was handsome and he was richly dressed. There was a money pouch on the table in front of him. I walked over and sat down beside him. He pushed me away but I treated it as a joke and remained beside him. Then he tried to focus his eyes on me and he mumbled something about my being Zoticus but I told him I was not. His manner changed and he became friendly but he insisted on calling me Zoticus.'

'No compliment to Zoticus,' Antoninus said.

'I could see that he was very drunk and there were some rough characters hanging around, watching him. Some of them would have been only too willing to lure him out of the back door and slit his throat for the gold that was in his purse.'

'A pity they didn't,' Antoninus interrupted, 'but of course you wanted the gold more than they did.'

'Yes, I wanted it but let me say this. I wanted him too. I didn't wish him killed. So I suggested that if he wanted to go on drinking he could come to my rooms at the back of the tavern. At first, like all drunks, he argued about going, but I pulled him up and inched him along to the door of my room. I ordered more wine to be sent in and finally got him into my bedroom where he collapsed on my bed.'

'Whereupon you undressed him.'

'That is part of my business, Great Caesar.'

'And then?' Antoninus leaned forward anxiously.

'And then he came to and called for wine and more wine and more wine.' Apollonius stopped. He looked down at Antoninus, hoping to read some mitigating expression in his face but there was none.

'And did you . . . ?'

'No, Great Caesar. I tried, but the man was too drunk. He had passed into a weeping stage and kept calling me "beloved" and when I touched him he pushed me away.'

'Then you didn't . . . ?'

'No, Great Caesar.'

Antoninus sat back, relieved. 'And you, Hierocles, do you still refuse to talk?'

'What can a Carian slave, a chariot driver, the dung of stables, say to the great Augustus of Rome?'

'Nothing!' Antoninus snapped back at him. He turned to the Centurion who had accompanied the Praetorians to his chamber.

'These men are under arrest.' He pointed to Apollonius. 'Take this one to the camp of the Alban Legion. Say that Caesar makes a present of a thousand-*sestercii* whore to the men of the legion, and that Caesar hopes they all enjoy him before morning. In the morning give him to the whips and see to it that when they have finished with him, not one inch of skin remains on his body. Then take him out and crucify him head down.' He looked at Hierocles's face, hoping for some sign of relentment, but there was none.

'As for the other, do not torture him but crucify him along with the first.'

'Head down, Great Caesar?'

'Yes, he holds his head too high for what he is. Yes crucify him head down and sew his eyelids open so that he cannot close them.'

Still the expression on Hierocles's face did not alter. Antoninus regarded it carefully then, unable to meet the condemning eyes, he dropped his head. He did not look up but he knew from the sounds of the soldiers' boots on the floor that they were forming two lines with Hierocles and Apollonius between them. He heard the order to march and the sound of the hob-nailed boots on the marble. Someone was sobbing. He knew it was Cleander. Was he in love with Hierocles too? He raised his head without realizing what he was doing. Why look at Hierocles now when he could see him on the cross tomorrow? Hierocles on a cross?

'Stop!' The word came without Antoninus's thinking.

The procession halted and the rear guard parted so that Antoninus could see the top of Hierocles's head, over the flaming red locks of Apollonius.

'Turn around.'

Hierocles and Antoninus faced each other. Antoninus got up from the chair and stumbled forward a few paces. All the bitterness had drained from his face. 'Carissimus, have you nothing to say to me? Nothing at all?'

Hierocles stared at him. Slowly he got down on one knee. 'Great Caesar,' the words came slowly. 'I believe it is not unusual for a man condemned to die to be granted one last request.'

'It is customary.' Antoninus tried to keep his voice from quavering. 'Speak, and Caesar may be willing to grant your request.'

'Then Great Caesar, this Carian slave begs but one thing. He asks that as he is nailed to the cross, Caesar will be there to watch and while he hangs there Caesar will remain until he dies.'

'Caesar had planned it that way. Your request is granted. But why do you ask it?'

'That my eyes may rest on Caesar as long as I live, for

301

since the first day I saw him my eyes have worshipped nothing else, neither god nor man.'

A solemn hush came over the assembly. Cleander's sobs had ceased. All Antoninus could hear was his own heart pounding. He continued to stare at the figure in the doorway. He took a step forward, placing his foot searchingly on the floor as if he feared it would give way under him then, with arms outstretched, tears streaming down his cheeks, he ran wildly across the room, threw himself on the floor before Hierocles and clasped his knees.

'Oh, Carissimus! Forgive me! Forgive me for all that I am and all that I have done. Forgive my vile temper, my stupidity, my jealous rage. Forgive me for forgetting, and forgive me for remembering. Forgive me for the precious hours we have spent together and for the miserable hours I have caused you. Forgive!'

Hierocles brought his face down level with the Antonine's. His hands were still bound behind his back and he could not touch Antoninus, but with his cheeks he brushed away the streaming tears. 'Mine is the blame. I deserve to die.'

'Then let me die alongside you.' Antoninus had become maudlin in his sorrow.

'No, little Caesar, let us live.'

Antoninus reached up and drew the sword from the scabbard of the nearest Praetorian. He turned Hierocles round and cut through the bonds. Hierocles's free hands lifted Antoninus up. They were oblivious of the soldiers and the tragic figure of Apollonius. It was Antoninus who suddenly became aware of their audience.

'Go!' he commanded.

'And this man?' The Centurion pointed to Apollonius.

Antoninus smiled ruefully.

'Take him not to the camp, spare him the whips and the cross. Let him live. Conduct him to his home behind the tavern of the Doves of Venus and give him time to pack his belongings. Then conduct him to Ostia and put him on the first ship that sails. Give the captain orders to disembark him at some little fishing port along the coast of Africa –

some poverty-stricken little town where there is nothing but mud houses and a few fishermen. There let him ply his trade.' He turned to Apollonius. 'Were you paid for tonight? I forgot that you live on your body.'

'No, I was not paid.' Apollonius was still fearful but he felt the truth might be more acceptable.

'Then wait.' Antoninus went to a cabinet on the other side of the room, called Cleander and instructed him to open it. From within he took a heavy pouch of gold and carried it back to Apollonius.

'You must have spent some four hours with Caesar,' thus he reinstated Hierocles, 'and I believe you charge one thousand *sestercii* an hour?'

The other didn't answer.

'Speak up!' Antoninus was insistent.

'Some of my clients have been good enough to pay me that.'

'And are you worth it?'

'I have been told so, Great Caesar.'

''Tis more than I ever got. Here are twenty-thousand *sestercii*. When you arrive at wherever you are going, you can advertise yourself as a five-thousand-*sestercii* whore.' He handed the bag to one of the soldiers. 'Take him away and give it to him.'

The boots marched out and the door closed. Antoninus dismissed Cleander. For a long moment he looked at Hierocles.

'Your poor wrists are bruised.'

'So was my heart.'

'Your feet are bleeding.'

'But your lips are smiling and happy again.'

'And so is my heart, beloved.

'Oh, Hierocles, what fools we are. Why do we behave so insanely?'

'Because we love so much.'

'Then why did I go to Zoticus?'

'Because you are Antoninus.' Hierocles essayed a smile.

29

ALTHOUGH THERE WAS neither anger nor recrimina-
tions to mar the night that followed, there was little sleep
for either Hierocles or Antoninus, or for the palace. With
the breaking of dawn, Antoninus had dropped into a fitful
slumber, only to awaken an hour later, shaken by violent,
uncontrollable sobbing. He became incoherent and delirious
and all Hierocles could make out of his frantic ravings was
that Antoninus imagined Hierocles already on a cross.

The screams and wailings from the imperial apartments
woke the entire palace and Julia Maesa, Annia Faustina,
Soaemias, Mamaea, and even the ailing Alexander, attended
Caesar's bedside. Antoninus recognized none of them – he
was still witnessing Hierocles's execution. In his ravings, he
became more violent, mistaking Hierocles and his relatives
for executioners, and although Hierocles did his best to
restrain him it took four husky palace slaves to hold Antoninus down. The Greek physician finally quietened him
with doses of poppy extract. When he awoke, he was quieter
but still incoherent in his ravings. At times he recognized
Hierocles, at others he wept violently for his lover's supposed
death.

Once, Hierocles having gone to summon Cleander, they
returned to find Antoninus had discovered Hierocles's sword
and had pressed it against his chest, poised ready to fall on
it. They managed to take it away from him whereupon he
reviled them both for keeping him from joining Hierocles
on the other side of the Styx.

For several days and nights, Antoninus wandered in a
strange land of horror, peopled by weird phantasies and
heart-breaking imaginations, pursued by the Tribune Agrippa, sword in hand witnessing over and over again in fear-
some detail the torture and crucifixion of Hierocles. Every
imagined nail that entered Hierocles's palms and feet pro-

duced a like torture in him and he cried out time and time again as the nails entered his flesh. He suffered pain, thirst and hunger on the cross the while he was witnessing another die.

With two ailing members of the imperial family on her hands, Julia Maesa was torn between the one and the other. If Antoninus should become mad should she depose him and put the ailing Alexander on the throne? If Alexander should die, would Antoninus continue being Caesar?

Then, as suddenly as the madness had taken him, Antoninus recovered and became himself again, recognizing those about him, able to separate the real from the unreal. But the memories persisted and he called several times a day for Hierocles to reassure himself of the other's actuality, and many times in the night he would waken at the spectre of Agrippa's sword. The sickness, though mental, had produced physical effects and Antoninus, for the first time in his life, appeared worn and haggard.

With his return to normal, Julia Maesa breathed deeply again and allowed herself to be concerned only over Alexander who, since the discontinuance of the poisoned mulsum was regaining some semblance of health.

Once more the palace settled into its usual routine which the convalescent Antoninus no longer found boring. He was seemingly content. The terrible ordeal he had forced upon Hierocles, which in the end had punished himself, had bound the two of them even closer, and the hours of mothering which Annia Faustina gave him endeared her still more to him.

He was now bent on righting as many wrongs as possible and to this end he gave freedom to Cleander and Rufus, neither of whom, however, chose to leave the palace. Cleander was devoted to Antoninus in the same degree that Rufus was to Alexander and although now nominally freedmen, they continued in the same duties they had had as slaves. Cleander, however, replaced his thin silver collar, which had been his badge of slavery, with a gold necklace decorated with carnelians which he had wheedled from Antoninus.

Rufus, once the iron collar had been filed off, continued to dress in the same rough tunics and shabby sandals as before.

Antoninus, in excess of charity, suddenly became interested in the lot of Roman prostitutes, both male and female, and wanted to better their lot. He founded a home for female prostitutes with the purpose of teaching them honourable ways of earning a living – sewing, weaving and cooking – but after the first week attendance dropped off and the women were only too happy to resume their usual places on the streets and in the wine shops. Why work all day for the same amount of money they could earn, more easily and pleasantly, in half an hour? With the boys he had even less luck, for after one look at the cheerless barracks he had intended for them they departed back to their cosy cubicles in the baths and the Suburra.

Life for Antoninus had become principally a matter of the palace and the family. They had never lost their Syrian clannishness. Even as the imperial family of Rome they were still typical Syrians. The family had been a closely-knit group in Emesa, where their kingship and priesthood had lifted them above the rest of the city and they remained a closely-knit group in Rome, where they had never been really accepted by the old Roman Patrician families.

Old Julia Maesa had always had a palace stud, but she had managed her love affairs with a modicum of restraint. She had never allowed the pleasure of the couch to interfere with her driving ambition to rule Rome.

Mamaea had inherited these traits from her mother but the plain faced Mamaea had never had a true love affair, for no man appealed to her unless he first became the property of her sister, Soaemias. Every man Soaemias looked at, Mamaea desired. She was an unattractive woman, tall, gaunt, cold, without any of the compelling beauty of her sister. Her clothes were drab and unbecoming.

Soaemias gratified every wish. Soaemias wanted fine clothes, expensive jewels and handsome lovers. Now she had achieved another desire, for Antoninus, her son, was on the throne and Mamaea and Alexander were still in the background. Soaemias treated her sister with indifference but did not actually dislike her. Mamaea hated Soaemias although she made some attempt to disguise it. But the fire under Mamaea's cold exterior was always smouldering and occasionally it came to the surface. Her resentment was most pronounced when Soaemias had a new lover. So had it been with Caracalla, and with the hundreds of others who had passed in and out of Soaemias's arms. Mamaea was even jealous of the slaves Soaemias possessed. Now it was Aegenax who was the particular object both of her desires and her hatred.

Her jealousy of Soaemias, her frustrated longing for Aegenax, and the fact that she had no position at court were the underlying causes of her sudden flare-up one night at a banquet soon after Antoninus had fully recovered. It started over such an inconsequential thing as the order in which they would mount the platform and take their seats at the formal dedication of Antoninus's statue, that which had replaced the gilded statue of Alexander, at the Praetorian Camp on the morrow.

The Palace Praefect had drawn up a plan of the seating arrangements and the order of the procession. When the whole family, including Alexander who was also able to come to the table, had assembled for the evening banquet, Antoninus casually passed the wax tablets, containing the seating arrangements to his grandmother, asking her to pass it along to the others to brief them for their places the next morning. Julia Maesa glanced at it quickly, found her own place and then passed it to Soaemias. Making sure that Aegenax would be beside her, she tossed it to a green-eyed young slave.

'Pass it to the Lady Mamaea, Lyxon,' she whispered.

Mamaea opened the tablets. One glance at them was the spark that set off the tinder of her smouldering emotions. Antoninus, as Caesar, came first, followed by Hierocles and then by Alexander as son and heir. This disposed of the male members of the family. Annia Faustina as Augusta of

307

Rome followed, then Julia Maesa. Soaemias came behind her mother and accompanying her was Aegenax, in his official position as High Priest of Elah-ga-baal. Next came Soaemias's female slave to carry the train of the long mantle which Soaemias and the imperial ladies always wore. After the slave came Mamaea, at the very end. Antoninus, Hierocles, Alexander and Eutychianus, as host, were in the front row. Annia Faustina, Julia Maesa, Soaemias with Aegenax beside her were in the second row but Mamaea was relegated to the third row along with Soaemias's female slave.

Mamaea's face flamed red, then the colour drained from it. She turned to Lyxon who was standing beside her, waiting to return the tablet to the Palace Praefect. With a loud snap, she closed the ivory covers and instead of handing it to the boy, she flung it in his face – enough that he was a slave of Soaemias to warrant her anger. The corner of the tablet bit into his cheek bringing blood and he, surprised at the blow, staggered backwards, upsetting a tray of food carried by another slave. The man tried to regain his balance, slipped and fell, tipping the whole tray over Antoninus and Hierocles. It was an elaborate concoction of purple sea snails swimming in a rich sauce of lobster and the whole gaudy mess liberally doused Antoninus and Hierocles.

Antoninus rose from the table, sputtering epithets at his aunt but she ignored him and began screaming at Soaemias. 'You and your Persian jackass! Who is he to precede me? Send him back to the gutter where he came from.'

Soaemias smiled aloofly while Antoninus and Hierocles tried to scrub the snails and sauce from their faces. Lyxon was wailing from the cut in his face. Mamaea continued screaming at Soaemias and Julia Maesa started shrieking even louder. Annia Faustina was helping Antoninus and Hierocles and adding her words to the general confusion. With the exception of Alexander who continued to eat placidly, the entire imperial end of the table was in an uproar – a Syrian family brawl, which the Romans present, although not daring to comment openly, sneered at quietly.

'Whore!' Mamaea screamed at Soaemias, 'You'd sleep with any man who would have you.'

'And how you wish just one man would have you! 'Tis common gossip that even your slaves would rather cut their wrists than be forced to sleep with you. No man ever looked at you and no man ever will unless you purchase him at the slave block and blindfold him.'

'I have my reputation to look after. Nobody can say a word against me.' Mamaea tried a tone of righteous indignation.

'And nobody can say a word for you either. Could you but see yourself with your long face, your stringy hair, your flat breasts. Even your breath stinks like the Cloaca Maxima!'

'Sleep with your studs then. Sleep with them and I hope one of them kills you.' Mamaea was screaming and sobbing now at the same time. 'I hope someone kills you soon. You wicked woman.'

Antoninus, with the help of Annia Faustina, had managed to get some of the mess from his face.

'Stop it!' He howled at his aunt and sent a silver platter flying in her direction which she managed to avoid. It landed on the floor with a loud clatter. He followed it with a murrhine goblet which splintered on the edge of Mamaea's couch. With an attempt at dignity, she gathered her plain grey stola about her and stood up, but Antoninus let drive with a handful of purple snails which caught her full in the face. She turned, only to get another bombardment in the rear. Still screaming vituperations, she fled from the room, Alexander following her.

The three remaining women tried to out-talk each other, and in the high-pitched pandemonium, Antoninus and Hierocles started to leave. Antoninus noticed Lyxon trying to staunch the blood from the cut on his face with a napkin. He pushed the slave ahead af him. 'Come to my apartments, boy! My slave Cleander will attend to your face.'

Half way to their apartments, they met Cleander running towards them. He stopped short, amazed at their bedraggled appearance.

'Run and prepare our baths,' Antoninus said. 'And get a bandage for this boy's face. My beloved aunt has been on a rampage tonight!'

Cleander said, 'I was on my way to bring you a message. You have a visitor – a most unexpected one.'

'Who?' Antoninus quickened his steps.

'Eubulus.'

'But only a few days ago we heard from him in Smyrna. He was still searching for the twin of Hierocles.'

'And he has not only found him but arrived almost before his letter. They are in your apartments.'

'And does the one he found look like Hierocles?' Antoninus quickened his steps.

'Really like me?' Hierocles matched his steps to those of Antoninus.

'It would be hard to tell the difference,' Cleander confirmed the fact.

Antoninus ran ahead. 'Hurry, Hierocles, we must see this other paragon. Oh, Hierocles, he may look like you but he cannot be like you. Nobody can be like you.'

But he *was* like Hierocles. Practically identical! Eubulus presented him after they had both made their obeisances to the Caesars, and Antoninus could only stare from one to the other. Eubulus introduced the fellow as Dionexus, a sailor from the city of Miletus, which, being a Carian city might account for his resemblance to Hierocles. There might even be some distant blood relationship. The youth, overwhelmed at being in the presence of two Caesars, quite lost his tongue.

'Oh, what a surprise we shall have for Gordius.' Antoninus was dancing around the bewildered lad. 'I shall be almost jealous of him, beloved, for this Dionexus is so like you. Oh, thank you. You shall be rewarded.'

'I have never failed Caesar yet,' Eubulus answered smugly, wondering how large the reward would be.

'Then go with my thanks, dear Eubulus, and return to the palace tomorrow afternoon after we finish with the ceremonies at the Praetorian Camp. Now leave us, that we may feast our eyes on this phenomenon.'

310

He waited until Eubulus left, then pushed the newcomer beside Hierocles. Separated they were almost identical but side by side there were certain small differences. Hierocles was about half an inch taller and more strongly muscled. His hair was a brighter gold, his skin finer, his nose more Grecian, his eyes a clearer violet. In such close proximity, Dionexus became merely an inferior copy but the close resemblance was there – like two Greek statues, one by the master Praxiteles and the other by a student.

'Off with your tunic,' Hierocles said.

The boy flushed under so many staring eyes – the expectant eyes of Antoninus, the rather anxious ones of Hierocles, the curious ones of Cleander and the startled green eyes of the slave Lyxon who had been entirely forgotten. Slowly Dionexus unpinned the brass fibula that held his tunic at the shoulder and let it fall to his feet.

Antoninus stared . . . and laughed. Hierocles sighed with relief. The resemblance to Hierocles stopped with the face. Where the gods had been over-generous with Hierocles, they had been most niggardly with Dionexus.

'Poor Gordius!' Antoninus laughed. 'How he has been cheated.'

'Not at all.' Hierocles could afford to be jubilant. 'It will make no difference to Gordius. But come, young fellow,' Hierocles flung off his own tunic rather boastfully, 'we bathe.'

'And you attend us, Lyxon of the green eyes,' Antoninus noticed the boy. 'Cleander will clean your wound which seems to be more blood than anything else.' He began to study Lyxon rather carefully.

'Do you notice anything, Hierocles?' he asked.

'Where?'

'Here,' Antoninus pointed to Lyxon. Hierocles studied the slave.

'No.'

'But see! He resembles me. Not as Dionexus does you, but there is a likeness. He is exactly my height and looks to be my weight. His hair is the same colour as mine. His complexion is the same, even though his eyes are different.'

Hierocles shook his head. 'He looks no more like you than I do.'

'Yes, he does,' Antoninus insisted. 'Dressed like me, he would bear a certain resemblance. Tomorrow we shall play a joke on Gordius. He usually arrives with his daily load of meats at the Praetorian Camp in mid-morning, which is when we shall arrive. We shall summon him and when he reports, this Dionexus and Lyxon will be in the room – both dressed as we are. We shall be hiding and it will be worth a million *sestercii* to see the expression on Gordius's face. Lyxon will be talking to Dionexus when Gordius enters and he will see only Lyxon's back but Dionexus's face. Then we shall burst out and surprise him and present him with Dionexus. Oh, 'twill be fun! But come! Into the water. I stink like the mother of all the lobsters and you like their father, Hierocles. After we have finished we'll dress the two in our clothes and give them a rehearsal. Poor Gordius! He'll have only Dionexus but I shall have you, until the day I die.'

'Don't talk that way, Little Caesar.' Hierocles's smile vanished. 'When that day comes, I shall die too. Life without you would be worse than death. I would not desire to live if I could.'

30

GORDIUS WHIPPED THE heaving horse which was nearly spent, praying to the entire pantheon of gods, Roman and barbaric, that the animal would last another few miles. As he turned off the paved road, he slowed down and gave the horse a moment's respite. According to the hasty directions he had received, this should be the right place – he was to turn off on a narrow road at the left just beyond the fifteenth milestone. Well, he had passed the milestone and this was the first road on the left. About a quarter of a mile away, up in the hills, he could see the tiled roofs of a villa, reddened by the lights of the fast setting sun. He was not sure it was the right one but he would try. He whipped the poor beast again but the animal could not increase its pace. It was plodding wearily now, putting one slow hoof before the other.

The heavy wooden gates to the villa were closed and Gordius cursed the length of time it took for a slave to emerge from the gatehouse. The man, a handsome negro and white hybrid was wiping the crumbs of his evening meal from his mouth. He sauntered leisurely around to the front of the closed gates.

'Hurry, man!' Gordius tried to hasten the slave's lagging footsteps. 'Is this the villa of Aurelius Zoticus?'

'It is, but my master won't see you. He receives no visitors tonight.'

'He'll receive me. Open the gates!' Gordius drew his sword and threatened the man. 'I come directly from Caesar with a message for your master. Open up. Don't make me get down and run you through.'

'He said not to let anyone in.' The slave hesitated between his duty to his master and the obvious authority of the man who said he came from Caesar.

'I don't care if he's bedded with six women. Where is he?'

The slave pointed to a leather curtained doorway on the other side of the open *peristylium* and Gordius ran to it, trampling the roses and myrtle, splashing through the marble pool rather than skirting it. He gained the doorway, lifted the curtain and stood for a moment on the threshold, gazing into the brilliantly lighted room. It was an awkward time to interrupt a man but every moment counted. The olive-skinned back and the heaving flanks could belong to none other than Zoticus, whose preoccupation with the owner of the white legs which were wound around his back, had prevented him from hearing.

'Aurelius Zoticus!' Gordius called out, whereupon the man turned quickly and in so doing disengaged himself from the woman.

'Who are you and what do you want here? Get out of my room or I'll have my slaves flog you. Who let you in?'

'It doesn't matter. I am Gordius. We made the trip from Nicomedia together.'

'So you're Gordius! I've not finished and by Isis I always finish what I start. Come back later.'

'There'll be no "later" Zoticus. Send the lady away. Get her out of here if you value your life.' He looked past Zoticus to the woman on the bed. 'Get out! Caesar's business cannot wait.'

The woman, frightened now, gathered one of the silk sheets around her and scampered from the room.

'What's the meaning of this? What does Caesar want now?'

'Nothing, but if you want to live listen to me. Dress yourself, take what gold and jewels you have in the house.'

'But Caesar! Caesar protects me.'

'Not this Caesar, Zoticus. Antoninus is dead, murdered! Alexander the Stupid is now Caesar, and that straight-back slut Mamaea is Augusta.'

'My little Caesar dead?' Zoticus put his hands to his eyes to stay the tears that were starting. 'Tell me, Gordius!'

'There is no time. Dress yourself. Order two horses saddled. I have work for you to do and only you can help me because in all Rome only you and I are left who loved the Antonine and Hierocles.'

Zoticus rummaged in the clothes press, found a pair of leather trousers, pulled them on and slipped his feet into a pair of heavy sandals. He took a plain linen tunic and a heavy woollen cloak but he still behaved as a man stupefied.

'And now your gold.' Gordius saw a leather bag and held it while Zoticus opened a chest and filled the bag with gold and several heavy, jewelled bracelets. Gordius dragged him from the room and to the back of the villa where he sensed the stables must be. He chose two of the strongest-looking horses, had the bewildered hostler saddle them, and hoisted Zoticus up. They rode down the drive into the fast gathering dusk.

314

'Why do you do all this to save me, Gordius?' Zoticus had recovered sufficiently from his shock to ask questions. 'We were never close friends.'

'Because you once loved the little Antonine and I have work for you to do. It is fitting that the only two men who cared for him and Hierocles should bury them.'

It was a distance of some twenty *milliae* from the villa of Zoticus to the little farm which still had the name of Hierocles carved over the lintel. On the way Gordius told the story of the day – the last day of Marcus Aurelius Antoninus Caesar, Augustus of Rome.

Perhaps Zoticus had heard of the troubles Antoninus had been having with the Praetorians? Yes, Zoticus had heard but he thought they were all solved. So had Antoninus, Gordius nodded, or he would not have gone to the Praetorians' camp this day to dedicate his own statue, which replaced that of Alexander. Gordius had arrived at the camp around mid-morning, his dray filled with the sausages, hams and bacon which he supplied daily to the garrison. Upon arrival, he had been told to report immediately on orders of Caesar, to the Officers' Quarters, to a certain small room off the guardroom. Gordius, who still wore the uniform of Praefect, was a familiar figure in the camp and still warranted a salute wherever he went and he returned the Praetorian's salute as he climbed down off the cart.

He arrived in the designated room to find it empty except for Hierocles and Antoninus, who were in a conversation at the farther end of the room. Hierocles waved to Gordius and bade him come closer but Antoninus did not turn around. When Gordius neared them and Antoninus turned, Gordius was dumbfounded to see that it was not Antoninus but a pretty green-eyed boy whom Gordius recognized as one of Soaemias's slaves. This was evidently one of the Antonine's little tricks but much to Gordius's amazement, when Hierocles spoke, it was not Hierocles at all although the man, dressed in the imperial robes with the silver laurel leaves on his head, was enough like Hierocles to be Hierocles himself.

Suspecting some trap, Gordius started to draw his sword

but before he had it out of the scabbard, he heard loud shouts of laughter and the real Caesars came running out from behind a stack of armour. They fell upon Gordius, throwing their arms around him and laughing at his puzzled expression until Antoninus reminded him of his promise to find the exact replica of Hierocles on the day he had dismissed Gordius as Praefect. This, then, this fellow by the name of Dionexus was the twin of Hierocles which Antoninus had promised! Antoninus and Hierocles had had their joke so Gordius was now presented with the second Hierocles for his own.

They were still laughing when the sound of women's voices shrieking imprecations at each other came from the guardroom. Antoninus airily dismissed the altercation and remarked that his mother and aunt were starting again where they had left off last night. There had been a banquet – they had quarrelled. It was unimportant. Antoninus had decided to let them finish it between themselves.

Antoninus paid little attention to the squabbling ladies and made no attempt to stop it. He was going to the *latrinae*, he said because he might be sitting up on the platform for an hour or more once the ceremony began. Hierocles started to accompany him but Antoninus waved him back.

A few moments after Antoninus had left they heard a high-pitched scream which was suddenly cut off. Hierocles had only one word – 'Antoninus' – and ran out of the room. Gordius was stepping through the door himself when he saw the leather curtain of the *latrinae* raised and a soldier came out. He recognized him as one of the Tribunes – a man by the name of Agrippa. He was waving a bloody sword and shouting and as soon as he saw Hierocles, he was upon him. Hierocles was unarmed and no match for Agrippa's sword. He fell to the floor and Agrippa had to place one sandalled foot on Hierocles's body to withdraw his sword. To the running Praetorians who issued from the guardroom Agrippa was shouting. 'I've killed the Beast of Rome and his stud.'

Gordius went back into the room and dropped the curtain. He heard the Praetorians passing and their shouts.

'Caesar is dead. *Ave*, Alexander Caesar!'

'Caesar is dead and his husband too!'

'*Ave* Alexander Augustus!'

'So with all depraved monsters like the Antonine!'

'Rome wants no painted queen to govern her.'

'Let us throw their bodies to the mob.'

'No, let them stay here. There is more important work to be done. Let us first proclaim Alexander Emperor. Then let the mob have the bodies.'

Above the clamour of the Praetorians, Gordius heard a woman's shriek. He peered out between the curtain and the door jamb. Soaemias, followed by Aegenax, came running down the hall, only to be spitted on Agrippa's sword. The other soldiers hacked at Aegenax, seeming to take a sadistic delight in mutilating his face and body. One of them pulled up the priestly robes and emasculated his corpse, waving the bloody trophy high in the air. Leaving Soaemias and Aegenax on the floor beside Antoninus and Hierocles, they continued on to the guardroom from whence came other and even louder shouts of '*Ave*, Alexander Caesar'. Gordius could hear Mamaea's hysterical shrieks above the rest.

Gordius motioned to the two impostors to follow him and they ran down the hall towards the *latrinae*. Hierocles's body was lying in the doorway and Gordius gathered it up into his arms. One glance informed him that Hierocles was dead. Antoninus was lying on the floor, blood flowing from a deep gash in his throat that had severed the jugular vein but his face was untouched and a curious smile still lingered on his lips.

A promise! Gordius remembered it now. A promise he had made to Caesar that these two should lie together under the stone pines at the little farm. He searched the room frantically with his eyes. Yes, it was there – the big wooden chest filled with ashes which military law demanded be kept in every *latrinae* to be sprinkled down the holes by every soldier each time he used one. Gordius flung open the chest. Fortunately it was nearly empty. With the assistance of Dionexus and Lyxon, he placed the bodies of Antoninus and

317

Hierocles inside and closed the cover. He had to work fast and think even faster. Between the three of them they carried the chest out into the hall. The clamorous uproar was still going on in the guardroom.

Godius hesitated in his tale.

'And what next?' Zoticus drew abreast of him. They were walking their horses a few paces to conserve the animals' breath.

Still Gordius hesitated. He was not proud of what he had done and yet he had done it for Antoninus and perhaps even more for Hierocles. He had fallen upon the unarmed Dionexus and Lyxon with his sword. Yes, he assured Zoticus, he had killed them quickly and mercifully but he could not forget the look in Dionexus's eyes that accused him with the very look of Hierocles. Gordius purposely did not mar the face of Dionexus but only that of Lyxon now mutilated beyond all possible identification. Yes, Gordius had hated to do it but he had a promise to carry out and the life of a slave and the life of a sailor from Miletus weighed very little in the scale against his promise to Caesar Augustus.

He abandoned the bleeding bodies on the floor and ran down the deserted corridor to a door that opened on the back. Outside he saw a maniple of Praetorians in undress uniform, sweeping a corner of the parade ground. Gordius called them over to him and, in his old uniform as Praefect, they ran to obey him.

'You there, help me, quick! I must take the big chest out and Caesar has already arrived. I don't want him to see a latrine chest being carried away as his procession rounds the corner. So back and get it for me and bring it to the south gate and help me load it into my cart.' He distributed a handful of coins among the men. They dropped their brooms, ran to get the chest and by the time Gordius had his cart at the door they were ready to load it on. Then he had driven away over the Roman road, the heavy chest bumping on the bottom of the cart.

He would have dug the grave then and buried the chest with all that was left of the two Caesars but he feared that his slaves would see him and suspect he was burying treasure and later after he had left, they would disinter the chest and reveal its true contents. So he had had it carried into the farmhouse and locked it in the inner room beside the palace bed with its silken sheets and mattress of rose leaves.

It was then that he had thought of Zoticus. Surely the true whereabouts of the Antonine's corpse should be known by more than a former slave chariot driver. Yes, Zoticus! Zoticus had been beloved by Antoninus. It was fitting that there should be two mourners at Caesar's burial – Zoticus for the Antonine, and Gordius for Hierocles. If the gods were with him, he could reach Zoticus before he was arrested, as arrested he surely would be.

Zoticus and Gordius quickened their horses as they saw the moonlight reflected on the armour of a maniple of guards coming down the road towards them. It was too late now to take shelter in the trees. To do so would evoke suspicion. Gordius whispered to Zoticus.

'We'll brazen it out. Let me handle this and you agree with whatever I say.'

As the soldiers approached, the Centurion recognized the uniform of Praefect which Gordius wore. Fortunately he did not recognize Gordius himself. The soldiers drew up their horses, blocking the road so Gordius and Zoticus could not pass, but the Centurion saluted and Gordius returned the salute, hailing them.

'Where to, fellows?' Gordius was jovial. 'It's a nice night to be riding but you seem a little far from Rome for Praetorians.'

'We go to arrest Aurelius Zoticus at a villa near the fifteenth milestone.'

'Zoticus, Zoticus?' Gordius tipped his helmet back and scratched his head. 'The name's familiar. Where have I heard it before.'

'Stallion and stud to the monster – he who was Caesar.'

Gordius nodded his head. 'Ah yes, now I remember. 'Twas common gossip that the bastard was hung like a stallion too.

But Caesar's got another one now, one Hierocles who used to drive for the Greens.'

'No more. We rid Rome of him today along with Caesar. Oh, the mob had a rare time with them today. They dragged the bitch's body through the streets of Rome along with that of his husband. And the things they did with those lifeless corpses! Ay, the most comical things you've ever seen. They laid them out in the Forum in all the positions they used in their depraved practices. Then when the mob tired of that they cut off Caesar's head and paraded it on a spear before they threw the bodies into the Tiber.'

'Good,' Gordius agreed. 'And who is Caesar now?'

'Ay, we've got a real emperor now. He's a fine upstanding young fellow, this Alexander. The Antonine's gone and every one of his hangers-on too, all the Palace Guards and the filthy priests. Now we're on our way to get Zoticus.'

'*Ave* Alexander!' Gordius's shout left no doubt as to its sincerity. 'And now, fellows, make way for me. This is Prince Shaipur, special envoy to Rome from the Indus. If he can't see one Caesar he can well see another.'

The soldiers parted and Gordius and Zoticus rode through. When they could no longer hear the maniple's hoofbeats, Gordius turned to Zoticus. 'Wasn't any too soon, was I?'

'You saved my life. My gratitude.'

It was fully night when they arrived at the little farm-house, deserted now in the silvery moonlight. Gordius carefully reconnoitred. There was nobody around, not even the slaves who had evidently run off to Rome to join the Saturnalia in the city. They tethered their horses in a grove of trees, well hidden in the shadows and made their way to the house on foot. Gordius opened the door slowly, half fearful that there might be soldiers within but the house was empty. There was no sound but the monotonous drip of the water clock. He led Zoticus into the bedroom and pointed to the dark outline of the chest on the floor.

'The Caesars.' He laid his hand on the chest. 'The little Antonine! He robbed me of something I wanted very much and yet I loved him. Let Rome say of him what it will, he was good. He had his faults and we all know what he was but was it any worse that he preferred to bed himself with legionaries than with Suburra whores? And with him is the other Caesar, Hierocles the chariot driver! Yesterday they were all powerful. Today they rest in a chest of ashes. Come, Zoticus, between the two of us we can carry this.'

'He never made me Caesar.' Zoticus stared down at the dark shadow of the chest. 'I wonder why.'

'Perhaps because you did not love him as much as Hierocles did.'

'I could only love him in my own fashion, Gordius.' He stooped to pick up one end of the chest and Gordius lifted the other. They stopped but once and that was at the barn for spades. From there they carried their burden down into the glade by the pool.

The moonlight, through the pine branches, striated the ground with splashes of black and white and by its light they dug the hole wide and deep. When only their heads appeared above the ground, Gordius signalled to Zoticus to stop. He jumped up and reached down a hand for Zoticus. They edged the chest over the deep hole.

Zoticus studied the heavy dark wood of the cover. Slowly he sank to his knees beside the chest.

'Just one glance, Gordius. Just one! I loved Antoninus. I loved him because he was Caesar and because his love brought me money and power. His love lifted me from being a common legionary to the most powerful position in Rome but when he tired of me, he did not desert me. Grant me one last look, Gordius.'

Gordius bowed his head.

Zoticus lifted the cover and the moonlight illuminated the inside of the chest. Antoninus lay, his head pillowed on Hierocles's arm. His cheek, in the narrow proximity of the chest, was against the cheek of Hierocles. The half smile was still on his face. He seemed content – content to lie through all the centuries in the close security of Hierocles's arms.

Zoticus pulled a kerchief from his sleeve and brushed the ashes from Antoninus's face. 'He always hated anything dirty,' he said as he handed the kerchief to Gordius who performed the same service for Hierocles. Together they fitted the cover back. They lowered it into the ground and then there was only the sound of their spades and the clods of earth as they struck the wood. When the hole was filled, they strewed it with pine needles.

They made their way back to their horses.

'Ride south, Zoticus,' Gordius advised, 'and I shall ride north. Get out of Italy as I shall and do not return. There still remains one thing for me to do to carry out the Antonine's wishes and some day I shall return to do it, but not now.'

They separated and rode in different directions. Of all the Antonine circle, only Gordius and Zoticus survived him.

EPILOGUE

THE SPRING WARMTH of an Italian sun shone down on the little roadside tavern and the drifting pink petals of an almond tree showered the rough tiles of its roof. A young man entered the wide open door – a fellow such as would have caused Antoninus to look twice and his fingers to itch, for he was tall, handsome and well formed. His arms were full of hyacinths, white, red and purple and he buried his face in them, half intoxicated by their smell. Another fellow followed him, this one as strikingly blond as the first was dark. They both had the polished skin of boys who spent much time in the baths. The blond boy fumbled in his pocket and produced a worn copper sestercius. He placed it on the counter.

'Two cups of wine,' he said, 'and if the money's not enough, water it well.'

The tavern keeper looked at the flowers and then at the boys' faces.

'Whose garden you been robbing?'

'Nobody's,' the dark boy spoke. 'Drusus and I were swimming in the pool up by the abandoned farmhouse and we discovered that the whole glade is filled with these blossoms. They were never there before because we know the place well. We often come out from Rome to spend the day there. So, we picked them to carry back to our room in Rome.' He turned and smiled at his companion. 'Drusus loves flowers.'

NOTES

DION CASSIUS: Epitome of Book LXXX

It was in this connexion that he won the Emperor's favour by a most remarkable chance. It seems that in a certain race,

323

Hierocles fell out of his chariot, just opposite the seat of Sardanapalus (Dion often calls Antoninus, Sardanapalus) losing his helmet in his fall, and being still beardless and adorned with a crown of yellow hair, he attracted the attention of the Emperor and was immediately rushed to the palace; and there by his nocturnal feats, he captivated Sardanapalus more than ever and became exceedingly powerful.

ibid.

It was thought a small thing that his (Hierocles's) mother should be brought to Rome by soldiers, and numbered among the wives of ex-consuls, she a slave.

ibid.

He (Antoninus) wished to have the reputation of committing adultery so that in this respect too, he might imitate the most lewd women and he would often allow himself to be caught in the act, in consequence of which he used to be violently upbraided by his 'husband' and beaten so that he had black eyes. His affection for this 'husband' was no light inclination, but an ardent and firmly fixed passion, so much so that he not only did not become vexed at any such harsh treatment, but on the contrary loved him more for it and wished to make him Caesar in very fact.

ibid.

Aurelius Zoticus, a native of Smyrna, who was also called cook after his father's trade incurred the emperor's love. This Aurelius not only had a body that was beautiful all over, seeing that he was an athlete, but in particular he greatly surpassed all others in the size of his private parts.

. . . caused a drug to be administered to him in wine that abated the other's (Zoticus) manly prowess. And so Zoticus, after a night of embarrassment, was banished from the palace.

The husband of this 'woman' (Antoninus) was Hierocles, a Carian slave, once the favourite of Gordius, from whom he had learned to drive a chariot.

He (Antoninus) married many women, yet it was not that he had any need of them himself but simply that he wanted to imitate their actions when he should lie with his lovers.

He used his body both for doing and allowing many strange things which no one could endure to tell or hear of.

He went to the baths and there committed his indecencies, always standing nude at the door of his room as the harlots do and shaking the curtain which hung from rings, while in a soft and melting voice he solicited the passers-by.

He would go to the taverns at night, wearing a wig and there ply the trade of female hucksters . . . He would collect money from his patrons and give himself airs over his gains; he would also dispute with his associates in this shameful occupation, claiming that he had more lovers than they and took in more money.

The circumcision which was carried out was a part of the priestly requirements of Elagabalus and he accordingly mutilated many of his companions in a like manner.

Dion Cassius refers to Antoninus as Sardanapalus, Tiberinus.

THE AMAZING EMPEROR HELIOGABALUS, by J. Stuart Hay.

The one real romance of the boy's (Antoninus's) life was with the fair-haired chariot driver, Hierocles. His identity is somewhat involved, although Dion Cassius states that he was a Carian slave, by profession a chariot driver. One day he was thrown from his chariot, right against the imperial pulvinar and lost his helmet. Elagabalus was there, and at once noted the perfect profile and curly hair of the athlete. He had him transferred to the palace where on account of a similarity of taste, the intimacy soon ripened into love and that again, according to Xiphilinus, into a contract of marriage.

Hierocles must have been the best and certainly was the most powerful of that army of sycophants which always thronged the Roman Court. We have no complaints against his exercise of authority.

He was a good son and in his prosperity was in no way ashamed of his mother. He openly purchased her from her owners and sent a company of the Praetorian Guard to bring her to Rome, there placing her amongst the women whose husbands had been Consuls.

Certainly Hierocles had no cause to fear; Elagabalus's affection was too feminine, too deep-rooted to do more than tease the man from whose hands, like many another woman in history, he was more willing to take ill-usage and stripes, if only they were signs of jealousy or proofs of affection.

Like Messalina Antoninus measured his attractiveness by the amount of gold he could carry home after his expeditions to the various lupanars of the city.

. . . a species of matrimony with the chariot driver Hierocles calling himself wife and empress – and that he was not attached to this man alone but to many others for whom inquisition had been made throughout the Empire on account of their looks and ability to satiate his mania more satisfactorily.

Antonine had his moments when he imitated a virgin at bay, still others when he expected to be a mother. He loved to dress himself in the clothes of women, even in the customary undress of the courtesan.

Modern investigation of such psychopathic conditions inclines us to admit that the boy was a sort of nymphomaniac.

The world has instinctively condemned Elagabalus, though probably without knowing why they did so.

The two chariot drivers, Protogenes and Gordius were made supervisors of his (Antoninus's) Sports. It is quite possible that he admired and liked these men for their proficiency in sport and that unwholesome minds saw more in the friendship than was warranted. Of Protogenes we hear no more. Gordius – probably the same person as above – was made Praefect of the Watch during the next year.

He (Antoninus) had conceived a notion of rendering his God (Elah-ga-baal) absolutely supreme by means of alliance with the worship of Vesta. Now this goddess and her Sacred Stone or Phallus, called the Palladium, her shields and bucklers, had been sent to Troy direct from heaven. Aeneas had brought them to Latium and they were the head and centre of Roman greatness. Pallas, or Vesta, was too powerful to be absorbed in the ordinary way. Antonine therefore considered that his god, being unmarried, might well acquire possession of Vesta by a matrimonial alliance. As Pontifex Maximus, he was head of the Vestal worship and had a perfect right to enter her shrine when and how he pleased. Antonine certainly did go to her shrine at this time, and took the Sacred Fire, carrying it to the Eliogabalium. Lampridius asserts that the high priestess, being jealous of the loss of her charge, tried to palm off a false vessel upon him but that the Emperor saw the deceit and broke the jar in contempt for the foolish fraud. He also transferred the sacred stone at the same time and in pursuance of his plan, celebrated the nuptials on which he had set his heart. Being himself free, he decided to marry one of the Sacred Vestals from the shrine of the god's new wife . . . one Aquilia Severa, a woman no longer in the first flush of youth, to judge by her effigy, but one whom his religious as well as personal predilections pointed out as a fitting consort. Pallas and Elah-ga-baal were united in a heaven-ly union like so many others amongst Syrian and Egyptian deities.

ibid.

But even the Senate seems to have protested and a plot in which Pomponius Bassus and Silius Messala were implicated (probably inspired by that upright lady Julia Mamaea) was set on foot. It was an attempt to substitute some other personage for the youth who knew so little of Roman feeling as to commit this act of sacrilege. These two men were well known busybodies who had already dethroned one Emperor and were obviously anxious for further employment in the same direction. Unfortu-nately for them, the plan was discovered and their secret court, held to consider the Emperor's actions, raided. They were im-mediately arraigned before the Senate and condemned for the crime of *lèse-majesté* or treason, probably both.

The result was that the Emperor published a statement, by no means conciliatory in character, which announced that his God liked not so martial a wife (as Vesta-Pallas-Minerva) in consequence of which he had decided to return her to her own shrine and send for Astarte from Carthage instead. Tanit of the Carthaginians, Juno Coalistis or Magna Mater, as she was called in Italy . . . Generally she was called a moon goddess. As queen of the heavens, she directed the moon and the stars. Latterly in Rome, she had been identified with the cult of Mithras which had taken such a hold on the popular mind and was now at the summit of its power. Undoubtedly the introduction of this God-dess into their midst, especially since it could hurt no local superstition, would be a popular move and Elah-ga-baal would gain the reflected glory, at least among the ignorant and reli-gious minded. From the Emperor's own point of view the mar-riage was fitting, since the queen of the heavens was not only second in authority to the sun but was also rich, and with her came her treasure.

About the same time, Antonine married again, presumably

at the instigation of his grandmother and to gain the allegiance of the patrician classes. His bride was the widow of that busy-body Pomponius Bassus, lately deceased. The lady, though by no means in her first youth (she being about forty-five years of age) was of imperial lineage. Undoubtedly the Emperor soon tired of her charms, which were scarce likely to please a boy of eighteen, and consequently he did not keep her long. She was a friend of his grandmother's . . . and fell in with Maesa's plan of appointing a sort of nuptial guardian to the boy.

Both Maesa and Mamaea were now working together, for both were determined to consolidate in their hands the power that was Antonine's by right. From this moment there is one continuous policy of corruption, vilification and grab, while the women, their greedy paws ever stretching out, filch from the boy his popularity, his friends and his reputation.

The trump card in this game was played by Maesa's diplomacy; she knew that the only way to win the boy was to attach herself to his religious ideals and she therefore seems to have fallen in with his scheme for the union of Elah-ga-baal and Urania.

Very insidiously she wormed her way into his boyish confidence, lulled his mind to rest and then suggested her great plan: the appointment of Alexianus to assist in the secular affairs which so sadly hampered the Emperor's spiritual and sacerdotal functions.

(Re Alexianus)

Lampridius has produced a spasmodic and unenlightened discourse on his hero's (Alexianus's) moral qualities. He assures us that Alexander had a regal presence, great flashing eyes and the nature and health of a soldier. Unfortunately this description is in no way borne out by portraits still extant. Alexander, in the Vatican bust, has certainly the appearance of strength but it is such as is possessed by a lusty coal-heaver, with a bull neck and a thick skull; the undecided features of the face, the weak mouth and chin, the low forehead, half hidden by the hair, all betoken mild-mannered vacuity rather than manliness. It is the face of a half-caste Phoenician such as he chanced to be. Alexander was an absolutely perfect tool for his grandmother's schemes.

The Emperor (Antoninus) was used to her (Maesa's) wiles;

she had tried cajoling him before but had failed; this time it was on the score of his religion, on the necessity that he should devote his full energies to the furthering of this great and all-embracing scheme, that she attacked him. Maesa must at this time have been close on fifty years of age and we are assured on all hands that she was in close alliance with her daughter Mamea who had long since conceived a holy horror, not only for the sins of her nephew but for the person of the sinner. So strongly was she convinced of her righteousness, that she had already thought it her bounden duty to attempt the corruption of the guards and to support the plots, all and sundry, which disaffected functionaries might attempt against the person of the Emperor.

The question of Seius Carus (who attempted the corruption of the Alban Legion) is one of considerable interest in this point of view. The gentleman was wealthy and of the patrician order, which did not prevent him from spending his money freely amongst the soldiery. Unfortunately he hit upon the wrong legion, the body which was now quartered near Rome and had joined Antonine so readily at Apamea. In the year 220, this legion had set up an inscription to Antonine's Victoria Aeterna, which monument had expressed the greatest possible devotion to the reigning Emperor, and gave the lie direct to those stories of Dion and Lampridius which assert that as early as the winter of 218, the soldiers cordially hated Antonine and placed all their hopes on Alexianus.

Lampridius gives a very poor reason for this – because, forsooth, they could not stand the thought that he was as ready as they themselves were to receive pleasure through all the cavities of the body. Dion relates Seius's trial, and informs us that the gentleman suffered for a crime which was absolutely unknown to any other legal system except it be the ecclesiastical.

But to return to the imperial ladies. They were spending much time searching out disaffected subjects; further, they were making much use of Antonine's most foolish resolve to cut down military expenditures at the price of possible unpopularity.

In the month of June, 221, the Dowager Empress propounded a scheme; an attempt, she said, to transfer the odium of Antonine's neglect in secular matters to other shoulders and to set the boy free to carry out his great policy for the advancement of

329

religious unity throughout the world. The work which he proposed was great and important and had been neglected for the good of the state. Now, to neglect the great god angered him and those to whom the family owed their position. To neglect the affairs of state angered the people and gave rise to disturbances – of this Antonine had had recent examples. Surely it would be advisable to appoint a co-adjutor in the affairs of state, and for obvious reasons, one of his own family, someone who would naturally have no other desire than to serve Antonine; there was a relative ready and willing. Why did he not adopt Alexianus? Perhaps the boy was insignificant. Well, so much the better, but at any rate, he might be used to advantage. All this was most plausible and may have blinded the Emperor for the moment but we can easily understand from what we know of Antonine's nature that even if he saw through the very specious pleas here put forward, he would enjoy meeting his grandmother on her own ground.

He was hard pressed. He was more anxious for the fate of his god than for the fate of the Empire.

There had been two plots to dethrone Antonine, and Julia Mamaea was behind both to replace him with Alexianus. Why not take the boy into his own keeping, adopt him as Maesa suggested and by taking their tool from their hands, neutralize the influence of both aunt and grandmother at one swoop. He could then train him in his own way. Alexianus was twelve years old at the time.

His friends knew that he was dealing with two able and crafty women but he refused to listen to them, for some time early in July, Antonine took his cousin Alexianus to the Senate and there in the presence of the women, this boy of sixteen summers, went through the solemn ceremony of adopting the child of twelve. He then solemnly declared his intention of training his 'son' himself, fitting him for the business of Empire early in order that he might be free from solicitudes about a successor. He told the assembled fathers that he was acting on the commands of the great God.

The name Alexander was then imposed upon Alexianus.

Antoninus did not give Alexianus any governmental powers although he gave him the titles of Augustus, Emperor and Caesar.

Maesa and Mamaea must have been wild with rage at having

gained so little and it must have been a very disagreeable awakening when they found that their plan had not succeeded. Maesa was now genuinely frightened. She thought that Antonine's religious mistake had created a real wave of bad feeling in the city, and that if anything should happen to Antonine, her position would be gone for good and all. With patience and determination, she set to work to gain for herself, and for Alexander also, what had not accrued when the adoption took place.

The boy was utterly unresponsive to the affection which Antonine was anxious to lavish on him, utterly incapable, so the Emperor said, of any sort of training at all for the position he was to occupy.

It must have been very annoying for the Emperor to be saddled through his own stupidity with a nincompoop of twelve. Were he one half as nasty as Lampridius asserts, we can well imagine the devil in Antonine striving to undermine his cousin's prejudices, trying to persuade him to run, dance, play; to wake him up from the self-satisfaction which so ill became his years. All of this, we are told, Antonine did under the generic terms of corrupting his morals which is, after all, the sum total of Antonine's enormities.

Here Mamaea stepped in. She was not going to stand by and see her work dissipated. The Bassiani developed young, and Alexander had no desire to change. His character was moulded and he had no desire to change or to enjoy the gifts which the gods had given to men. Antonine thought that something might be done for the cousin he pitied by turning him loose; he found it was no good and soon lost patience. Friction arose at every turn.

Antonine resolved to get rid of Alexander. To do this, however, he had to quarrel openly with his relatives and by a *coup d'état*, regain paramount authority in the state.

On the 10th of July, he sent to the Senate, ordering the fathers to withdraw the title of Caesar which he had conferred on Alexander and which they had confirmed. The Senate were silent.

At this time, Antonine became suspicious of his old advisers as he had seen them paying court to the young Caesar and his mother. He dismissed them and put men into offices, especially those about the palace who, from a personal and too intimate relation, he felt he could rely on. As ever, such appointments were a gross mistake. As mere friends, such men would have tended to his undoing – as officials, they tended to revolution.

Following up his command to the Senate, Antonine sent messengers to the army. They demanded that the army should relieve Alexander of the title of Caesar and the messengers were charged to deface the statues of Alexander in the camp. This was unwise because the property belonged to the regiments and not to the Emperor.

Next comes the record of an attempt to assassinate Alexander. Herodian does not refer to it at all and Dion thus 'Much as Sardanapalus loved his cousin, when he began to suspect everybody and learnt that the general feeling was veering towards Alexander, he dared to change his resolution and did all in his power to get rid of him. He tried one day to have him assassinated and not only did not succeed but nearly lost his own life in the attempt as well.'

From Lampridius, we learn that Antonine sent men to assassinate Alexander and also sent letters to the boy's governors (who were working for Mamaea) with promises of wealth and honours if they would kill their charge in any way they thought best, either in the bath, by poison or the sword.

Antonine went to his gardens for an afternoon's exercise in chariot driving, without taking any guard. The soldiers, upon hearing of this, were roused to the highest pitch of anger. They ran, some to the palace where Alexander was living with his mother and some to the gardens where they would find Antonine; their intention being to carry out Mamaea's wishes on the person of the Emperor. Soaemias went to warn Antonine. Antonine was preparing for a chariot race when he heard the noise approaching and being frightened hid in the doorway of his bedroom behind the curtain. Next, he sent his praefect Antiochianus to find out the reason of the tumult. This man easily managed to dissuade the soldiers from their murder.

At last Antonine's eyes were fully opened to his danger. He now knew how far Mamaea's money and the influence of Maesa were tending. There had been a military arising, not strong enough to effect its purpose, it is true, but still able to cause confusion, strife and divided allegiance in the city.

With courage almost unprecedented in a boy of his age, he went straight to the camp, resolved to show himself in their midst and settle the matter once and for all with the Praetorians. It was undoubtedly one of the finest acts of courage in his life, this going alone and unprotected into the midst of a camp which was supposed to be in a mutiny; a camp where he had just learned that at least a certain section of the men were in his aunt's pay and to which his aunt, cousin and grandmother had just retired for safety.

The arrival of the Emperor put a stop to the trouble, and there was a conference at which Alexander's name was never mentioned. The subject of complaint and mutiny was that certain freedmen had been appointed to offices for which there had been others better qualified than Antonine's friends. With a considerable amount of good sense, Antonine acceded to the soldiers' demands; he dismissed four out of five of the persons mentioned, amongst whom were Gordius from the Praefecture of the Night Watch, Murissimus from an unknown office, and two other friends. Hierocles's name was also mentioned but the Emperor refused to listen to it. He said he would die rather than give up Hierocles.

The family returned to the palace and tried to brazen out their treachery and Antonine continued to have command of the boy's person. The net result of this plot was the retirement of Alexander from public notice.

During the period between this plot and the next, successfully managed by Mamaea, both Dion and Lampridius assure us that the Emperor made daily attempts on the life of his cousin. To circumvent these, Mamaea refused to allow Alexander to eat anything from the imperial kitchens and set up a kitchen of her own in the palace. Antonine seemed to be quite indifferent as to what was going on. He knew that his position was precarious. Syrian divines had told him that his doom was near. He lived his life in which the spintries, a form of amusement with which Tiberius had refreshed an equally worried frame, figured largely, along with other reprehensible enjoyments.

Mamaea got Alexander designated Consul for the year of 222. Here Antonine struck. He refused to go to the Senate to be invested unless someone else was designated instead of his cousin. This time Maesa herself does not seem to have tried to influence the boy. That crafty old sinner had already managed to worm herself back into the friendship of the boy and his mother by putting the odium of recent trouble entirely on the shoulders of her daughter Mamaea. She begged Soaemias to make clear to

Antonine that by refusing to take the consulship, it would be his own undoing. Rome would never endure such a breach of the usual order. Suddenly, yielding to his mother's entreaties, he consented to the plan and going to the Senate, he associated Alexander with himself in the consular dignity, thereby signing his own death warrant.

January 1, 222 was the beginning of the end. The office of Consul was vitally necessary for Alexander's promotion. It was shortly after midday when Antonine went to the Cura and there in the presence of his grandmother, he consented to give that official power and authority which they had struggled to obtain.

The reason for the murder of Antonine is not clear. Lampridius assigns no adequate reason, giving instead suppositions of his own – first that the Praetorians feared Antonine's vengeance on account of the attack made on him some months previously, second because of his refusal to give them donatives they resolved to rid the Republic of him. First they would get his friends out of the way, and then openly attack Antonine in the *latrinae* and kill him.

Dion's account is more circumstantial and brings Alexander and Mamaea into the scene. His story is that the two Consuls, during a meeting of the Praetorians, summoned on account of one of the multitudinous plots against Alexander, went into the camp, with their two mothers, fighting one another as usual, each imploring the soldiers to kill her sister's son. We are then told, that Antonine, quite contrary to his custom, got frightened and rushed from the scene and disappeared into a chest from which he was soon dragged to have his head cut off while his mother held him in her arms. As the operation of killing one without the other in such a position was difficult, Soaemias perished along with her son.

Herodian substitutes for the story of the sudden dissolution of the Senate, a report which he says Antonine caused to be circulated. It was to the effect that Alexander was so ill he was likely to die at any moment. By this means, Antonine hoped to keep the boy shut up in the palace until the soldiers and citizens had forgotten him, when he could be put out of the way quietly. The turbulent Praetorians, when they began to miss the young Consul, decided to mutiny again, the present form being a refusal to turn out the palace guard until Alexander should re-appear.

When the guards refused to come to the palace, Antonine, in-stead of killing Alexander, did the one thing that no terrified person could possibly have done: he set out in a litter for the camp, utterly unprotected. The litter is fully described, namely the state litter, sparkling with gold and precious stones. With Antonine went Alexander. It was as usual a journey in which the Emperor courted death. When the litter arrived at the gates of the camps, the consuls were conducted to the chapel which occupied the central position in the enclosure. The chapel was an ominous place as it was here that Caracalla had played the farce of regretting his part in the murder of his brother Geta. The visit did foster loyalty to Alexander who was acclaimed as a deliverer, and raised to a fever pitch the evil passions against Antonine who was received with perfect coldness. Despite this inauspicious reception the Emperor elected to stay the night in the camp chapel the better to meditate on his wrongs, which was obviously an unlikely proceeding on the part of the young Sybarite.

The next morning, he held a court martial to try the soldiers, who had made themselves conspicuous by the warmth of their reception to Alexander. Antonine condemned these men to death as seditious persons. The soldiers transported with rage at his treatment of their companions, and filled with hatred of the Emperor, conceived the notion of succouring their im-prisoned brethren by upsetting the dishonoured Emperor. Time and pretext were admirable, they killed both Antonine and Soaemias, and then included in the massacre all those of their cortege who were in the camp, and known to be Antonine's ministers or accomplices in his crimes. They then gave the bodies to the mob to be dragged about the streets of Rome, finally throwing that of the Emperor into the Tiber from the Aemilian Bridge.

A careful comparison of these three stories, reveals the fact that none of the eye-witnesses saw the same things and none ascribe the deed to the same motive. All agreed, however, in shifting the responsibility from the former conspirators to the Praetorians. Let us attempt to construct the events of that memorable day.

From Herodian we learn that the state litter was used and

that in it travelled the two Consuls, accompanied at least by Soaemias, Fulvius Diogenianus, Praefect of Rome, Aurelius Subulus, Chancellor of the Exchequer, Hierocles the Emperor's friend and husband, who had recently been designated Caesar, and two out of three of the Praetorian Praefects.

Lampridius says that Antonine tried to escape by hiding in the *latrinae*. What would have been easier than for one of Mamaea's party to seize the boy, unprotected in the *latrinae*? The Emperor gone, the obvious thing would be for the conspirators to remove as quickly as possible all those persons who might make things difficult for his successor. Of these Soaemias would certainly be the most troublesome.

To account for the treatment of Antonine's body at the hands of the mob is certainly difficult. We know that he had done nothing which could have rendered him obnoxious to the populace. To ascribe it to intolerance of his psychopathic condition shows not only ignorance of Roman susceptibilities but also a foolish pre-dating of popular prejudice. We certainly have no record of this Emperor's sepulchre and we have no record of the defilement of the corpses, but it is possible that Mamaea's money invented this scheme for disgracing her nephew's memory.

Antonine had the stigma of all crimes imputed to his memory and Alexander the Good arose, superior to all human frailties. Then, and not until then Rome began to be shocked. Men whose fortunes Antonine had made by his liberality, the Senate whom he had snubbed so unmercifully, and the army to whose donatives he had not properly attended, all these found it advisable to adopt the views of the new administration; their education in ingratitude is complete. Instead of the generous, fearless, affectionate boy whom the populace had known, there emerged the sceptred butcher, ill with satyriasis, the taciturn tyrant, hideous and debauched, the unclean priest, devising in the crypts of the palace infamies so monstrous that to describe them, words had to be coined. It was Mamaea's work and for 1,800 years no one has had the audacity to look below the surface and unmask the deception.

THE CAESARS, by Ivar Lissner. G. P. Putnam's Sons, New York.

The Emperor was constantly accompanied by a huge athlete from Smyrna called Aurelius Zoticus.